THE WAYSIDE
AND WOODLAND
SERIES 🙟 🙟

THE MOTHS OF THE BRITISH ISLES

Garden Tiger *and varieties.*

THE MOTHS

OF THE

BRITISH ISLES

BY

RICHARD SOUTH, F.R.E.S.

AUTHOR OF
" THE BUTTERFLIES OF THE BRITISH ISLES "
EDITOR OF " THE ENTOMOLOGIST," etc.

EDITED AND REVISED BY
H. M. EDELSTEN, O.B.E., F.R.E.S.,
D. S. FLETCHER, F.R.E.S., AND R. J. COLLINS, F.R.E.S.

SECOND SERIES

COMPRISING THE FAMILIES
*LASIOCAMPIDAE, ARCTIIDAE,
GEOMETRIDAE, COSSIDAE,
LIMACODIDAE, ZYGAENIDAE,
SESIIDAE, and HEPIALIDAE*

WITH COLOURED FIGURES
AND DRAWINGS OF EARLY STAGES

FREDERICK WARNE & CO. LTD.
LONDON & NEW YORK

Copyright in all countries signatory
to the Berne Convention

FREDERICK WARNE AND CO. LTD.,
LONDON, ENGLAND

First Published	.	.	.	.	1908
Second Impression	.	.	.	.	1917
Third Impression	.	.	.	.	1918
Fourth Impression	.	.	.	.	1919
New Edition	.	.	.	.	1923
Do.	Reprinted	.	.	.	1926
Do.	Reprinted	.	.	.	1933
New Edition	.	.	.	.	1939
Do.	Reprinted	.	.	.	1941
Do.	Reprinted	.	.	.	1943
Do.	Reprinted	.	.	.	1946
Do.	Reprinted	.	.	.	1948
New Edition					
© FREDERICK WARNE & CO. LTD., 1961					
	Reprinted	.	.	.	1972
	Reprinted	.	.	.	1973

PRINTED IN GREAT BRITAIN
ISBN 0 7232 0002 5

PREFACE TO THE PRESENT EDITION

A NEW edition of this volume having become necessary, it was deemed a fitting opportunity to bring the subject matter in line with our present knowledge of the structure, habits, distribution, and nomenclature of the species considered therein. This has been established in collaboration with the lepidopterists in the Department of Entomology of the British Museum (Natural History). With this end in view, the new facts have been incorporated in the text as far as possible. Scarce and occasional visitors have also been included.

The whole of the coloured plates have been redrawn by the late Mr. H. D. Swain, F.R.E.S. Where examples were not otherwise available, specimens were lent from the collections of the British Museum (Natural History) by permission of the Trustees. The figures on black-and-white plate No. 19 were drawn by Miss A. Walters. The text figures are from photographs taken by Mr. J. D. Bradley, F.R.E.S.

We are very greatly indebted to Mr. W. H. Tams, A.L.S., F.R.E.S., for his assistance with the nomenclature and his kind help and advice on the many problems which arose in the revision of the volume ; also to the late Dr. E. A. Cockayne, O.B.E., F.R.E.S., and Mr. C. N. Hawkins, F.R.E.S., for many useful notes and corrections. Additions to the food plants of larvae have been added in some cases from " Larval Food-plants " by Mr. P. B. M. Allan, M.B.E., M.A., F.R.E.S., whose assistance is hereby acknowledged.

The Irish records have been brought up to date as far as

possible from " The Catalogue of the Macro-Lepidoptera of Ireland," by the late Lt.-Col. Donovan.

A new General Index and also a Specific Index have been provided.

H. M. EDELSTEN.

D. S. FLETCHER.

R. J. COLLINS.

ORIGINAL PREFACE

In the present and previous series of " The Moths of the British Isles," over 750 species have been portrayed on the plates and described in the text—a number that includes all those insects formerly grouped under the now obsolete term " Macro-Lepidoptera." The task of dealing with so many species in two volumes has necessarily imposed brevity in their treatment ; but it is hoped that nothing has been omitted that could be legitimately regarded as falling within the scope of volumes especially designed for the votaries of Nature Study.

To have comprised in this scheme the large contingent of our moths known as " Micro-Lepidoptera " would have reduced further the space available for those species which experience shows appeal to the majority of nature students in a way that the minuter forms may not do. Even then, only a few general remarks on each group would have been possible, with, perhaps, a portrait or two of representative species. Such a course seemed hardly likely to prove of practical utility. The " Small Fry," as they have been called, exceedingly interesting though they may be to a limited number of students, have therefore been left for separate treatment at some more convenient season.

Both classification and nomenclature are always under revision, and we are probably a long way from hearing the last word concerning either. These are, however, matters that cannot be ignored even in a popular work ; consequently I have ventured to adopt sundry changes in arrangement and in names which, although not departing from the old style in any very large way, still approach pretty closely to the new.

I have again to tender my sincere thanks to Mr. Robert

7

Adkin, F.R.E.S., for kindly lending specimens of rare species and varieties for figuring ; and also to Mr. B. Adkin, F.R.E.S., Mr. G. T. Porritt, F.R.E.S., and Mr. A. J. Scollick, F.R.E.S. I desire also to gratefully acknowledge the loan of further beautiful coloured drawings by Mr. Alfred Sich, F.R.E.S. These figures have been most accurately reproduced in black and white by Mr. Horace Knight, to whom I am greatly indebted for his able assistance in connection with the numerous drawings of ova, larvae, and pupae. In some cases the preserved skin of a caterpillar had to serve as a model, and where this occurs the fact is mentioned. A few figures of larvae have been copied from Dr. G. Hofmann's " Die Raupen der Schmetterlinge Europas," 2nd edit., by Professor Dr. Arnold Spuler. All such reproductions are duly noted in the text.

Mr. Knight is also responsible for the coloured drawings for Plates 1, 13, 36, 61, 96, 98, 100, 104, 134, and 148 ; the figures on which, except that of *Zygaena filipendulae ab. chrysanthemi*, are from specimens.

" A Forester," Mr. H. Main, F.R.E.S., and Mr. W. J. Lucas, B.A., F.R.E.S., were good enough to furnish prints of some of their excellent photographs depicting life-history details of moths and caterpillars in repose, as met with in nature.

RICHARD SOUTH.

The plate references in the present Edition
do not apply to the above.

LASIOCAMPIDAE

Lackeys and Eggars

Staudinger in his catalogue of Palaearctic Lepidoptera refers twenty genera comprising sixty-three species to this family. Of these, eleven species belonging to ten genera occur in the British Isles. According to some authorities a twelfth species, *Dendrolimus pini* Linn., should be included. This is the *Eutricha pini* of Stephens (1828) and the " Wild Pine tree Lappet moth " and " Pine tree Lappet " of the more ancient authors. The claim of this species to a place in the British list rests chiefly on a specimen captured in the Norwich Hospital, in July, 1809, by Mr. Sparshall. Wilkes (1773) states that he once found a caterpillar near Richmond Park, but the moth was not reared. For generations the species now classified as Lasiocampidae have been referred to Bombycidae, but the silkworm (*Bombyx mori* Linn.) is typical of that family, which has but few genera in it, and none of them occurs in Europe. Although some of the moths are of considerable size, most of them are not large. The general colour is some shade of brown. Both sexes have the antennae bipectinated, but more strongly in the male than the female.

In his treatment of the species here included under Lasiocampidae, Tutt (" A Natural History of the British Lepidoptera," vols. i., ii.) separated them into two families, Lachneidae and Eutrichidae. The first family was divided into five sub-families and the same number of tribes. The latter family had three sub-families and three tribes. The whole were embraced in a super-family styled Lachneides. Lasiocampidae disappeared as a family name, but the genus *Lasiocampa* was retained for *quercus* L., whilst *trifolii* Schiff. was referred to the genus *Pachygastria* Hb., and these with *Aurivillia* Tutt, not represented in Britain, constituted the Pachygastriidi tribe

9

of the Pachygastriinae, a sub-family of Lachneidae. All this
will no doubt appear very complicated to the beginner, but
he need not worry himself very greatly about the matter at
present. When he feels that he has a fair knowledge of the
species in the group he will be in a position to grapple with
the niceties of classification.

The Lackey (*Malacosoma neustria* Linn .)

The colour of the male ranges from pale yellow ochre,
through pale brown to reddish or dark brown ; and in the
female from pale brown to reddish brown ; two cross lines
are generally present on the fore wings ; the space between
the lines is usually darker in the female, and sometimes in the
male also, forming a dark central band. All these colour
forms were reared from some caterpillars taken by South at
Byfleet, Surrey, in 1901. Another year a few caterpillars
taken at Esher produced ochreous coloured males and pale
brown females only ; the bands of the latter were narrower
than usual and much contracted below the middle. As the
females last mentioned are somewhat under the normal size
South was inclined to think that the caterpillars from which
they were reared had been on short commons during their
last stage. Two males and a female are shown on Pl. **2,** 1–3.

The greyish brown eggs are laid during July and August in
a ring cluster around a twig as shown on Pl. **3,** 1*a*, and so they
remain exposed to all weathers during the winter. In April
the caterpillars hatch out, and as they live in company
throughout the greater part of their larval existence, the
first business is to construct a silken tent-like web. The
exterior of the tent affords a suitable surface upon which
they can lie when they take a sun bath, which they seem
fond of doing whenever the opportunity offers. It is also
used, as well as the interior, for the process of skin-changing.

The full-grown caterpillar (Pl. **3,** 1) is slaty blue above ;
along the middle of the back is a bluish white line, bordered

on each side by a reddish orange-lined black stripe ; towards the lower limit of the slaty blue colour is a black-edged reddish orange line, and below this again the ground colour is flecked with orange, sometimes forming a line in the region of the spiracles ; there are two velvety black spots on the back of the ring nearest the head, and a smaller black spot on each side of the next two rings ; the hairs are brownish, rather more numerous on the sides than on the back. Head slaty blue with two black eye-like spots. It feeds from April to June on hawthorn, sloe, and various fruit trees in orchards and gardens ; also on birch, elm, oak, sallow, willow, etc.

Chrysalis (Pl. **3,** 1*b*, 1*c*) blackish, rather downy enclosed in a double oval-shaped cocoon ; the inner compartment is of rather closer woven silk, and is thickly covered with a yellowish substance, which is ejected by the caterpillar as a fluid, and after drying forms a sulphur-like powder on the cocoon, and in a lesser degree on the chyrsalis also. The moth is on the wing in July and August, but it is rarely seen in the day-time, and not often at night, except when attracted by light into the house, or to the gas or electric lamps. It is exceedingly easy to rear, either from eggs or from collected caterpillars ; the latter are often abundant.

Generally distributed throughout England, but becoming scarcer from the Midlands, to Lancashire and Yorkshire, and not often occurring further north than the last-named county. In Ireland it is unknown in the north, but occurs in many parts of the south and south-west.

The Ground Lackey (*Malacosoma castrensis* Linn.)

This also is a variable species. Most frequently the fore wings of the male are pale buff, cross lined, and more or less clouded with brown ; hind wings brown. The female has all the wings reddish brown, the front pair being crossed by two pale buff lines. The fringes are pale buff, chequered with brown in both sexes. Colour and marking are, however, subject to considerable variation. Sometimes all the wings are pale buff (male), or reddish brown (both sexes), and the fore wings without marking. The cross lines on fore wings of the female may be either very slender or very broad ; occasionally almost the whole of the basal area up to, and including, the first cross line is buff. Two examples of each sex are shown on Pl. **2**, 4–7.

The eggs are laid in a similar manner to those of the last species, around stems of wild carrot, sea wormwood, and other plants that flourish in the insects' favourite haunts, which, in this country, are the salt marshes along the estuaries of the Thames and Medway.

The caterpillar is black, inclining to bluish between the rings ; along the back are four much broken reddish orange lines and a central bluish line ; a bluish stripe followed by a reddish one along the sides, and below this the colour is bluish, speckled with black ; the hairs are golden brown. Head blackish grey, without black spots (Pl. **3**, 3).

The chrysalis and its cocoon are similar to those of the Lackey, and spun up among herbage.

The moth emerges in July and August and, although it may be occasionally attracted by light, is rarely seen in the open. The caterpillars are to be found, most years, in plenty from May to July. They feed on almost every kind of plant growing on the salterns, and as they are fond of sunning themselves on sea wormwood, sea plantain, etc., are easily seen at such times. In dull weather they retire to their webs, which are generally rather low down in the herbage. In confinement they will do very well if supplied with fresh sprays or leaves of almost any fruit tree, or of birch, whitethorn, etc. The receptacle containing them should be constructed and placed so that the caterpillars get plenty of air and sunshine. It is considered desirable to sprinkle both food and caterpillars with water now and then ; some rearers deem it necessary to put a tiny pinch of salt in the water used for sprinkling ;

and in his own experience South found that better results were obtained when the food was thus treated than when the salt was omitted.

On the Continent this species occurs in woods, and on heaths, etc., but in Britain it is seemingly confined to salt marshes. Although it has been recorded from the Suffolk coast, and other places, the best localities for it are probably the salterns, from Gravesend to the Isle of Sheppey, and at Southend and Shoeburyness. It also occurs on the Sussex coast.

Malacosoma hybr. *schaufussi* Standf.—In 1884 Dr. Standfuss made some experiments in crossing three species of *Malacosoma*, and one of these was the pairing of *M. neustria* ♂ with *M. castrensis* ♀; the offspring he christened as above. Since that time others have succeeded in crossing the two species with varying results.

On August 13, 1906, Mr. Percy Richards sent South a small batch of eggs (Pl. **3,** 2a) laid by a female, *M. castrensis*, that emerged in a breeding cage, and had paired with a captured male, *M. neustria*, he introduced. The larvae hatched out one or two at a time, from April 7 over a period of more than a fortnight. Few of the caterpillars would commence to feed, and of those that took to the plum and sallow with which they were supplied, only four reached maturity. Three of these pupated during late June and early July, and three moths, all females, emerged in due course, one on July 28, another on August 6, and a third on August 13. The second specimen was very much crippled, probably owing to the cocoon having been accidentally injured. One caterpillar was still feeding on August 14, but died about the 26th.

The mature larva (Pl. **3,** 2) has the head and markings thereon like *neustria*, also the black spots on the first thoracic segment, but they are rather large and inclined to unite. The bluish line along the sides is dotted and freckled with black rather more thickly than in *castrensis* ; the dorsal line is very thin, but bluish as in *castrensis*, and the red lines on each side of it are broad.

In colour the three moths are deeper brown than any form of either parent species that South had seen, but the transverse lines, and especially the outer, are most like those of *neustria*.

It should be mentioned that much information on hybridism in the Lackey moths and other species will be found in Tutt's " British Lepidoptera," vol. ii.

The Pale Oak Eggar (*Trichiura crataegi* Linn.)

In its typical form the male of this species (Pl. **4,** 1, 2) is ashy grey, with a darker central band on the fore wings ; and the female is dusky greyish brown, also with a darker band. The colour of the male varies in shade from almost whitish (ab. *pallida* Tutt), to blackish grey ; in the paler forms the central band of the fore wings is often of a purplish tint, and in the darkest forms the band is almost black. The female ab. *pallida* is pale buff.

The eggs, which are brownish, inclining to reddish on the micropylar area, are covered with dark grey hairs from the body of the female and laid side by side in a chain-like arrangement on a twig of hawthorn or sloe (those figured on Pl. **8** were deposited in a box, and not securely attached). From eight to twelve is said to be the usual number in a batch, and each female will deposit an average of 160 eggs.

The caterpillars do not hatch out all at the same time, but by ones and twos, at intervals spreading over a period of two, or perhaps three, weeks. Several forms of the caterpillar have been described, but the ground colour is generally more or less black above and greyish on the sides ; the ornamentation comprises interrupted white or whitish stripes, streaked or clouded with reddish, and reddish warts ; the hairs are reddish brown. The black larva with orange rings is very like that of a young *M. rubi* and is often mistaken for one.

The example figured on Pl. 8 was from eggs laid by a female moth in Selkirk, South Scotland. From the age of three weeks until it became full grown it was black marked with yellow on the back and orange on the sides ; hairs pale greyish mixed with black ones, especially on the back towards the black, glossy, and somewhat hairy head. It hatched on April 26, was reared on plum, pupated early in June, and the moth, a darkish grey female, emerged on July 31. Another caterpillar that hatched on May 1, and two others from still later hatchings, were then in chrysalis.

The caterpillar may be found from April to June on hawthorn and sloe, and it is said also on birch, oak, sallow, apple, bramble, etc. Those that South found resting by day on shoots of hawthorn, apparently enjoying the sunshine, had almost invariably been " ichneumoned " (Cockayne mentions that, in his experience, it is not so), but others that came up after sunset to feed on the shoots were generally healthy. Usually the caterpillar feeds up and pupates the same year, but on the moors in Aberdeenshire and some other parts of Scotland it is said to hibernate and to complete its life cycle the following summer and autumn. Furthermore, the moths from these winter larvae are much darker than normal, and have been doubtfully referred to subsp. *ariae* Hübn, a form found in the Alps, Scandinavia, and Finland.

The moth is out in August and September, and occurs in wooded districts throughout the southern half of England, but northwards from the Midlands it is uncommon ; it is found in several parts of Scotland to Inverness and in the Outer Hebrides. In Ireland it is reported (Birchall) to have occurred in Killarney, and Kane mentions that " a blackish form was taken at Magilligan, near Derry, by W. Salvage. Its larvae were feeding on blackthorn." The range abroad extends through Europe to Armenia and Asia Minor.

The December Moth (*Poecilocampa populi* Linn.)

This is a rather thinly scaled moth ; the general coloration is sooty brown ; the wings are suffused more or less with greyish ; there are two pale ochreous cross lines on the fore wings, the first enclosing a reddish brown basal patch ; hind wings rather paler with a diffuse whitish central band ; fringes brown chequered with pale ochreous. Head brown, collar brownish, tipped with pale ochreous in the male. The female is rather larger than the male. The moth is figured on Pl. **4**, 3, 4, and the eggs and caterpillar on Pl. **5**, 1, 1*a*.

The eggs, which are laid on the bark of trees, are whitish grey, variegated or mottled with darker grey.

The caterpillar hatches out in April, and when nearly full grown is ochreous, but so thickly dotted and freckled with black as to appear of a dark brown coloration ; the back is clothed with dark short hairs, and the sides with long paler hairs ; on the back of the first ring is a reddish brown mark divided by a white line ; a double row of whitish dots along the back, most distinct on rings two and three, where they are placed on a velvety black bar ; on each side of the white dots is a reddish brown interrupted line. Head ochreous brown, thickly dotted with black and clothed with pale hairs. Underparts ochreous, spotted and lined with blackish. Feeds on the foliage of most trees, and is said to eat lettuce. Found April to June.

Chrysalis glossy red brown, in a cocoon spun up among dead leaves, etc., under loose bark, or on the ground.

The moth does not emerge until October, and in that month, but more frequently in November and December, the males may be seen around gas lamps quite late at night.

Although found chiefly in woods it is not essentially a woodland species, as it occurs in districts where there are no woods but plenty of trees growing in parks, fields, or even hedgerows. It is fairly common generally throughout England and Wales, but becoming rather more local northwards to Cumberland.

1, 2, 3. The Lackey.
4, 5, 6, 7. Ground Lackey.

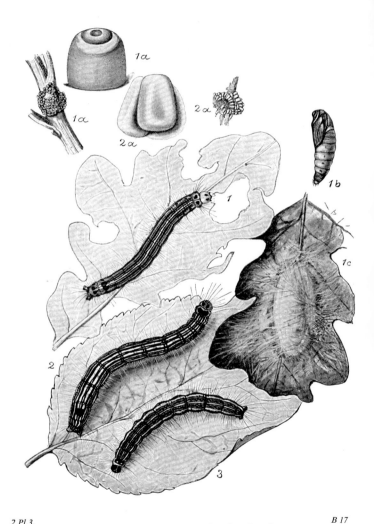

1, 1a, 1b, 1c. **The Lackey:** *eggs, caterpillar, chrysalis and cocoon.*
2, 2a. **Hybrid between the Lackey and Ground Lackey:** *eggs and caterpillar.*
3. **Ground Lackey:** *caterpillar.*

It occurs through Scotland to Sutherland, but is nowhere common. In Ireland it is widely distributed, and not uncommon near Dublin, and at Favour Royal, Tyrone. Abroad it ranges through northern and central Europe.

The Small Eggar (*Eriogaster lanestris* Linn.)

Also a brownish insect with somewhat thinly-scaled wings (Pl. **4,** 5, 6). The fore wings are light reddish brown with a whitish patch at the base, a white spot about the centre, and a whitish transverse line beyond ; the hind wings are smoky brown and have a pale central band. The female, which is larger than the male, has a conspicuous greyish anal tuft, the hairs from which she uses to cover over her pale oily green eggs when they are deposited in clusters on twigs of hawthorn or sloe in February or March (Pl. **5,** 2*a*).

The caterpillar is black or greyish black, with reddish brown hairs, and a series of black-edged yellowish brown, or reddish brown blotches on each side of the back ; these blotches are outlined in pale yellowish and occasionally connected by a line of the same colour (Pl. **5,** 2). From the time they are hatched until nearly mature the caterpillars live in companies on a closely woven web of silk on a branch of hawthorn or sloe, only leaving their habitation to feed. These webs may often be seen on hedgerows from May to July. The brown chrysalis is enclosed in a solid-looking oval cocoon of a pale ochreous or whitish colour. Not all the moths emerge the following year : some will remain in the chrysalis over two or three winters, and occasionally they have been known to emerge seven years after pupation. The moth is said to be fully formed within the chrysalis all the time, but for some reason will not emerge, although if extracted from its shell, it has been known to expand its wings in the ordinary way. Barrett states that in the middle of February, after a moth had emerged, he " put a large number of cocoons upon a warm mantelpiece and obtained scores of moths within a few hours."

Generally distributed over the southern half of England ; plentiful in some years in the southern and eastern counties. Northwards and in Scotland it is local and less frequent. Kane states that in Ireland it is very locally abundant. The range abroad is through central and northern Europe to southern Lapland, and eastward to Siberia and Amurland.

The Oak Eggar (*Lasiocampa quercus* Linn.)

The two moths, one male and one female, shown on Pl. **7** 1, 2, were reared from caterpillars obtained in Kent, and they represent the more or less ordinary South English forms of the species. Sometimes the ground colour of the male is more distinctly reddish, or rust tinted, and the yellowish bands narrower on all the wings. Or the bands may be much broader than in the male figured, and the widening is effected by extension in the form of rays towards the outer margins of the wings. A form that has been referred to, in error, as ab. *roboris* Schrank (*marginata* Tutt =), has the outer margins of all the wings broadly yellow. South had not seen an English example of this form, but he had a reddish specimen in which the yellow band on the fore wings is broader than usual, and the whole of the outer third of the hind wings yellow, with a slight brownish shade on the external margin ; this is *semimarginata* Tutt, and is also identical with ab. *roboris* of other British authors. The white spot usually present on the fore wings varies somewhat in size and shape ; it is often seen on the under as well as the upper surface of the wings, except in the lighter coloured forms.

Subsp. *callunae* Palmer (The Northern Eggar) is shown on Pl. **9**, 1, 2. The chief features of this form are the generally darker coloration in both sexes, the yellow patch at the base of the fore wings of the male, and the outward turn of the lower ends of the yellow bands. All these characters are subject to modification ; the yellow bands may be very narrow at one extreme, or greatly widened at the other, and the hind wings may occasionally be bandless ; the basal patch is often of large size, but in some examples it is entirely absent. Sometimes the bands are greenish in colour (ab. *olivaceo-fasciata* Cockerell), and more rarely, perhaps, the greenish tinge extends over the whole of the wings (ab. *olivacea* Tutt). It should be noted here that the ab. *olivaceo-fasciata* has occurred once or twice in South England, but this phase of aberration seems to be more connected with *callunae* than with *quercus*. Both these forms are common in Caithness.

Callunae was not recognised as British until the year 1847, when it was introduced as a species distinct from *quercus*. The late Richard Weaver, who gave it the English name of the " Scotch Eggar," took specimens of the moth at Rannoch in 1845, and he found caterpillars in that year, as well as in 1844 and 1846. It is now well known to occur not only in Scotland, including the Hebrides and Orkneys, but also on the moors of northern England, and in Ireland and Wales. In Devon it is found not uncommonly in the Exmoor and Dartmoor districts, and it has been recorded from various parts of the New Forest in Hampshire.

The egg of *callunae* is figured on Pl. **6.** It appears rather polished, and in colour is pale brown mottled with darker brown. The eggs are stated to be deposited whilst the female is on the wing, and consequently they fall to the ground or are arrested in their descent by the herbage over which they are scattered.

The full-grown caterpillar of *quercus*, beneath the brownish fur with which the body is clothed, is dark brown on the back and rather violet brown on the sides ; the ring divisions are velvety black ; there is a white stripe along each side and below the stripe some reddish marks ; the ring nearest the head is edged with reddish, and the next two rings each have two reddish-centred white spots. The dull purplish brown chrysalis is enclosed in a hard oval-shaped cocoon which is spun upon or near the ground in a flimsy web among herbage, dead leaves, etc. Sometimes it is placed among the twigs of the food plant (Pl. **6**).

In southern England the caterpillars hatch from the egg in August and usually hibernate when quite small. They feed up during the following spring and early summer, perhaps in June or July, and the moth appears in July or August. Occasionally, however, a few individuals depart from the general habit and complete their growth the same year, hibernate in the pupal stage, and produce moths the next year, possibly earlier than hibernating caterpillars. On the other hand, perhaps owing to adverse weather conditions, feeding after hibernation may be continued well on into the autumn, when the caterpillars pupate, but emergence of the moth is postponed until the following year, the second after hatching from the egg.

In the case of *callunae*, at least as regards its normal habit in Scotland and southwards to the moorland districts of Yorkshire and Lancashire, the young caterpillar hibernates the first winter, feeds through the following summer, and passes the second winter as a chrysalis, the moth emerging in the following May or June.

Generally speaking, then, it may be stated that *quercus* has a twelve-month life cycle, whilst that of *callunae* extends almost or quite to twenty-four months, of which at least twelve months are passed as a caterpillar. However, as has been noted, *quercus* sometimes passes one winter as a caterpillar, and another as a chrysalis, thus assuming the *callunae* habit ; whilst *callunae* occasionally attains the perfect state during the summer following that in which the caterpillar left the egg.

The food plants comprise bramble, dogwood, hawthorn, heather (*Calluna*), and various low plants ; it is even content with ivy.

Newman, in the *Entomologist* for 1845, gives a life history of the northern Eggar (*callunae*), and from this the following details are extracted   The male flies rapidly over the heather

1, 2. **Pale Oak Eggar,** *male and female.*
3, 4. **December Moth,** *female and male.*
5, 6. **Small Eggar,** *male and female.*

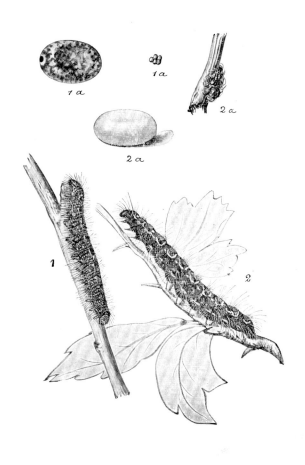

1, 1a. **December Moth:** *eggs and caterpillar.*
2, 2a. **Small Eggar:** *eggs and caterpillar.*

by day at the latter end of May or beginning of June ; its flight is jerking or zigzag, and its object is evidently to find the female, who rarely moves until impregnation has taken place. Subsequently the female flies over the heather, dropping her eggs at random as she flies, and the eggs, having no glutinous covering, do not adhere to any object which they may accidentally touch in falling. On emergence from the egg the young caterpillar is dark ash coloured, the divisions between the rings of the body being indicated by two minute orange streaks, each of which is accompanied by a small black spot. After the first moult the ground colour becomes more smoky, the divisions velvety black, and on each ring a triangular orange spot appears ; these markings become more conspicuous later on, and by the end of October, when it hibernates, they are very distinct. It rests in a straight position, and, if disturbed, falls off its food plant, and rolls in a ring with its head slightly on one side.

The habits of the Oak Eggar moths (*quercus*) are prettp much the same as those of the Northern form, except that the moths fly in July and August, and frequent hedgerows, the borders of woods, heathy commons, and cliffs and sand dunes at the seaside.

A bred female of either form will attract numerous males, and even the receptacle in which a newly emerged female has been placed is almost as effective as the lady herself. When staying at a cottage on the edge of a moor near Lynton, North Devon, years ago, South had some pupae of the Oak Eggar. One day, late in July, quite a number of males entered the cottage and made their way to the cage in which the pupae were, and he had no difficulty in boxing several of them. The next day he put the female moth, which had emerged the previous day, into a roomy chip box, and carried it in a satchel to the moor, where it was placed on the ground. The males began to arrive soon afterwards and some fine examples were secured. Although the female was taken on the moor only on the one occasion, that satchel continued to be an object of interest to the male Eggars for several days afterwards.

Generally distributed, and often common in some localities, throughout the British Isles. Abroad, its range extends over Europe into Asia Minor, Armenia, and Siberia.

The Grass Eggar (*Lasiocampa trifolii* Schiff.)

This moth is usually brown in colour. The fore wings are inclined to dark reddish brown, and have a pale ochreous brown curved band or ring at the base, a slightly curved line or band of the same colour beyond the middle of the wing; central spot white, finely margined in black. Except that the female is generally larger, and the cross lines usually less distinct, the sexes are much alike. This brown form occurs most frequently in Britain, but in parts of the Kentish and Sussex coast, and especially the Romney Marsh district, a yellowish form is obtained. The Dungeness race is paler and yellower while the Cornish is darker brown than other races. In some specimens the cross lines are darker. In others one or both cross markings may be faint or quite absent, and even the white central dot, which varies in size and shape, may be missing. Sometimes the outer band is distinctly broad and outwardly diffuse (Pl. **7**, 3, 4).

The eggs (Pl. **11**), which appear to be laid loosely, are pale whitish brown, roughened with darker brown, and the micropylar area is purplish brown. Some that South received on March 2, 1907, appeared to be on the point of hatching on the 5th of that month, but no larva came out, although one of the eggs was chipped at one end. It has been frequently stated that the caterpillars hatch out in the autumn and hibernate, but as has been pointed out by Tutt ("Nat. Hist. Brit. Lep.," ii. 20), the eggs of this species probably do not hatch until some time during February or March, although when kept indoors the caterpillar has emerged from the egg in January.

The full-grown caterpillar is black, velvety between the rings, covered with golden brown hair on the back and greyer hair on the sides, among which are some black ones ; three interrupted whitish lines on the back ; some of the hairs along the middle of the back stand erect and form a ridge, looked at from either end. Head lightish brown in colour, lined with black. Feeds in the spring months and up to June chiefly on various kinds of grass. Among many of the plants that it has been known to eat are trefoils, bird's-foot (*Ornithopus*), sea thrift (*Statice*), heather, sallow, hawthorn, sloe, plum, bramble, etc. With regard to the food, it is interesting to note that although one rearer will find that sallow is excellent for the caterpillars, another considers that sallow or hawthorn are but poor substitutes for kidney vetch (*Anthyllis vulneraria*) upon which the caterpillars were feeding when found (Pl. **11**).

The brownish chrysalis is enclosed in a hard but somewhat brittle, brown, oval cocoon, and when spun upon the surface of the ground, protected by an outside covering of loose silk webbing. In August and early September the moths appear. Emergence from the chrysalis usually takes place soon after midday ; the males are early on the wing, and when reared in captivity they should be secured as soon as the wings are dry, or they may spoil themselves in their efforts to escape. Reared females are apt to be deformed, but for " assembling " they may probably be as useful as more perfect examples if the rearer happens to be able to exhibit the attraction in a locality for the species. Both sexes have been taken at electric light.

The best known localities for the species in England are, besides those already mentioned, the sand hills on the Cheshire and Lancashire coast. It is, or has been, found also on the coast of Cumberland ; Lyndhurst and Ringwood, in Hampshire ; Isle of Purbeck, Poole, Swanage, and Bloxworth, in Dorset ; Devonport, Bolt Head, and Salcombe, in Devon ; and Penzance and the Scilly Isles. Its range extends through central and southern Europe to Asia Minor and North Africa.

The Fox Moth (*Macrothylacia rubi* Linn.)

The male is reddish brown, and the female generally greyish brown, but sometimes is of a reddish grey coloration; the fore wings in both sexes are crossed by two pale ochreous lines on the central area (Pl. **9**, 3, 4).

The ground colour in the male ranges in tone from foxy red to dullish red brown or to greyish red brown. The cross lines in either sex may be widely apart, near together, or even united throughout their length, forming a band (ab. *fasciata* Tutt); sometimes one of the lines (ab. *unilinea* Tutt), or both lines, are absent from the fore wings, or from one of them.

The brown clouded greyish eggs are laid in batches, during June, on stems and stalks of plants, or on heather; sometimes they have been found on a fence, a rock, or a stone. The caterpillars hatch out at the end of June and through July. At first they are black, including the glossy head, and covered with long hairs which are black with some white ones amongst them; the ring divisions are pale yellow; later on they are more chocolate brown with yellow bands which, however, do not encircle the body entirely.

When full grown, in the autumn, the caterpillar (Pl. **12**) is velvety black, and above this colour is most in evidence between the rings; the back is clothed with dense, short, bright reddish brown or tawny hair, and the whole body is covered with brownish hairs, varying in length, but always much longer than the tawny ones; along each side are some whitish hairs. Head blackish covered with brownish hairs. It feeds in August and onwards to October, when it seeks winter quarters, reappearing in the following spring, but not feeding again. After enjoying the sunshine whenever the opportunity offers through the early months of the year, it finally pupates in March or April. The cocoon is a long, more or less tubular, brownish construction of silk and larval hairs. It is spun up, usually somewhat upright, low down among the food plant, or at the roots of grass, etc. ; sometimes among moss, when the rounded head end can just be seen above the moss.

In certain localities and seasons the caterpillars have been seen in enormous numbers, but such profusion only happens now and then. In some districts they may be abundant one year, and then scarce or quite absent for several years.

When handling the larvae it will often be noted that the tips of one's fingers are thickly felted with the tawny hairs from the creature's back ; if these hairs get transferred to the face or neck considerable irritation may be the result.

The late Mr. Robson used to collect the caterpillars on fine days in early spring, put each caterpillar into a separate paper box about two inches square, and keep them on a shelf over the kitchen fire, where they would duly pupate. Various methods for keeping these caterpillars through the winter have been described, and all appear to have been fairly successful. The most simple would seem to be the following : bore a number of holes in the bottom of a roomy box, and fasten wire gauze on a close fitting frame to serve as a top. Cut a tuft or two of heather to cover the floor space of the box. Caterpillars collected in the autumn may be put into this receptacle and supplied with food, such as bramble or sallow, as long as they seem inclined to feed. Do not crowd too many into the box, and let it stand out in the garden, preferably on the soil.

The moths emerge in May or June. The males are very active on the wing in the afternoon sunshine, and later on, and may often be seen in numbers dashing hither and thither in an apparently erratic flight over heaths and open spaces, in search of the females. The latter do not fly till night, and occasionally they are attracted to a bright light.

Except that it has not been noted in the Shetlands, the

species occurs throughout the British Isles. Abroad its range extends over Europe, and it is found in Amurland.

The Drinker (*Philudoria potatoria* Linn.)

The male is reddish brown, more or less clouded on the fore wings with ochreous; and the female is yellow, or whitish ochreous. Sometimes this colour distinction of the sexes is reversed, and the males are pale whilst the females are dark. In the fens of Cambridgeshire notably, pale or yellowish males are not altogether uncommon. Barrett mentions, among other aberrations, male specimens from South Wales with the whole of the fore and hind wings deep rich glossy purplish chocolate.

There is variation in the two whitish or silvery marks on the fore wings, the upper one is often very small, sometimes quite absent, and the lower one reduced to a crescent. The chocolate brown cross lines, of which there are usually two on the fore wings, are sometimes faint or entirely missing. Tutt has named nine forms, chiefly colour aberrations, and two others had previously been named. (The moth is figured on Pl. **10,** and the early stages on Pl. **15.**)

The eggs, which are white with bluish grey markings, are laid in clusters on grass stems, etc.

The caterpillar is slaty grey inclining to blackish; the lines on the back are formed of yellowish dots and dashes; two rows of tufts of short black hairs on the back, with longer brown hairs between; low down on the sides are shaggy tufts of white and yellowish hairs and longer brown hairs; an erect pointed tuft of brown hair on second ring, and a similar one on ring eleven but the latter inclines backward. Head greyish, striped and lined with brown and yellowish brown, and clothed with brown hair. It feeds on coarse grasses, including the ribbon grass grown in gardens, and reed, in August to September or October.

In the latter month it goes into hibernation, being then but little over an inch in length. About April it resumes feeding and becomes full grown in June or thereabouts. The long yellowish or whitish brown cocoon in which it changes to a brown chrysalis is more or less pointed at the lower end, and generally attached to a culm of grass or a reed. A showery season seems to suit these caterpillars better than a hot, dry one. The partiality of the caterpillar for a drop of dew, mountain or otherwise, has frequently been noted. The old English name of The Drinker Caterpillar (1682) is therefore not only an appropriate one but shows that this larval habit was observed even at that early date. The specific name *potatoria* given to the moth by Linné is of similar significance.

The moth emerges in July. It seems most addicted to damp grassy lanes, ditch-sides, fens, marshes, moorlands, and sandhills ; and is not really uncommon in very many suitable districts throughout the United Kingdom. Abroad, it is common over the greater part of Europe and its range extends to Amurland and Japan.

The Small Lappet (*Epicnaptera ilicifolia* Linn.)

This exceedingly local and rare British moth has the fore wings pale reddish brown, suffused on the outer marginal area with grey ; about the centre of the wings there is a short black line preceded by a whitish mark ; beyond is a blackish, indistinct, wavy line ; the greyish outer area is limited by a brown line, and this is inwardly edged with whitish : hind wings purplish brown with the central area whitish and crossed by a blackish line. Fringes whitish, marked with brown at the ends of the veins (Pl. 13, 1, 2).

Kirby states that the caterpillar is rust-coloured, with a black stripe on the back, on which stand white dots ; and with reddish yellow transverse spots on the second and third rings. Another form is grey, and the back white, with a broad black central stripe interrupted by rust-coloured spots dotted with black.

The following brief description is taken from an inflated skin

of an immature caterpillar received from Dresden : brownish
inclining to reddish, paler between the rings ; clothed with
short greyish hair, and longer hairs from and above the fleshy
tubercles low down along the sides ; there is a hair-clothed
eminence on ring eleven.   The only conspicuous markings are
on rings two and three ; each of these has two orange spots
separated and narrowly edged externally with velvety black ;
there are two small black spots on the back of each of the
other rings, and indications of reddish circles around some of
these.   Head blackish, covered with greyish hairs (Pl. **17**, 2).

In this country the caterpillar feeds on bilberry (*Vaccinium
myrtillus*), but on the Continent it is said to eat the foliage of
sallows and willows, also of birch.

The cocoon is spun up among the leaves of the food plant.
That figured on Pl. **17**, 2*a*, of foreign origin, was on a shoot of
bilberry ; a moth emerged from it on April 5, 1907.   The
first detailed account of this species in Britain is that in the
Zoologist for 1852, in which Mr. Atkinson records that he took
a specimen in May, 1851, at Cannock Chase in Staffordshire.
A year earlier two larvae were found by Mr. Green on a moor
near Sheffield, and one of these attained the moth state in
April, 1851.   After this moths and caterpillars seem to have
been taken in varying numbers down to 1896, when a specimen
was captured by Dr. R. Freer of Rugeley.   Tutt, quoting
from a letter received from Dr. Freer, states that two moths
were reared from three caterpillars found at Cannock in 1898.
Newnham recorded larvae at Church Stretton in 1900 and a
moth was taken at Cannock just before the 1939–45 War but
was not recorded.   The only other known British locality was
in the neighbourhood of Lynton, North Devon, where a caterpillar, which, from the description, must have been this species,
was found in 1864.   It was taken on August 3 in a wood
abounding with bilberry.

The species ranges over central Europe, but seems to be
generally rare ; it also occurs in Amurland and Japan.

Oak Eggar: *eggs, natural size and enlarged, caterpillars and cocoon.*

1, 2. **Oak Eggar**, *male and female.*
3, 4. **Grass Eggar**, *male and female.*

The Lappet (*Gastropacha quercifolia* Linn.)

Warm reddish brown is the prevailing colour of this fine moth. The wings are more or less suffused with purplish grey, and crossed by blackish lines—three on the fore wings and two on the hind wings. Except in the reddish tinge, which may be bright or dull approaching chocolate, this species is pretty constant in its coloration. Barrett mentions a specimen of a light brown colour, and another of a pale buff. The first of these forms seems to approach the ab. *meridionalis* Hormuz. (Tutt), and the other to ab. *ulmifolia* Heuäcker, which are well known on the Continent. In certain favourable seasons a second generation of the moth has been obtained, chiefly perhaps, in confinement, and on the Continent; although in Britain a caterpillar or two will sometimes feed up and attain the perfect state the same year they hatch from the egg. These examples, which are much smaller, but do not otherwise differ from normal specimens, are referable to ab. *hoegei* Heuäcker.

The moth is figured on Pl. **13,** 3, 4, and the eggs and caterpillar on Pl. **17,** 1, 1*a*.

The eggs, which are whitish in colour with greyish markings, are laid, in July or early August, in twos, threes, or more, on twigs or the undersides of leaves of sloe, apple, sallow, hawthorn, etc. A single female moth has been known to lay over a thousand eggs, but this is perhaps exceptional, and somewhere about half that number is possibly near the average. Even the latter would take the moth some time to distribute here and there in small batches.

The caterpillars hatch out in about a fortnight, feed for a few weeks, and in the autumn, when about three-quarters to one inch in length, take up their winter quarters low down on the stems of the food plant, but, in confinement, often on a withered leaf.

Caterpillar dark grey, so thickly sprinkled with minute black dots as to appear almost black; the whole body is clothed with fine and rather short blackish hair; low down on the side there is a fringe of brownish hair, and this covers the fleshy lappets (the older writers named this larva the " Caterpillar with the Lappets ") ; two white marks edged in front with black on the third ring, and a hairy prominence on the eleventh, are the most conspicuous features of this caterpillar. When the front rings are extended, the divisions between them are seen to be deep blue. Head grey, with darker stripe and paler lines. Occasionally several white marks appear on the back, and this is stated by Professor Poulton to occur more especially in the caterpillars when the twigs and stems of the food plant upon which they have grown up are covered with grey lichen. Sometimes the caterpillar has been reported as destructive in orchards ; two or three large ones feeding on a small apple tree would certainly afford evidence of their presence in the shape of denuded twigs, but it is doubtful if they ever occur in sufficient numbers to cause any very serious damage to fruit trees.

The chrysalis is dark brown, inclining to blackish, and covered with a whitish powder, which does not shake off. It is enclosed in a long, grey brown, tight-fitting cocoon of silk and hairs of the caterpillar, which is generally spun up among the lower twigs, or to the stem of the food plant.

The moth emerges in June or July, and is on the wing at night, when it may be sometimes netted as it flies along or over hedgerows. When caught in this way it dashes about so wildly in the net that it is rarely of much value for the collection. The same may be said of examples taken by light, which at times attracts the moths freely. When resting in the daytime, it very closely resembles a withered bramble-leaf or bunch of leaves. The fore wings are folded down, roof-like, over the hind wings, which are flattened out and their edges project beyond the margins of the fore wings. It is, however, very rarely seen in the open at such times.

The species does not seem to have been recorded from Ireland or from Scotland, but it has a wide distribution in England, although much less frequently met with in the north than in the south. In the Cambridgeshire fens it is perhaps more plentiful than elsewhere, but it is not uncommon in some parts

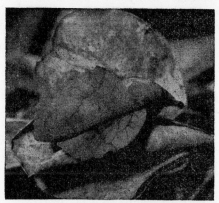

Fig. 1.—Lappet Moth at rest.

of Berkshire, Huntingdonshire, and Kent. The range abroad extends through central, southern, and eastern Europe, to Armenia, Tartary, Siberia, and Amurland ; it is also represented in China, Korea, and Japan.

SYNTOMIDAE

Similar in day-flying habits and in many cases in appearance to the Zygaenidae, but readily distinguished by the absence of vein 8 in the hind wing. The family is richly represented in tropical regions, especially in South America, but poorly represented in the temperate regions. A few species have been recorded in Britain from time to time ; most frequently they have been found in association with imported fruit.

Two of the very few European species of Syntomidae have

been recorded. A specimen of *Syntomis phegea* Linn. (Pl. **127,** 8) was found on the Kent coast between Dover and Folkestone on July 24, 1872, by J. C. Batchelor (1874, *Entomologist,* 7 : 88). A specimen of *Dysauxes ancilla* Linn. (Pl. **127,** 9), said to have been taken at Worthing in Sussex, was exhibited by E. Newman at a meeting of the Entomological Society in 1867 (Barrett, 1895, *Lep. Brit. Is.,* 2 : 138).

Occasional specimens of the beautiful African *Euchromia lethe* Fabricius have been found in Britain, probably imported in the pupal stage with bananas from West Africa.

Several specimens of the West Indian *Ceramidia musicola* Cockerell have been reported from widely scattered localities in Britain ; these too have probably been introduced with bananas. One of the earliest records is of a specimen found in Manchester in 1923 (*Entomologist,* 56 : 113, 1923).

ARCTIIDAE

We include under the above heading the *Nolinae, Lithosiinae, Arctiinae* and *Callimorphinae.* Of the first sub-family only five species occur in the British Isles, sixteen of the second, thirteen of the third, and three of the fourth. In all groups the caterpillars are hairy but the hairs are usually longer in those of the " Tigers " than in those of the others.

NOLINAE

The moths of this sub-family are of rather small size, less, in fact, than some of the so-called " Micros," among which they have been placed in the past. Probably they may, for this reason, be overlooked. They mostly sit head downwards on the trunks, branches, or leaves of trees, sometimes on palings, but the rarer ones hide themselves among the thick, low herbage. The time of flight is after dark, and the moths

Pale Oak Eggar: *eggs, enlarged, and caterpillars.*

1, 2. **Northern Eggar,** *male and female.*
3, 4. **Fox Moth,** *male and female.*

occasionally visit the sugar patch. The caterpillar has only eight false legs (prolegs), the pair on the third abdominal segment being absent ; the body is clothed with tufts of hair, the hairs of the front and rear tufts longer than the others. When full grown it spins a more or less spindle-shaped, toughish cocoon of silk mixed with the larval hairs, which is usually coated with particles scraped from the surface of twig or stem upon which it is spun up.

The Short-cloaked Moth (*Nola cucullatella* Linn.)

The fore wings are whitish or greyish, with a dark, almost black, patch at the base ; this patch is marked with whitish, and is limited by the first cross line, which is black and curved ; the second line, also black, is wavy and curved inwards towards the front margin ; between these lines is a dusky central shade, commencing in a blackish spot on the front margin, and sometimes forming an inward border to the second line ; a raised tuft of white, grey-capped scales on the basal patch, and two other tufts beyond it and in a line with the front margin ; hind wings dark grey, paler towards the base (Pl. **14**, 1, 2).

The caterpillar is reddish brown, clothed with short greyish hairs ; the spots and central line on the back are whitish. It hatches from the egg early in August, and after feeding for a while, retires to winter quarters, selecting some sheltered cranny, such as a chink in the tree bark, where it spins over itself a few strands of silk. Feeding is resumed in May and June, after hibernation, usually on the upperside of leaves of sloe and whitethorn, and also of fruit trees, such as apple and plum, and sometimes pear (Pl. **18**, 1*a*, 1*b*).

The moth is out in June and July. It flies at dusk.

Widely distributed and generally common in the south of England ; somewhat rare in Scotland—perhaps overlooked. It has been reported from Ireland, but is not mentioned by Kane in his catalogue of Irish Lepidoptera.

The Kent Black Arches (*Nola albula* Schiff.)

Fore wings white, largely light brown between the obscure cross lines ; outer marginal area clouded, and front margin dotted with light brown ; three tufts of raised scales placed as in previous species ; hind wings of the male, greyish white, browner on the outer margin ; of female, brownish grey. Varies in the amount of light brown, and sometimes this is much reduced ; more rarely it disappears entirely (Pl. **14,** 3–5).

The caterpillar varies in colour from ochreous with pink tinge to bone white ; the warts are set with pale hairs and those along the back and at each extremity are longest ; a double greyish line along the middle of the back, and a series of black marks on each side ; these marks unite across the back on rings six and ten. After hibernation, it feeds in spring until June, on the young growth of dewberry, and according to Mr. H. Symes (1953, *Ent. Rec.*, 65 : 247) the larvae are usually to be found on the under-surface of the leaves of the lower-growing plants that are partially hidden among coarse grass. Other recorded foodplants are raspberry, strawberry, cinquefoil (*Potentilla reptans*), and hemp agrimony (*Eupatorium cannabinum*). The brownish cocoon is constructed on a stem of grass and in appearance looks not unlike a swelling of the stem (Pl. **18,** 2*a*, 2*b*).

This species was first observed in England in the year 1859, when four specimens were taken in July at Chattenden Roughs, a large hilly wood in north-east Kent. Barrett noted a specimen from the Isle of Wight, and it has again quite recently been found there. Mr. G. T. Porritt stated that he saw one of two examples captured in South Devon in 1901 ; and another, a male, was recorded as taken at light in a house near Weymouth, Dorset, in August, 1904, and from Lewes in 1906.

Though no longer occurring in the original Kentish locality, it has been recorded from near Dymchurch and from Sandhurst in Kent since 1950. It is known also from Sussex, Hampshire, and Dorset, being found commonly between Swanage and

Wareham in 1951. A specimen was taken at light at Arkley in Hertfordshire in August, 1954, and the species has also been recorded from Suffolk and South Wales.

At the time the first specimens were met with in England the species seems to have been rare or little known on the Continent. Since then knowledge of its distribution has vastly increased, and it has now been found not only in many parts of central Europe, but also in Finland, Italy, Dalmatia; Asia Minor, Persia, and extending into Amurland and Japan.

The Small Black Arches (*Nola strigula* Schiff.)

Fore wings greyish white, freckled and dusted with grey brown at the base and on the front and outer margins; two black wavy and toothed cross lines; between the base of the wing and the second line are three raised tufts of grey brown tipped whitish scales: hind wings dark grey, paler towards the base (Pl. **14**, 6, 7).

The caterpillar feeds, probably after hibernation, from April to June, on the undersides of oak leaves. It is pale ochreous in colour, with pale reddish brown warts and star-like tufts of hair; a blackish bar on the back of ring six; head blackish.

The moth emerges from the chrysalis in July. It occurs in oak woods in Kent, Surrey, Sussex, Hampshire, Somerset, and Gloucestershire; also in Berkshire, Norfolk, Suffolk, Hertfordshire, and Essex, but it is very local and seems to be restricted to a more or less limited area in all its known haunts, among which the most favoured are perhaps the New Forest in Hampshire and Abbots Wood in Sussex. In some years it may be fairly common, or even plentiful, and then becomes quite scarce during several seasons in the same place.

The Least Black Arches (*Celama confusalis* Herr.-Schäff.)

Very similar to *Nola strigula*, but whiter; the first line is curved towards the second tuft of raised scales, thence gently curved to the inner margin, above which there is a slight

inward angle or elbow ; the second line is less wavy ; hind
wings whitish grey with a black central dot, and in the male
whiter along the inner area.   The head and palpi of this species
are white, but *strigula* has a greyish white head and dark palpi.
Again, the antennae in the male of the present species are
ciliate, but in male *strigula* they are bipectinate (Pl. **14,** 8, 9).
A grey form, ab. *columbina* Image, occurs in Epping Forest.

The caterpillar, which feeds in July and August on the leaves
of oak, beech, sloe, and apple, etc., is reddish, inclining to
yellow on the back, which is traversed by black lines, the
central double and interrupted on rings seven to nine by rusty
V-shaped marks.

The moth flies in May and June.

This species appears to have a wider distribution than either
of the others.   It is the only one known with certainty to
occur in Ireland, and it is widely spread in that country.   In
Scotland it is found in Perthshire and Ayrshire, and probably
is present in other parts ; a specimen was taken on the Isle
of Canna on May 27, 1956.   In England it is obtained in most
counties, except perhaps the northern, although it has been
recorded from various parts of Yorkshire.

The Scarce Black Arches (*Celama tuberculana* Bosc.)

The general colour of this moth is white ; the fore wings
more or less sprinkled and clouded with brownish grey or dark
grey, and crossed by two black lines, the first curved and the
second slightly waved, indented and edged inwardly with
ochreous brown ; the three raised tufts are white, capped with
grey (Pl. **14,** 10–14).

This is the only really variable species among the five
occurring in this country.   In some specimens the space
between the cross lines is largely filled in with dark grey, and
in other specimens the wings are almost entirely white, traces
of the cross lines being the only markings.

The late Robert Adkin, who reared this species from the

1, 2. **The Drinker**, *males*.
3, 4. **The Drinker**, *females*.

Grass Eggar: *eggs, natural size and enlarged; caterpillar.*

egg, allowed South to select specimens from his fine series to illustrate the range of aberration ; these are figured on Pl. **14.**

Caterpillar brownish inclining to purplish, with an ochreous line along the middle of the back and some brown V-shaped black marks. Head blackish brown. It feeds in May, after hibernation, on various clovers, preferring the blossoms, and bird's-foot trefoil (*Lotus corniculatus*).

The moth appears some time between mid-July and mid-August. The late Mr. Tugwell, by keeping some larvae, reared from the egg, in a warm room induced them to feed up instead of hibernating, and they attained the moth state in December.

This is another exceedingly local species in England. It was first taken at Bembridge in the Isle of Wight in 1858, and one or two specimens have since been obtained in that island. Examples have also occurred on the cliffs near Hastings, and at Folkestone ; one was recorded as taken in a light trap at Woodbridge in Suffolk, July 21, 1904, and it has recently been reported from Norfolk (July 16, 1947, R. G. Todd), and from Dorset (July 21, 1951, E. H. Wild). The headquarters for the species in this country are the Deal sandhills, on the Kentish coast, where it was discovered over a quarter of a century ago, and probably occurs still.

LITHOSIINAE

Footman Moths

The members of this sub-family of Arctiidae occurring in the British Isles are not numerous ; we can only muster some sixteen species, and although a few are not uncommon, several are exceedingly local.

The moths of the genus *Lithosia*, when resting, fold their drab or buff-coloured wings down closely along the body, and they then have a very elongate and stiff appearance which probably gave rise to their English name " Footmen." Most of them are very inactive or even torpid during the daytime. They repose on the branches and leaves of trees and bushes, or among heather and other low herbage, and often fall to the ground when disturbed. At dusk they become active and then fly pretty briskly. Unlike the " Tigers " they have long tongues and some of them are attracted by " sugar."

The caterpillars are very hairy, the hairs arising in tufts from warts (tubercles) are usually short, but in some species are of moderate length. The majority hatch from the egg in the late summer, and do not complete their growth until the following year, about May or June. Some of them are known to be more or less active through the winter. In a state of nature, most of the caterpillars feed on lichens and algae growing on trees, bushes, rocks, or on the ground, but many kinds in confinement will thrive on a diet of lettuce or even withered leaves.

In all cases the chrysalids are enclosed in silken cocoons, and these are spun up among the lichens, in crevices of bark, or other suitable crannies.

The Red-necked Footman (*Atolmis rubricollis* Linn.)

When newly emerged from the chrysalis this moth is black on all the wings, but it soon loses its early velvety sheen and becomes sooty in appearance ; the last rings are orange, but all the rest of the body is black ; the thorax also is black, but the part nearest the head, termed the collar, is red, hence the common English name Red-neck moth given to it by Harris (1778). Haworth called it the " Black Footman."

The caterpillar is greyish, more or less freckled with ochreous ; three lines along the back, the central one whitish, the others black and interrupted ; the hairs arising from reddish warts are brown or greyish brown. Head black. It feeds from July to October on green algae (*Pleurococcus naegelii*), growing on fir and oak, but also on beech, and on old palings. Chrysalis, glossy dark red brown in a tight-fitting cocoon of silk mixed with the hairs of the caterpillar ; spun up among the lichen. The moth is shown on Pl. **16,** 1, and the caterpillar and chrysalis on Pl. **45,** 2, 2*a*.

The moth is on the wing in June and July ; in forward seasons as early as the end of May. On a sunny afternoon it may be seen careering around trees, generally pretty high up. When resting the moths sit about on the trees or on the herbage under them. In some years it occurs in large numbers, but it is not usually very abundant, and sometimes even in its best localities only a few specimens will be seen during the season. It frequents woods, especially the larger ones, throughout the southern half of England up to Norfolk on the east, and Hereford on the west. Recently reported from Caernarvonshire. In the northern counties it is rare, and is not common in Scotland or Ireland.

Abroad, its range is through central and northern Europe, except the extreme north, to Dalmatia, Altai, and Amurland.

The Muslin Footman (*Nudaria mundana* Linn.)

This delicate little moth has the semi-transparent fore wings pale greyish, faintly tinged with brown ; crossed by irregular brownish lines ; the hind wings are paler, shaded with a darker tint on the outer margins. Occasionally all the wings have a smoky tinge. The moth is shown on Pl. **16,** 3, and the caterpillar and chrysalis on Pl. **25,** 2, 2*a*.

The caterpillar is greyish, with a broad whitish or yellowish stripe along the back, divided down the centre and edged by blackish lines; a velvety black mark on ring seven; raised warts and hairs dark greyish. Head black, shining ; face yellowish. It may be found in April and May, after hibernation, on rocks, stone walls, especially those formed of loose cobbles or shale, trees, bushes, and even gate posts. South beat them from an old hawthorn hedge bordering a damp meadow in Middlesex, and collected them in numbers from the hollows of field boundary walls in North Devon. They feed on the tiny lichens and algae that grow in such places as those indicated. The green, or yellowish green, chrysalis is enclosed in a rather loose muslin-like silken cocoon, and is not difficult to obtain, especially from walls. It appears to be pretty generally distributed throughout England and Wales, except perhaps the midland and eastern counties ; it occurs in the east and west of Scotland. In Ireland it is common, and often abundant, locally.

Distribution : northern and central Europe.

The Round-winged Muslin (*Thumatha senex* Hübn).

As indicated by Haworth's English name the wings of this moth are rounder in outline than those of the Muslin Footman, also named by Haworth. In general colour it agrees with that species, but it differs in having a larger central dot, and the cross lines are represented by blackish dots which, however, are not always well defined (Pl. **16, 4**).

The caterpillar, as described by Buckler, is deep reddish grey, thickly covered with hairs which are of two kinds ; the majority are pale brown with black points and slightly feathered, others are longer, black, and densely feathered with soft pale brown plumage. Head black and shining. It feeds in August and, after hibernation, in May on algae growing on dead reeds and mosses growing on the ground in marshes and fens. It is known to eat *Peltigera canina*, and the mosses *Hypnum sericeum*, and *Weissia serrata*. Although occurring, in July and August, in marshy places in several parts of southern England and Wales, it is especially common in fen land. In such localities as Wicken, for example, it flies at early dusk in hundreds all over the fen on favourable nights, but if there happens to be a breeze the moths will not leave their retreat among the herbage. Later on in the night, if on the wing, they readily assemble around a brightly burning lamp, and are satisfied to sit on the herbage illuminated by its rays. In northern England it is known to be not uncommon in some districts of Yorkshire, and it probably occurs in other counties also. There appear to be only two records from Ireland and one from Scotland.

The Rosy Footman (*Miltochrista miniata* Forst.)

The fore wings of this pretty little moth are ochreous yellow tinged with pink ; the front and hind margins are bright pink, in some cases approaching vermilion ; the markings are bluish black ; hind wings rather paler (Pl. **16,** 2). It varies in the amount of black markings, which are sometimes almost absent, and in colour ranges from yellow to orange. Specimens of a yellow form ab. *flava* de Graaf. have been taken.

The caterpillar is dark drab covered above with blackish and mouse-coloured plumed hairs ; on rings one and eleven the plumose hairs are replaced by short simple ones ; the hairs of the side tufts are plain. Head brown, the cheeks outlined in black (adapted from Hellins). Algae and dog lichen (*Peltigera canina*) growing upon the stems and branches of trees supply this caterpillar with food. It will also feed on dead moist oak and sallow leaves and lettuce. It seems to nibble on all favourable opportunities throughout the winter. It hatches from the egg in August, and is full grown in May. Boden, writing in September, 1896 (*The Entomologist*), noted that some caterpillars had then attained the perfect state, while others were still feeding, and he adds that the caterpillars actually attacked and ate up the moths. Although there seems to be few records from the Midlands, this species appears to be widely distributed over England as far north as Yorkshire. In Ireland it has been recorded from Claring Bridge and East Galway. The moth is out in July. It is a wood-loving insect, but is also found on heaths, and even in lanes and the borders of fields when plenty of trees occur in such places. It may occasionally be beaten out of trees and bushes in the daytime but it is on the wing at dusk, and although it is a high flier, specimens come within reach now and then. Light and sugar both attract it. The species ranges through central and northern Europe, and in Asia to Japan.

The Dew Moth (*Setina irrorella* Linn.)

Varies in colour from yellowish buff to creamy white, the colour on the margins always deeper ; the rows of black spots on the fore wings are usually well defined, but sometimes those of the two central series are very faint, or quite absent, whilst an unusual number appear in the outer marginal series. Occasionally black scales appear on the veins, connecting the spots, and forming the figures ⋜ more or less distinctly ; such forms are known as ab. *signata* Borkh. The moth appears in June and July (Pl. **16,** 5, 6).

When resting, the moth hangs from a blade of grass, or leaf of some plant ; it then has a very transparent appearance. Barrett suggests that this gave rise to the English name it now bears, and by which it was known to Haworth and entomologists of his time.

Buckler and Hellins describe the caterpillar as blackish brown above, and dark reddish grey or purplish grey on the sides ; a series of yellow spots along the middle of the back, then a white and yellow interrupted line, followed by a light yellow stripe under the spiracles ; raised spots blackish, some white ; hairs blackish brown ; head black.

It feeds, in the sunshine, on the black and yellow lichens growing in the haunts of the species, which are edges of cliffs and rough stony places near the sea, and also on hillsides. The species occurs, perhaps, more abundantly on the Kentish and Sussex coast than inland, but it is certainly not confined to the cliffs at Dover and Folkestone in Kent, or at Ventnor, Isle of Wight. Among inland localities for it are Box Hill, Ranmore, Reigate, and other places on the Surrey hills. It has also been recorded from the Cotswolds in Gloucestershire ; the Isle of Man ; St. Davids, South Wales ; Aberdeenshire,

Sutherlandshire, and the Tweed, Tay, Clyde, and Argyll districts in Scotland. For Ireland, Kane gives Mayo; " Ardrahan, County Galway, and west through the Burren of Clare, widely spread."

The Four-dotted Footman (*Cybosia mesomella* Linn.)

Fore wings pale creamy white, the margins yellowish : a black dot near the costa, and another below near the inner margin ; hind wings suffused with blackish grey. Rarely the fore wings are yellow with a whitish central shade, and the hind wings are yellowish (Pl. **16,** 7).

The caterpillar is velvety blackish grey ; warts thickly set with densely feathered blackish hairs. Feeds in April and May, after hibernation, on algae growing on heather. In confinement it will, according to Buckler, eat heather and fresh or withered leaves of sallow.

Fairly well distributed over England. It appears to be absent from Ireland, but in Scotland it is known to occur in the Clyde, Solway, and Moray districts, and has been recorded from Aberdeenshire. In the South of England it affects heaths and the more open woods ; sometimes not uncommon in such places. The moth, in June, may be disturbed from bushes, or put up from the heather as one walks through. As the sun goes down it may often be seen on the wing, but later in the evening is its chief time of activity. In Lancashire and Cheshire it is found on the mosses, and Cannock Chase in Staffordshire is a noted locality for it. Still obtained in Chippenham, Wicken, and other Cambridgeshire fens, also at Wood Walton Fen, Huntingdonshire.

The Four-spotted Footman (*Lithosis quadra* Linn.)

The sexes of this species are very different in appearance. The fore wings of the male are grey tinged with yellowish, except on the outer fourth ; the basal fourth is yellow. The female is larger and yellow in colour ; each fore wing has two black spots, sometimes unusually large, sometimes mere dots, and more rarely absent altogether (Pl. **19**, 1, 4).

Caterpillar blackish with four wavy yellow lines along the back, the spaces between the lines powdered and freckled with yellow giving a grey appearance ; raised spots on the back red, those on the sides greyish ; a black cross on rings three, seven, and eleven ; hairs grey mixed with black. Head black and glossy. It feeds, after hibernation, in May and June, on lichens, preferring those upon oak trees. In the breeding cage it is apt to eat its companions, especially when many are crowded into a small receptacle (Pl. **25,** 3, 3a).

The moth emerges in July, and during that month, and sometimes in August, it may be seen on tree-trunks ; but it more often reposes on the branches, from which it may be dislodged by jarring the boughs with a stick, when it drops rather than flies towards the ground, but generally manages to arrest its downward course by catching hold of a spray of bracken or some other plant and there awaits capture. Night is the usual time of flight, but it is on the wing at dusk. It is partial to " sugar " and has been known to visit flowers.

This species has been recorded from a large number of localities in England extending from the Scilly Isles to the Scottish border. From the circumstances connected with many of such captures one is led to suspect that the insect has migratory habits. In England the most favoured locality is the New Forest in Hampshire, where it abounds in some seasons, but is quite scarce in others. It occurs, more or less regularly, in the larger woods in Dorset, extending into Devon ; also in Sussex ranging into Kent, but is only occasionally common in either of these counties. Generally considered to be uncommon in the eastern counties, but has been reported to occur in large numbers at Aldeburgh in Suffolk. In Ireland very local from Louth to Kerry.

Distribution : central Europe, southern Sweden, Livonia, Dalmatia, Armenia, Amurland, Korea, and Japan.

Fox Moth: *caterpillars.*

1, 2. **Small Lappet,** *male and female.*
3, 4. **The Lappet,** *male and female.*

The Buff Footman (*Lithosia deplana* Esp.)

Fore wings, ochreous grey, tinged with yellow on the basal half of the front margins ; hind wings paler, becoming greyer on the outer area ; fringes of all the wings yellow. The male is fairly constant in colour, but the female sometimes has a distinct yellow stripe on the front margin of the fore wings extending to the fringes (ab. *ochreola* Hübn.) ; more rarely in the New Forest, Dorset, and S.W. Ireland, a form occurs with the fore wings orange buff, and the hind wings only slightly tinged with grey (ab. *unicolor* Bankes) (Pl. **16,** 8, 9).

Caterpillar, greyish, or greenish grey, freckled with darker, hairs grey inclining to brownish ; a broad creamy or yellowish stripe, edged with black and traversed by a dark central line along the back. Head blackish and glossy. From August to June on green algae (*Pleurococcus*) growing on stems and branches of yew, oak, and beech. In confinement will eat withered leaves of sallow and lettuce (Pl. **23,** 1–1*b*).

A local species, and although recorded now and then from several other parts of the country, and also from Killarney in Ireland, seems to be pretty much confined to the counties of Surrey, Sussex, Hampshire, Dorset, Devon, Norfolk, and Kent. The moth, which is out in July, rests during the day upon the boughs and among the foliage of oak, beech, and yew, the latter especially in the Dorking district of Surrey.

Distribution : central and south-east Europe, southern Scandinavia, Livonia, northern Italy, and Russia.

The Dingy Footman (*Lithosia griseola* Hübn.)

Haworth's English name for this moth was the " Dun Footman." In its typical form the fore wings are pale greyish with a yellowish front edging ; the latter most distinct towards the base ; the hind wings are whitish ochreous more or less suffused with grey. The pale form, ab. *flava* Haw. (*stramineola* Doubl. =), at one time considered a distinct species (the Straw-coloured Footman of Haworth), has pale straw-coloured fore wings and white ochreous hind wings (Pl. **19,** 2, 3).

Caterpillar, sooty brown, with a darker line down the middle of the back and an interrupted yellow or orange line or stripe on each side of it ; dark brown hairs arising from dark warts ; head glossy black (described from a skin). It may be looked for in the spring moths on the lichens affecting alders and sallows growing in fens and marshy places (Pl. **20,** 2).

The moth is abundant in the Cambridgeshire, Huntingdon shire, and Norfolk fens, and is common in boggy places in the New Forest, but it probably occurs in all suitable places throughout England and Wales. It does not seem to have been observed in Ireland, but has been recorded from Moray in Scotland. The yellow variety, which by the way is not known to occur abroad, is found with the ordinary form, chiefly in the fens and in the New Forest ; but it is also to be obtained, though less frequently, in Surrey (Weybridge district), Berk-shire (Reading district), and still more rarely elsewhere. It is out in July.

Distribution : central Europe, southern Russia, Ural, Altai, Amurland, Korea, and Japan.

The Common Footman (*Lithosia lurideola* Zinck.)

Fore wings, leaden grey with a yellow stripe terminating in a point at the tip of the wing ; collar yellow tipped with leaden grey ; the hind wings are pale ochreous yellow. It appears in July, or sometimes at the end of June.

Caterpillar, dark greyish covered with blackish hairs arising from black warts on the back, and yellowish hairs from similar coloured warts on the sides ; three black or blackish lines on the back, and an orange stripe along the sides from the fourth to eleventh rings ; head black. August to June. Generally supposed to feed, in a state of nature, on algae and lichens growing on trees and bushes. It has been reared on the foliage of sallow, apple, and oak ; also known to eat buckthorn, clematis, dogwood, etc. South occasionally beat it from old hedgerows, and frequently saw it on trunks of poplar and ash upon which not much in the way of lichen could be seen. Such caterpillars, when taken, have almost invariably spun up soon afterwards. The moth is shown on Pl. **19,** 5, 6, and the caterpillar on Pl. **23,** 2.

This species is perhaps the commonest and most generally distributed member of the genus in England. It becomes much less frequent in northern parts of Lancashire, and in Yorkshire it is local, but recorded as common in the south-east of that county. It occurs in Scotland, whence it has been recorded from Clydesdale, Aberdeenshire, and Moray. Kane states that it is common near Galway, and also gives Castle Bellingham, Clogher Head (not rare), and Athlone as Irish localities. Also reported from Wicklow, Cork, and common in Clare (Donovan).

Distributed over Europe, except the extreme north, Andalusia and southern Italy; the range extending to Asia Minor and Armenia.

The Scarce Footman (*Lithosia complana* Linn.)

Very similar in appearance to the last species, the yellow stripe along the front edge of the fore wings, however, does not terminate in a point, but is continued through to the fringes; the male has a costal fold with a tuft of scales beneath, which *L. lurideola* does not have; collar orange throughout; the hind wings are sometimes distinctly yellow, and with but little, if any, greyish shading on the front area (Pl. **19,** 7, 8).

Caterpillar, brown or brownish grey above, and paler beneath; a white-edged black line along the middle of the back, and a row of orange spots, alternating with whitish ones, on each side of the line; the orange spots faint or absent on rings one to three; an interrupted yellow or orange stripe along the sides; the brownish warts are thickly studded with short greyish brown hairs. Head black and glossy (described from a skin). From August to June. The most usual food is probably algae on trees, but it is said to eat moss, knotgrass, clover, bramble, and the flowers of bird's-foot trefoil, etc. (Pl. **23**, 3).

The moth is out in July and part of August, and may be disturbed in the daytime from its resting-place among heather and low herbage. It is on the wing in the dusk of the evening, and when the weather is favourable, flies freely. As it has a weakness for " sweets, " it should be looked for at night, by the aid of a lantern, on the flowers of knapweed and thistle. It chiefly affects heaths, but it is also found in woods, and on sandhills by the sea, as in Norfolk, also at Wood Walton Fen, Huntingdonshire. A local species, but usually to be more or less frequently met with in all the eastern and southern counties, and in some of the midland. Rare in Wales, Cheshire, Lancashire, and Yorkshire. Only doubtfully recorded from Scotland. In Ireland it is widely distributed, and, according to Kane, not uncommon where it occurs.

The Northern Footman (*Lithosia sericea* Gregson)

Gregson named and described this insect in 1860, and in the following year Guenée described it as *L. molybdeola*. It seems to be peculiar to England, and only occurs on the mosses of Lancashire and Cheshire. The fore wings are somewhat narrower and darker in colour than those of the Scarce Footman ; and the hind wings are suffused, to a greater or lesser extent, with dark grey. Some entomologists maintain that this is probably only a small form of *L. complana* Linn. According to Mr. Pierce it cannot be specifically separated from that species or from *L. pygmaeola* Doubl. by the genitalia, the usual test in such matters. Prout, however, has stated that Speyer, in 1867, pointed out structural differences, not only in the shape of the wings, but also in the size of the costal tuft of scales on the underside of the fore wings. It should be added

1, 2. Short-cloaked Moth.
3, 4, 5. Kent Black Arches.
6, 7. Small Black Arches.
8, 9. Least Black Arches.
10, 11, 12, 13, 14. Scarce Black Arches.

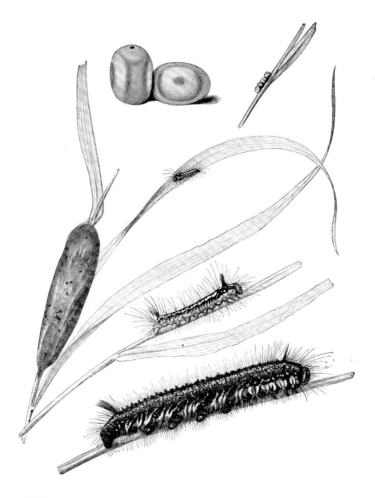

The Drinker: *eggs, natural size and enlarged, caterpillars and cocoon.*

that there does not seem to be any material difference between the caterpillar of *complana* and that of *sericea*. The caterpillar is said to feed on algae growing on heather. Anyway, the question of form or species may here be left open. The fact of the Northern, or Gregson's, Footman being an exclusive British production invests the insect with an interest greatly above that attaching to many of our moths. Both sexes of the species are depicted on Pl. **21**, 1, 2.

The Pigmy Footman (*Lithosia pygmaeola* Doubl.)

Ochreous white, sometimes tinged with greyish, or with yellowish ; hind wings clouded with greyish on the front area. Female almost always smaller than the male. The fore wings vary a good deal in the matter of colour, the extremes being yellow and dark grey (Pl. **21**, 3, 4).

Buckler describes the caterpillar as brown on the back, with a central thick black line, and two dark brown lines ; sides paler brown, with a dusty white line along the spiracles ; the warts (tubercles) with short brown hairs, and the head black. August to June.

This extremely local little moth was unknown as an inhabitant of Britain until 1847, when it was described as *L. pygmaeola*, by Doubleday in the *Zoologist* for that year, and noted as having been found among rushes on the coast of Kent. Two years later the insect was again referred to, and it was then stated to be confined to a " space of about four hundred yards in extent, on the coast of Deal." It then became known as the " Deal Footman." During the past hundred years or so large numbers have no doubt been removed from this locality, which was the only British one it was known to occur in. It is still to be found there, although said to be less common than formerly. In the *Entomologist* for September, 1912, this species was recorded as not uncommon on marram grass growing on the Norfolk coast. It has also been recorded from south-east Kent.

The Hoary Footman (*Lithosia caniola* Hübn.)

Fore wings silky whitish grey with a yellowish streak along the front edge; the hind wings are whitish with a faint yellowish tinge. Some of the specimens are entirely whitish (ab. *lacteola* Boisd.). July and August, sometimes earlier (Pl. **21**, 5, 6).

Caterpillar greyish brown, with a black line along the back, and a series of irregular orange marks, representing stripes, on each side of it ; these orange marks are outwardly edged with black ; an orange line low down along the sides ; warts greyish or brownish, each bearing a tuft of short pale hairs. Head blackish, shining, notched on the crown, and studded with pale bristles in front. Fed on lettuce from April 30, **the date they** were received from Mr. Walker of Torquay. They **were then** quite small, **the** largest not more than half an inch in length. They pupated in June, and the moths emerged in July, all fine specimens (Pl. **20**, 1, 1a).

In the open the caterpillar feeds upon the black lichens growing on rocks, etc., by the sea ; also upon Dutch clover (*Trifolium repens*), kidney vetch (*Anthyllis vulneraria*), and bird's-foot trefoil (*Lotus corniculatus*).

This species was not known to occur in any part of the British Isles until August, 1861, when the late Mr. C. G. Barrett took four specimens on the Hill of Howth in Ireland (*vide Ent. Annual*, 1862, p. 106). A large number were subsequently captured or reared from caterpillars obtained in the same locality by others. Kane ("Cat. Lep. Ireland") remarks that the colony flourished at Howth for many years, but that the species seemingly perished in the severe winters of 1878 or 1879, and unless a specimen taken in 1890 was this species, has not since been seen there. The only other Irish locality from which it has been recorded (August, 1866) is on the coast near Waterford. A single specimen was taken there in 1954 by Dr. de Worms and the late R. E. Ellison. Torquay, where the species was first observed in 1864, is now a noted locality, and it is said to occur in places along the coast to Babbacombe.

Other localities in Devon are Dartmouth, Torcross, and Bolt Head. Barrett found the species rarely in two places by the sea in South Pembrokeshire, and mentions Rye in Sussex, and south-east Kent. Recently reported from Cornwall.

Mr. J. Walker informed South that the moths fly at dusk, and that they all seem to get active at almost the same moment, and settle again in the same way at the end of their first flight, which lasts about half an hour. After dark the rays of a lamp directed downwards into the bushes will attract them from their retreat. Occasionally they visit " sugar."

Abroad this is a southern species, but its range extends to western Germany, the Tyrol, Switzerland, and South Hungary, as well as to England ; also to Asia Minor.

The Orange Footman (*Lithosia sororcula* Hufn.)

This moth is orange yellow on the fore wings, and a paler shade of the same colour on the hind wings. Except that the tint is brighter in some specimens and darker in others, there is nothing to mention in the way of aberration (Pl. **21**, 7, 8).

The caterpillar is white on the back with five black stripes, the outer ones broader than the others ; all these stripes are broken up by brownish patches, and they fail to show at all on the eighth ring, which, therefore, is conspicuously white ; the sides are smoky grey marked with white on the second and third rings ; the warts are reddish, bearing smoky grey hairs. It may be found from July to September on the lichens and algae growing on the trunks of oak trees. The moth does not appear until the following May or June, when it may be beaten from branches. Not uncommon in the woods, chiefly oak, of Norfolk, Suffolk, Essex, Kent, Surrey, Hampshire, and Dorset ; it also occurs in Cambridgeshire and Sussex. In Berkshire and Buckinghamshire it is fairly common, but seems to affect the beech woods in those counties. Recorded from Ireland by Birchall, who stated that it was abundant at Killarney. Donovan doubts this record.

The Dotted Footman (*Pelosia muscerda* Hufn.)

The fore wings are pale grey suffused with pale reddish
brown except on the costal area : there are six black dots,
two before the middle of the wing and placed above the inner
margin, and four beyond the middle in an oblique series from
the costa ; the hind wings are pale brownish grey, becoming
somewhat darker towards the apex (Pl. **21,** 9, 10).

Caterpillar velvety blackish brown, marbled with reddish
grey ; stripe along middle of the back, and a line on each side
of it deep black ; warts and hairs brown, the latter short but
numerous ; a pair of red spots on ring one, and another pair
on ring twelve ; beneath the spiracles is a fine reddish grey
line ; under surface pinkish grey ; head small and blackish
(Buckler). So far it has escaped detection in its fenny home,
but it has been reared from eggs laid by a captured female.
Caterpillars obtained in this way seem to have thrived on a
mixed diet of algae growing on alder and sallow, mosses, and
withered leaves of bramble, sallow, also on lettuce. August
to May. Buckler states that the dark chestnut brown pupa
is enclosed in a double cocoon, the inner a webby one of
greyish silk, and the outer one thinner and composed of white
silk. The whole affair was formed in a curled-up bramble
leaf. The caterpillar is figured on Pl. **20,** 3.

The moth is out in late July and through August. It has
been obtained in a certain marshy locality in the New Forest,
Hampshire, and also in some marshes at Sandwich, Kent. Its
chief haunts are, however, in the fens of Norfolk, such as
those on the River Bure, and Brundall fen on the Yare, but
Horning and Ranworth are, perhaps, the headquarters of the
species. It may be mentioned that when Stephens wrote
about this insect in 1829 only two specimens had then occurred
in Britain, and these had been found in a marsh at Horning
floating upon the water in a ditch.

Distribution : central Europe, Denmark, Sweden, Livonia,
Dalmatia, Corsica and Sardinia, Amurland and Japan.

1. **Red-necked Footman.**
2. **Rosy Footman.**
3. **Muslin Footman.**
4. **Round-winged Muslin.**
5, 6. **Dew Moth,** *male and female.*
7. **Four-dotted Footman.**
8, 9. **Buff Footman,** *male and female.*

1, 1a. **The Lappet**: *eggs, natural size and enlarged, and caterpillar.*
2, 2a. **Small Lappet**: *caterpillar and cocoon.*

ARCTIINAE and CALLIMORPHINAE

Tiger Moths

The moths in this sub-family have short, or, rather, stout bodies, and ample wings ; and as the tongue is imperfectly developed in most of the species, flowers have no attraction for them.

The White Ermine (*Spilosoma lubricipeda* Linn.)

Older English names for this generally distributed and often common species are The Great Ermine Moth of Wilkes (1773), Harris (1778), and The Large Ermine of Haworth.

On Pl. **22** will be found three colour-forms of the moth. Fig. 1 has the typical whitish colour, Fig. 2 is creamy on the fore wings, and Fig. 3 has the fore wings buff. The last represents a specimen from Scotland, where, especially in the western parts of the country, and also in the north of Ireland, and the north-west of England, buff forms, both paler and much darker than the one figured, are not uncommon. Sometimes the Scottish specimens have smoky hind wings. As regards the black spots on the wings, the species is subject to considerable variation. In some examples almost all the markings are entirely absent ; in others they are very small and numerous, or large in size and number ; the central spots on the fore wings are often united, forming irregular designs. Again, there may be an unusual amount of black spotting on the outer margins, and all other parts of the wings free of spots. All these aberrations in marking, except, perhaps, the central cluster, seem to occur in the various colour forms. An uncommon form, known as ab. *walkerii* Curtis (Pl. **27,** 5), has the black scales gathered together into streaks along the nervures of the fore wings of which the ground colour is pale brownish ochreous. The more usual streaked specimens are known as ab. *godarti* Oberthür, which is recessive.

The caterpillar which is often not uncommon in gardens in

August and September, or even later, is brown, with long hairs, and a reddish stripe along the middle of the back. It feeds on the foliage of low-growing plants, and does not appear to be specially attached to any particular kind. The chrysalis is dark brown, in a close-fitting cocoon of silk and hair from the caterpillar, spun up in odd corners on the ground or at the base of a wall or fence, sometimes between the pales (Pl. **28**).

The moth emerges in June, and may be seen sitting on walls, fences, trees, or on the herbage growing on hedge banks ; or even on the bare ground. It often flies into houses when lighted up, and is a frequent attendant at the public gas lamps and electric lights. The geographical range of this species extends through northern and central Europe southward to North-west Africa, and eastward to Amurland.

The Water Ermine (*Spilosoma urticae* Esp.)

The specimens of this white moth, depicted on Pl. **22**, 7, 8, are of the form usually met with in Britain. To Haworth, Stephens, and other early entomologists this was known by the English name of the " Water Ermine " (*S. papyrata* Marsham), whilst a rarer form—with a minute dot on the disc of the fore wings, and three dusky spots on the hind wings, as in the White Ermine—was the " Dingy White " of Haworth. Occasionally specimens are obtained with extra black spots on the basal and front areas of the fore wings.

Caterpillar, dark brown with a purplish tinge, the hairs, arising in spreading tufts from black warts, are dark brownish ; spiracles white ; head black and glossy. Feeds in July and August on a variety of marsh plants, among which are yellow loosestrife (*Lysimachia vulgaris*), mint (*Mentha aquatica*), lousewort (*Pedicularis*), water dock (*Rumex hydrolapathum*), and iris. It seems to affect plants growing under bushes, rather than those more exposed. It is, presumably, not difficult to rear in confinement, as there is a record of eight broods belonging to three generations, and all descendants of a captured female, having been reared by Mr. Bacot. Chrysalis dark reddish brown, in a cocoon similar to that of the last species.

The moth, which emerges in June, is rarely seen away from its favourite haunts, which are marshes and fens ; its English name is therefore a very appropriate one. It is not often observed in the daytime, but is on the wing early in the evening, and later on is pretty sure to be attracted to any strong light that may be set up in its neighbourhood. The best localities for the species seem to be the fens of Norfolk, Suffolk, and Cambridgeshire, but it used to be fairly plentiful in many suitable parts of Hertfordshire and East Kent, and may still occur in some of the marshes between Dartford and Gravesend : it is found in Sussex in the Lewes and Brighton districts, and has been recorded from Kimmeridge in Dorset, from the Isle of Wight, from near Burton-on-Trent, from the Lancaster district, and from Pembrokeshire, South Wales. In Scotland it is rare, and is not known to occur in Ireland.

The distribution abroad extends over central and northern Europe, through South Russia to Amurland.

The Buff Ermine (*Spilosoma lutea* Hufn.)

This species is now known by the English name of the Buff Ermine, but the names bestowed upon it by some ancient writers were perhaps hardly more suitable. Thus Wilkes in 1773 called it the " Spotted Buff Moth," and Harris five years later dubbed it the " Cream-dot Stripe." The ground colour is generally some shade of buff, in the paler specimens merging into cream, and in the darker to yellowish ochre. In the matter of black marking the range of variation is extensive ; Tugwell named a fasciated form ab. *fasciata*. The specimens figured on Pl. 24 illustrate something of this variation, both as regards colouring and marking. The females are, as a rule, paler than the males, but occasionally examples of the latter sex are quite as pale as any female. Figs. 7 and 8 approach ab. *zatima* Cramer. Originally this form was only known to occur in Heligoland. The same form, or a modification of it, was described by Haworth as *radiata* from a Yorkshire specimen. Then, in 1837, specimens of the variety were reared with the normal form of the species from caterpillars obtained at Saltfleet in Lincolnshire ; and subsequently a few more examples were reported from the last named county, and elsewhere. In 1891 a specimen of ab. *zatima* emerged from an assortment of chrysalids sent to Harrison of Barnsley (*vide Entom.*, xxvii. 95–7). This particular specimen was of the female sex, and it paired with a male which was also an aberration, but not of the *zatima* form. Some of the offspring resulting from this union were of the female parent form, others favoured the male parent, and others again were inter-mediate. In the course of a few generations almost entire broods of the *zatima* variety were obtained. Allowing the sexes of *zatima* to mate with those of more or less ordinary *lutea*, the late W. H. Tugwell obtained many very interesting aberrations, one of which he named ab. *eboraci*. The *zatima* form and its various modifications were reared by entomo-logists all over the country, and presumably directly or in-directly from the original Barnsley stock. In Yorkshire especially the form was improved ; the specimens were larger and darker, and there was a tendency towards the almost entirely black form known as ab. *deschangei* Depuiset.

The pale whitish green eggs are laid in batches on leaves, sometimes high up on birch trees, or virginia creeper, but more usually on the foliage of low growing plants ; it is often common in gardens. At first the caterpillar is tinged with yellowish, but it afterwards becomes greyish, and finally brownish. When full grown the hairs, with which the body is clothed, are brown ; there is a yellowish or whitish grey stripe along each side, and an obscure somewhat reddish tinted line down the middle of the back. Head glossy brown.

The glossy reddish brown chrysalis is enclosed in a dingy

coloured web-like cocoon, which is spun up among leaves or litter on the ground. The late R. Adkin found some of these cocoons spun up between the folds of an old brown blanket used as a covering for a rabbit hutch in winter. The moth emerges in June. Occasionally, in confinement, specimens will leave the chrysalis in the autumn instead of passing the winter therein, as they more usually do (Pl. **31**).

A common and often abundant species over the greater part of the British Isles. Its range abroad extends through central and northern Europe, South Russia, and Tartary to Amurland, Korea, and West China.

The Muslin Moth (*Cycnia mendica* Clerck)

The early British authors knew this moth as the " Spotted Muslin " or " Seven Spot Ermine " (Harris, 1778). The male is dark brown or blackish, with a few usually obscure black dots on each wing. The female is silky white, with more clearly defined, and often more numerous, black dots (Pl. **22,** 4–6). On Pl. **27** will be found figures of rarer and more extreme aberrations of the female. Those represented by Figs. 3, 4, 6, 7, were reared by the late G. T. Porritt, of Huddersfield, who at the same time obtained a number of other interesting intermediate examples (" Trans. Ent. Soc. Lond.," 1889, p. 441, Pl. 14). Variation in the other direction is towards the complete suppression of the black dots ; and I have seen specimens with only one such dot on each wing.

In the ab. *rustica* Hübn. shown on the same plate, it will be noted that the males approximate somewhat to the female coloration ; the specimens (Figs. 1, 2), were bred by the late Robert Adkin in 1887. This form was not known to occur in the British Isles until 1885, when Mr. de V. Kane detected specimens in a collection of insects made in Co. Cork, Ireland. It was next heard of from Belfast, and then, in 1886, again in Co. Cork, an example of each sex was taken. The female specimen laid eggs, and some of these were sent to the late

Mr. Adkin, who not only was successful in rearing the moths, but in 1889 obtained a pairing between an almost white male *rustica* and an ordinary English female. Only four eggs were laid, and from these two male moths resulted in May, 1890, both intermediate in colour between the two forms. Large numbers of specimens resulting from crosses between *mendica* and *rustica* were bred by Adkin, Onslow and Cockayne ; white is dominant to brown ♂, with a modifier. Adkin also named a form with dark grey wing veins, from the south of Ireland, ab. *venosa* (*Entom.*, lv. 79). In all its early stages *rustica* is identical with ordinary *mendica*.

Male specimens with pale yellowish grey coloured wings have been reared from eggs laid by a female captured at Eltham, Kent, exhibiting a tendency to the *rustica* form. In the Barnsley district, Yorkshire, the males are paler than usual, but in the Sheffield area of the same county the males are black. From North Durham chrysalids, South had a smoky greyish form of the male.

The caterpillar is brownish grey covered with yellowish brown hairs arising from greyish-ringed pale brown warts ; a paler line along the middle of the back, and some white dots forming a broken line below the black outlined spiracles. Head pale chestnut brown, glossy. When newly hatched it is whitish, tinged with yellow and semi-transparent ; the dots and hairs are dark grey. After the first moult the colour is greyish with black dots and blackish hairs. Head yellowish, brown tinged. It feeds in July, sometimes earlier, and August, and seems to thrive on the foliage of many kinds of low-growing plants, such as dandelion, dock, plantain, chickweed, etc., and also eats the leaves of birch and rose. Chrysalis, very dark brown, almost black, glossy, but minutely pitted, giving a roughened appearance ; enclosed in a close-fitting cocoon composed of silk and the caterpillar's hairs, with particles of earth on the outside. The early stages are figured on Pl. **26.** The moth flies at night, and except that a female

may occasionally be seen on the wing, this species is rarely
observed in the daytime.   May and June are the usual months
for this moth, but in 1906 a specimen was attracted to light
on November 3.

Widely distributed, and often common in most English
counties, in parts of Wales, and in Scotland as far north at
least as Ross.   In Ireland one male specimen of the typical
form has been obtained in Co. Galway, and one in Co. Clare ;
ab. *rustica* occurs in Co. Dublin, and Offaly, Waterford, Cork,
Kerry, and Galway.

The Ruby Tiger (*Phragmatobia fuliginosa* Linn.)

The English name given to this moth only suitably applies
to the southern reddish form of the species (Pl. **29**, 1 ♂).
In the north of England the fore wings are darkened with
brownish and the hind wings with blackish tints, until in
Scotland the only trace of red colour is found on the inner
edge of the hind wings (subsp. *borealis* Staudinger, Fig. 2 ♀).
In these dark specimens the body is also blackish.   Very
occasionally, specimens approaching the northern form are
obtained in southern England.   A female moth captured by
Mr. G. E. J. Crallan in May, 1901, at Bournemouth, laid
forty-eight eggs ;   thirty imagines were bred the same year,
two of which were *borealis*.   On the south and south-west
coasts the black band of the hind wings exhibit a tendency
to break up into spots ;   not infrequently this is completely
effected, and the specimens then approach the larger southern
European form *fervida* Staud.   In a fine series of this species
from Cornwall, seen in the late Mr. A. Harrison's collection,
were a few specimens that came very close to the last-named
form.   Yellow aberrations (*lutescens* Mosley) have been obtained in Denbigh and orange (*aurantiaca* Cockayne) at Wis-
bech.   The eggs are whitish and deposited in batches on leaves.
Up to the last moult the caterpillar is greyish or brownish, with
dark greyish or blackish warts from which arise star-like tufts

of brown hairs ; a reddish line along the middle of the back, and some reddish spots on the sides. When full grown it is black, and the reddish line on the back is almost hidden by closer and more compact tufts of black hairs. Head black and glossy (Pl. **33**, 2).

The leaves of various low-growing plants afford it nourishment, but it is very partial to dock, dandelion, golden-rod (*Solidago*), and plantain ; it is also fond of groundsel and lettuce in confinement, but these plants have been found unsuitable if given too frequently. In the open it seems to feed through the summer, hibernate when full grown, reappear in the early spring, and in due course spin its brownish cocoon among herbage generally low down near the ground ; on moors it often makes the cocoon among the twigs of heather as shown on Pl. **33**, 2*a*. The chrysalis is black, marked with yellowish on the hind edge of each ring. The vitality of the caterpillar is extraordinary. One known to have been embedded in ice for fourteen days at least, became active in less than half an hour after the ice around it melted. It pupated shortly afterwards.

When eggs are obtained early, it is possible to have three generations of the moth during the same year. Thus eggs deposited on May 8 produced caterpillars which fed up quickly and attained the moth state in July. From July eggs some of the caterpillars will outstrip their companions, pupate in September, and appear as moths about a month later. The moth is to be found in May and June, sometimes in July or August, in wood clearings, on moors and rough hillsides, and also in water meadows, etc. It flies at night, is attracted by light, and although it occasionally flies in the sunshine, it is, as a rule, not often seen in the daytime. Occurs throughout the British Isles to the Orkneys. Distribution : Europe, western and central Asia, Amurland, Japan, North-west Africa, North America.

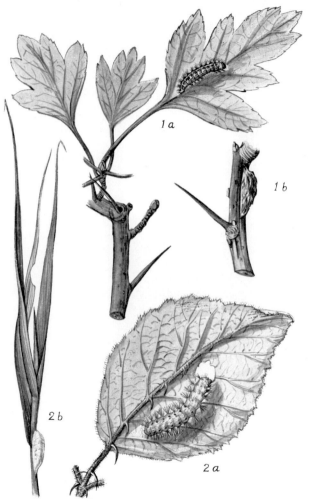

1*a*, 1*b*. **Short-cloaked Moth**: *caterpillar and chrysalis.*
2*a*, 2*b*. **Kent Black Arches**: *caterpillar and chrysalis.*

1, 4. **Four-spotted Footman,** *male and female.*
2, 3. **Dingy Footman.**
5, 6. **Common Footman,** *male and female.*
7, 8. **Scarce Footman,** *male and female.*

The Clouded Buff (*Diacrisia sannio* Linn.)

Fore wings of the male yellow, with a reddish and greyish central mark ; hind wings whitish, with blackish central spot and outer band ; the inner margin, fringes, and front edge light crimson. The female has orange fore wings with reddish margins, veins, and central mark ; hind wings orange, with black basal area, central spot, and outer band (Pl. **30**, 1, 2).

The female of this species is so different in appearance from the male that it was described by Linnaeus as distinct, under the name *russula*.

Although the central spot of the fore wings is subject to minor modification in size, shape, and colour, it is in the hind wings that variation chiefly occurs. In the male the blackish grey band on the outer area of the hind wing may be broad and complete, or it may be broken up by the veins into a series of bars ; then, again, the bars tend to become smaller and smaller until only tiny portions remain. Usually, the basal third of the hind wings is more or less greyish, but sometimes the whole surface almost, or quite up to the outer band, is clouded with dark grey. The black markings of the female hind wings are apt to vary in a very similar way.

The caterpillar is reddish brown, covered with brown hairs ; a yellow-marked whitish stripe along the back, and two darkish stripes on the sides ; a white spot below each black margined spiracle. It hatches from the egg in July, and as a rule hibernates when still small, completing growth in April and May. It feeds on the leaves of many low plants, among which are dandelion, dock, chickweed, and plantain (Pl. **34**). The chrysalis is brown, streaked with greyish, and is enclosed in a flimsy cocoon among herbage, generally on the ground.

The moth, which inhabits heaths and mosses, is on the wing in June and early July ; the male may be put up on sunny days, but the female is not often seen until early evening. After dark both sexes may be found on the heather.

It should be noted here that there are usually two broods of this species abroad, and that in confinement it will develop a more or less complete second brood in September with us. An instance is recorded of sixty-three out of sixty-six caterpillars from eggs laid in early July, feeding up and producing moths in the last week of September. The caterpillar is not an easy one to deal with during hibernation, so that it would always be to the advantage of the rearer to get it through to the perfect state the same year, whenever possible.

The species is widely distributed over the south and east of England, and South Wales. It occurs in Cheshire in all suitable places ; in Lancashire it is common on the moorlands, as at Witherslack and Methop, and it is not uncommon near Quernmore, Clougha, and other places, in July. Local and somewhat scarce as a rule in Yorkshire, but recorded as not uncommon in the Scarborough district. In Scotland it is found in Roxburghshire, and northwards to Aberdeen ; and, according to Kane, it is widely spread, although local, in Ireland.

The Wood Tiger (*Parasemia plantaginis* Linn.)

On Pl. **29**, figures 3–7 show some of the forms of this attractive and somewhat variable species. Figs. 3, 4, are male and female of the typical form found in England. The most usual phase of variation is in the narrowing or widening of the pale yellowish markings of the fore wings, and the black markings on the hind wings ; occasionally the yellow or the black increases to such an extent that the fore wings appear to be almost entirely of the one colour or the other. The hind wings range in colour from the normal yellow through orange to red, and through pale shades of yellow to white ; on the other hand they are sometimes almost entirely black. The ab. *hospita* Schiff. (Fig. 7) has all the wings white, and although it has been reported from Shropshire, West Durham, the Lake District, etc., it has been chiefly obtained in the Hebrides and in the highlands of Scotland. Only males of this form are known ; the females found with them have heavy black markings on the hind wings, almost crowding out the reddish ground colour. The creamy markings of the fore wings are narrow, and the central spot small.

The full-grown caterpillar is blackish above with greyish black warts from which arise tufts of blackish hairs, except on rings four to six, where the hairs and the warts at the base of each tuft are reddish ; the black hairs of the hinder tufts are the longest (Pl. **33,** 1).

Twelve eggs laid by a female in Aberdeenshire were received on June 29, 1906. They were shining yellowish in colour, and were on a leaf of plantain (Pl. **33,** 1a). The caterpillars resulting from these eggs were reared on a mixed diet of forget-me-not (*Myosotis*), plantain, and groundsel, but evinced a decided preference for the former. Some died young in moulting but at the beginning of August five were full grown, and four duly pupated in a slight but roomy cocoon of silk, mixed with the caterpillar's hairs, in which the blackish brown chrysalis with the cast-off skin attached to the tail was plainly visible. Four moths, all female, emerged at the end of August, when the other caterpillar was still feeding, and seemingly about mature. That caterpillar did not, however, pupate, or survive the winter. As a rule the caterpillars hibernate when about half grown, and feed up in April and May of the following year. The somewhat unusual rate at which those just mentioned completed their growth was no doubt due to the heat of the summer of 1906.

The moth is to be found on heaths, moors, the slopes of chalk, and limestone hills ; also in woods that are not too thickly timbered and have a good undergrowth of heather, etc. The males may sometimes be seen flying in the sunshine, and they will then be noted to wing their way to some particular spot where most likely a freshly emerged female will be the attraction. The male is often started up from the heather or other herbage as one walks along ; or it may even rise from the bare ground upon which it sometimes has a fancy to sit. The female seems to be more sluggish during the daytime.

The species is widely distributed over the British Isles, and its range extends through central and northern Europe, and northern Asia to Japan.

The Garden Tiger (*Arctia caja* Linn.)

How frequently the collector has had introduced to his notice, by some non-entomological friend, or worthy cottage dame, a " fine butterfly," only to find that the supposed prize, usually imprisoned under an inverted tumbler, was just an ordinary specimen of the gaudy, but common, Garden Tiger. Few persons living in the country, and at all interested in the natural objects around them, will fail to recognise the portraits on Pl. 30, 3, 4 ; other figures, however, on Pl. 1 will appear strange, and yet they only portray some of the many forms which the moths assume. Possibly it would be true to say that no two specimens could be found that were exactly identical in tint and marking. Even the markings of any one example are frequently not precisely alike on corresponding wings. Normally the fore wings are white or creamy white with dark brown markings, and the hind wings are red with deep blue centred black spots, often ringed with yellow. The dark markings of the fore wings are most inconstant in size and in form ; in some cases they are so greatly enlarged that these wings might be described as dark brown with narrow, irregular whitish markings (Pl. 1, 1). On the other hand, but less frequently perhaps, the dark markings are narrowed, shortened, and reduced in number, until only spots remain on a white or creamy ground (Pl. 1, 2). The red colour of the hind wings is sometimes crimson in tone, or it assumes an orange tint, and less often it gives place to yellow ; the central spots often unite and form a band, or some, occasionally all, disappear ; the marginal spots some-

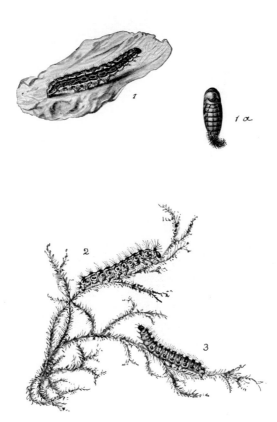

1, 1a. Hoary Footman: *caterpillar and chrysalis.*
2. Dingy Footman: *caterpillar.*
3. Dotted Footman: *caterpillar.*

1, 2. **Northern Footman**, *male and female.*
3, 4. **Pygmy Footman**, *male and female.*
5, 6. **Hoary Footman**, *male and female.*
7, 8. **Orange Footman**, *male and female.*
9, 10. **Dotted Footman**, *male and female.*

times run into a band. For variation in *A. caja* by Cockayne see *Trans. S. London Ent. and N.H. Soc.*, 1947–48, 155.

Besides aberrations such as that referred to above, curious abnormal specimens occur in the breeding cage from time to time, but these are often more or less deformed. It is, perhaps, remarkable, that so few " good things " in the way of varieties are obtained from collected caterpillars, even when these are reared by hundreds. Possibly, if the breeder started operations with a stock of eggs from unusually pale or unusually dark females, and then reserving only the lightest or the darkest, as required, of each generation to continue the experiment, some interesting light or dark " strains " might result in course of time. The objection to this is that before the desired result was obtained the stock might be weakened by " inbreeding," and the moths consequently deformed. If, however, the same line of experiment were conducted by several people, each living in a different part of the country, and with stock selected from the products of his own locality, eggs, caterpillars, or chrysalids might be exchanged, say, after the second year, and in this way the effect of " inbreeding " would be minimised.

The caterpillar, generally known as the " Woolly Bear," is not at all an uncommon object throughout the country, and is, perhaps, even more often noticed in gardens, including those of suburban London. The figures of the early stages of this moth, on Pl. **39,** are all from material obtained in South's own small garden.

The foliage of pretty well all low plants, and tall ones, such as the hollyhock and sunflower, too, seem to be equally acceptable to this larva. It is not often seen before hibernation, but in the early days of spring it will be noticed sunning itself on walls and fences that have a good crop of nettles, dock, or other weeds at their base or around them ; or it may be searched for on the undersides of dock, etc. The late Mr. Frohawk recorded these caterpillars as swarming from mid-May to mid-June, 1904, in the Scilly Isles. He stated that they occurred in such myriads that no vegetation escaped them, and that they devoured anything from stonecrop to the foliage of shrubs of various kinds. Every path and road-way was dotted all over with their crushed bodies.

In the open the moth is on the wing in July and sometimes in August. When kept indoors the caterpillars, or at least some of them, will feed up quickly and attain the moth state in September or October.

The species is distributed over the whole of Europe, except Andalusia, Sicily, and the southern part of the Balkan Penin-sula, and its range extends through Asia to Amurland, Korea, and Japan.

The Cream-spot Tiger (*Arctia villica* Linn.)

Although this moth does not vary to the same extent as its cousin the Garden Tiger, it is still subject to considerable aberration in the size, number, and position of the yellowish-white, or cream-coloured spots on the fore wings and of the black spots and hind marginal markings of the hind wings. The former are often much reduced in size, rarely perhaps so greatly as to leave the fore wings almost entirely black ; but they are sometimes so greatly enlarged and united that these wings appear to be cream coloured with black markings. On the hind wings the black spots nearest the base are sometimes widened and lengthened so as to meet and form a transverse band ; in other specimens the black markings on the outer area are run together into a patch. Occasionally both forms of hind wing aberration occur in the same specimen. South was not aware of any case in which the hind wings are spotless, but he had seen specimens in which this condition was very closely approached. Very rarely the hind wings are suffused with black, and at least two specimens with all the wings suffused with black have been recorded (Pl. **32,** 1, 2).

The pearly white eggs are laid in neatly arranged batches on

1, 2, 3. **White Ermine.**
4, 5. **Muslin Moth,** *females.*
6. **Muslin Moth,** *male.*
7, 8. **Water Ermine.**

1, 1*a*, 1*b*. **Buff Footman:** *caterpillars, chrysalis and cocoon.*
2. **Common Footman:** *caterpillar.*
3. **Scarce Footman:** *caterpillar.*

leaves. The caterpillars hatch out in July, feed for a few weeks, and go into hibernation while still small. They resume feeding in a favourable season as early as mid-March. Some that South obtained at the end of March, then about three parts grown, began to spin up on April 15. The full-grown caterpillar is black with several star-like clusters of brown hairs on each ring, the hairs on the back of the hinder rings rather longer and slightly curved backwards ; the head, legs, and claspers are red, approaching crimson. A diet of dandelion suits it very well, but it will also eat chickweed, dock, nettle, groundsel, and in fact almost any low-growing plant. The outer leaves of lettuce are useful on occasion but should not be given exclusively, and it also likes the tender shoots of gorse (*Ulex europaeus*). Chrysalis and cocoon somewhat similar to those of the last species (Pl. **40**).

The moth emerges in May and June. Occasionally a few larvae will feed up and the moths appear the same year, but this only happens in captivity and not in the open. When reposing in the daytime, on a hedgebank for example, with the fore wings closed down over and hiding the yellow hind wings this moth is not so conspicuous as one might suppose it would be. At night it is active on the wing and often flies into houses, attracted by the light. South put up specimens now and then in hay fields, and once found half a dozen along a short stretch of the Upper cliff at Ventnor, Isle of Wight.

It is perhaps most frequent in the south-west, but the species seems to be widely distributed and fairly common from Kent to Cornwall, and westward from Hampshire to Gloucestershire. It also occurs in the eastern counties to Cambridge and Norfolk. From Cheshire it has been twice reported, and two specimens are said to have been taken, a few years ago, in the Lancaster district.

The Feathered Footman (*Coscinia striata* Linn.)

Altogether there do not appear to have been more than six or seven specimens of this species (Pl. **35,** 3) recorded as British. Stephens mentions three of these, two males taken in the autumn of 1815, near Windsor; and one specimen, without date, in the Isle of Anglesey. Of the others one appears to have been taken in Yorkshire (1832), one in Essex, and another in North Wales (1859). Barrett also refers to a specimen, which was captured but afterwards escaped, near Bettws-y-Coed, North Wales, June, 1859, and gives some circumstantial details of the event. It appears, therefore, that of the very limited number of British *striata* North Wales has furnished almost half. The species is widely distributed in Europe, except the most northern part; the range extending into Asia Minor, Syria, Armenia, and Amurland. Abroad, it occurs on heaths, and in warm dry places. The caterpillar is blackish brown, marked with orange on the back, and white on the sides; the warts are yellowish, and the hairs arising therefrom are reddish brown; the head is black. It feeds in spring, after hibernation, on grasses, heather, and low herbage, and becomes full grown in May.

The Speckled Footman (*Coscinia cribraria* Linn.)

The fore wings are whitish, crossed by three rows of blackish grey dots, more or less connected, forming lines; and two streaks of the same colour through the length of the wings, but not always extending to the outer margin; a cross series of wedge-shaped marks or dots on the outer area; hind wings grey. Sometimes the fore wings are wholly suffused with the darker colour, and between such specimens and less frequent examples in which the wings are almost devoid of marking, there are many gradations (Pl. **32,** 3 ♂, 4 ♀; 5, 6 aberrations). The nearly spotless ab. *arenaria* Lempke has been taken occasionally at Dungeness, no doubt immigrants from the Belgian coast sand dunes. For variation in this species see *Entom.*, xxxiii. 67.

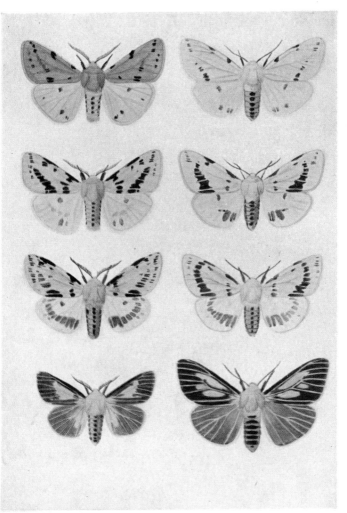

Buff Ermine *and varieties.*

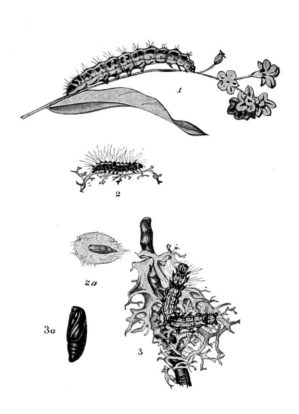

1. **Crimson Speckled**: *caterpillar.*
2, 2a. **Muslin Footman**: *caterpillar and chrysalis in cocoon.*
3, 3a. **Four-spotted Footman**: *caterpillar and chrysalis.*

Eggs received from the New Forest, June 25, 1907, were laid around a slender, bare, twig of heather, the batch measuring about three-quarters of an inch in length. At first they were golden yellow, but afterwards became pale purplish brown and very glossy (Pl. 36).

Although the eggs appear to be more frequently laid on heather than on anything else, the caterpillars do not seem to be very partial to the plant as an article of food if others are available. In October, 1907, South had about a score or so of young larvae feeding, and apparently thriving, on dandelion, lettuce, and grass, but they certainly seemed to prefer the first named. They were then rather over half an inch in length, and yellowish brown in colour ; there was a whitish grey stripe along the back ; the warts were shining black, and the hairs arising from them were black, mixed with a few longer white ones ; head blackish.

Caterpillars after hibernation have been found on the grass, *Aira caespitosa*, during March from about the 10th onwards ; they are then about a quarter of an inch long, and according to the late Mr. Fowler, always found on the sunny side of the clumps of *Aira* stretched out, and evidently enjoying the warmth of the sun. Some collected in that month were reared on groundsel, and produced moths from July 12 to August 20. The chrysalis is at first reddish, afterwards shining jet black ; in a slight egg-shaped white silken cocoon, spun up in tufts of grass. Some larvae which Kettlewell had hibernated twice.

In exceptional seasons the moth has emerged in late May, but June and July are the usual months, and it may occur as late as August. It rests among the heather, is easily disturbed on sunny days, and is very active on the wing, although it does not fly far before settling again. The species is very local in England, occurring on certain heathland in Dorset and in a heathy district between Ringwood and Verwood, and in a not generally known part of the New Forest.

The Crimson Speckled (*Utetheisa pulchella* Linn.)

This white moth, prettily speckled with black and red dots, is a native of warmer countries than ours. However, it not only visits us now and then in the course of its wanderings, but if the migrants arrive in England at a suitable time of the year, the females most probably deposit eggs from which caterpillars may hatch, and some of them feed up and produce moths later in the same year. Stephens, writing in 1829, mentions a specimen taken many years previously in Yorkshire. This was no doubt the earliest known British example of Haworth's Crimson Speckled. A second specimen captured in a field near Christchurch, Hampshire, in October, 1818, was figured by Samouelle in 1819. Between the year last mentioned and 1827, two other specimens occurred, both at Hove, Sussex. Stainton (1857) adds Epping, Manchester, Stowmarket, and Worthing. In 1869 three specimens were taken in the autumn ; and a specimen was found at Scarborough in June, 1870, and one in Sussex. In 1871 a record was established, when at least thirty specimens were obtained at various places on the east, south, and south-west coasts, and in the Isle of Wight ; one specimen being also recorded from Manchester. Two specimens were taken in Cornwall, May, 1874, and in the autumn of that year three occurred on the south coast, and one in Derbyshire. The moth seems not to have been noticed in the springs of 1875 or 1876, but twenty-four specimens were recorded later in the former year, and twenty-three in the latter. Between 1876 and 1892 less than twenty specimens were reported altogether, and the species was either entirely absent or overlooked in 1877, 1882, 1883, and from 1887 to 1891, inclusive. In 1892 several moths were captured in May and June on the coast ; one at Brighton in July, two in the Hastings district, and one at Folkestone in August. Since 1892 and up to 1907, a period of fifteen years, the species seems to have been rarely noted in England ; the records showing in 1894 (2), 1895 (1), 1906 (1).

In 1901 three specimens were reported as captured, and one seen at Earlsfield, Surrey, July 1 to 15. From 1907 to 1912 there do not appear to be any records. Two occurred in 1913, after which there was another gap until 1921 when several were taken. In 1922 one was bred from a larva found in South Devon. The species was reported in 1923, 1924, and 1925, and again in 1929, 1930, since when there have only been three records : August 11, 1947, at Bull Point lighthouse, North Devon, and two in 1953 (Pl. **35**, 4, 5).

In Ireland it has been reported from Dublin, Cork, Kerry, and Waterford.

The caterpillar is greyish with black warts from which arise tufts of hairs, blackish on the back and pale greyish on the sides ; a white line on the back, and one on the sides. Each ring is often barred with orange. Head reddish ochreous marked with black (Pl. **25,** 1). Feeds on forget-me-not (*Myosotis*), borage (*Borago*), etc. The chrysalis is reddish brown, enclosed in a white silken cocoon spun up among the food plant, or on the surface of the ground ; in the latter case particles of earth adhere to the outside.

The caterpillar is said to feed only in the sunshine, so that in our islands the weather conditions would often be most unfavourable to the species in the larval state. On the other hand its sun-loving habit would expose it to the attacks of parasitical flies and other enemies. Anyway, the Crimson Speckled seems quite unable to increase and multiply to any extent even for a season in any part of England. Along the African and European borders of the Mediterranean there are evidently several generations of the moth in each year ; the life cycle of the summer broods being short, but more protracted in the later brood. Brownlow states that eggs laid on October 20, hatched on the 22nd of the same month, and the caterpillar stage lasted until February of the following year. Distribution : southern Europe, Africa, Canaries, Madeira ; Asia Minor, Armenia, central Asia ; India, and Australia.

The Beautiful Utetheisa (*Utetheisa bella* Linn.)

A specimen of this American species was taken on Skokholm Island at the end of July, 1948, by M. C. Williams (Pl. **35,** 6).

CALLIMORPHINAE

The Cinnabar (*Callimorpha jacobaeae* Linn.)

This species was named the Cinnabar by Wilkes in 1773, such name of course referring to the more or less vermilion colour of the hind wings and the markings on the greyish black fore wings. The hind wings are often pinkish in tint, and probably it was to such specimens that Moses Harris gave the name " Pink Underwing." Very rarely the stripe on the front edge of the fore wings unites with the upper hind marginal spot ; still less frequently there are some crimson scales in addition connecting the two hind marginal spots. Occasionally specimens have been recorded in which the usual red colour is replaced by bright yellow. There is also a form (1) suffused with grey black or (2) even quite black, ab. *nigrana* Cabeau. (Lambill, 1928, 28 : 12). The moth is shown on Pl. **35,** 1, 2, and the early stages on Pl. **45,** 1, 1*a*.

The caterpillar is orange yellow and each ring is banded with purplish black ; the scanty hairs are short and blackish in colour. Head black. Feeds in July and August on ragwort (*Senecio jacobaea*) and sometimes occurs in such numbers as to completely clear large patches of the plant of every particle of green, leaving nothing but the tougher portions of the bare stems. It also feeds on groundsel, coltsfoot, etc.

The chrysalis is dark brown tinged with reddish ; in a slight silken cocoon just under the surface of the ground, or among any loose material on the ground.

The moth is on the wing at the end of May and in June ; odd specimens have occasionally been seen in April. It occurs on waste ground, sandy heaths, railway banks, downs, and hillsides. Although fairly common generally, in some years it is not at all plentiful even when caterpillars may have abounded the previous season. When disturbed from among its food plant or herbage around, it is not very active on the wing, and is easily captured. Its usual time of flight is in

FIG. 2.—CINNABAR CATERPILLARS FEEDING.

the evening. Light seems to have an attraction for it, as it has been taken at lamps in towns, some distance from any place where the caterpillar could have fed.

Occurs in all suitable places throughout the greater part of England and in Scotland up to Moray. Common in Ireland. Its range abroad includes all Europe, except the extreme north, and extends into Asia.

The Jersey Tiger (*Euplagia quadripunctaria* Poda)

This handsome species long known as *E. hera* Linn., but for which Poda's earlier name *quadripunctaria* must be adopted, has its English home in **South** Devon. The species had been recorded as British as far back as 1855, when one moth was taken at Newhaven in Sussex; in 1859 a specimen was obtained in North Wales, two were taken in Sussex, 1868, and in 1877 one was captured in the Isle of Wight where it has been taken subsequently. The late Sir Edward Poulton also took one in his garden at St. Helens on August 28, 1935. For the county of Devon, the earliest record is that of a specimen netted in a garden at Alphington, near Exeter, in 1871, followed soon after by a report of others at a place near Lodderwell. Ten or eleven years later the moth was found at Dawlish, and in that neighbourhood and in other parts of a wide area stretching from Exeter to Teignmouth, and perhaps further west, and also to the east, it has been taken almost every year up to the present time. Large numbers of eggs have been obtained and distributed among entomologists, many of whom have successfully wintered the caterpillars and eventually reared the moths.

The principal variation is in the colour of the hind wings and the body, which usually are red, but in ab. *lutescens* Staud. are yellow; between the red and the yellow forms there are all kinds of orange and other intergrades. The red form is the most common, yellow next, while the terra cotta form ab. *saturnina* Oberth. is the rarest. There is also variation in the black markings at the inner angle of the fore wings, some or all of which are sometimes absent. A specimen with the inner margin of the fore wings black instead of creamy white has been recorded, and a specimen with whitish hind wings is stated to have been seen but not secured. The moth is shown on Pl. **37,** 3, 4, and the early stages on Pl. **43,** 1, 1*a*.

The eggs, which are laid in batches, are pale yellowish when deposited, but assume a deep violet tint before hatching. Mr. W. Hewett (*Entom.*, xxviii.) states that in the case of seventeen female moths that he captured in August, 1895, the average number of eggs laid by each was 133, and as regards fourteen batches of eggs, the caterpillars hatched out in fifteen or sixteen days.

When nearly full grown the caterpillar is blackish with an orange stripe along the back and a series of creamy white spots on the sides ; the hairs, arising from shining light brown warts, are pale brown mixed with greyish ones ; spiracles black ringed with white, under surface greyish. Head black and glossy. It hatches from the egg in the autumn and goes into hibernation while still very small ; reappearing in the spring and feeding on until July, when it spins a flimsy silken web-like cocoon well down among moss and litter. The food plants are dandelion, white deadnettle (*Lamium album*), ground ivy (*Nepeta glechoma*), groundsel, plantain, nettle, borage (*Borago officinalis*), lettuce, and elm.

The moth emerges in July and August in a state of nature, but often as early as June in confinement. It sits by day among the herbage, and in the bushes of hedgerows, but readily quits its retreat when disturbed. The normal time of flight is at night ; and that light has an attraction for the moths is evident from the fact that they have been known to fly into cottages at the rate of three or four in an evening.

The species is distributed throughout southern Europe, its range extending to Holland, Belgium, and Livonia. It was known as an inhabitant of the Channel Islands long before it became established in England.

The Scarlet Tiger (*Panaxia dominula* Linn.)

This brightly coloured moth (Pl. **37,** 1, 2) has in the past been confused with species and forms occurring in parts of central and southern Europe and Asia Minor. Kettlewell (*Proc. S.L.E. and N.H.S.*, 1942–3, Pt. I) has shown that the names *rossica* Kol. *bithynica* Staud. and *persona* Hübn. should not be included in the British nomenclature. The black aberration (*nigra* Spuler-Hofman) from Kent has all the wings and body black, but retains the metallic green sheen ; it is exceedingly rare. In ab. *bimacula* Cockayne from north Berkshire, all the spots on the fore wings, with the exception of the two basal, are absent ; the dark markings on the hind wings are increased and form a band from the costa to the anal angle. Another form (ab. *lutea* Staud.) has the hind wings and body yellow.

Caterpillar, black, hairy, with bands of more or less connected spots, yellow or yellowish in colour, down the middle of the back, and along the sides ; the hairs, arising from shining black warts, are grey with some black ones intermixed. Head, glossy black. It hatches from the egg in July or August, feeds for awhile, then hibernates, and completes its growth in April or May. A number of plants have been mentioned as suitable food for these caterpillars, but the favourites are, perhaps, nettle, groundsel, hound's-tongue (*Cynoglossum officinale*), bramble, sloe, sallow, and comfrey (Pl. **43**, 2–2*b*). The chrysalis is dark reddish, rather blacker above ; enclosed in a silken cocoon spun up among leaves, etc., on the ground.

The moth emerges in June, and seems partial to marshy ground. It is found in the district between Dover and Deal commonly, and in other parts of Kent more rarely. Also in Hampshire, Devon, Dorset, South Wales, Gloucestershire, Wiltshire, Berkshire (water meadows by the Kennet), Oxfordshire, and Hertfordshire (rare). Some years ago South found a few specimens in the Brandon district, but it is not plentiful in Suffolk, and is rare in or absent from Norfolk. It was found in Cambridgeshire, chiefly in Wicken and Chippenham Fens, but not recently.

GEOMETRIDAE

Caterpillars of this family of moths, with very few exceptions, have only two pairs of claspers or prolegs ; when there are

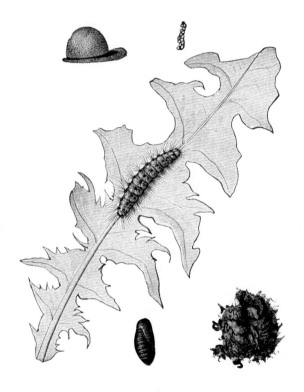

Muslin Moth: *eggs, natural size and enlarged, caterpillar, chrysalis and cocoon.*

1, 2, 3, 4, 6, 7. **Muslin Moth** *varieties.*
5. **White Ermine (ab.** *walkeri*).

more than four claspers, the extra ones are only rudimentary and therefore useless. In moving from place to place the caterpillar stretches out to its full length, first to one side and then to the other, as though measuring the distance. When a hold is secured with the true legs the body is arched and the claspers are brought up almost to the point held by the true legs ; the latter are then thrust forward and the measuring business proceeds as before. Some kinds perform the looping manoeuvre very deliberately, but others at a quick rate. In common parlance among British entomologists the caterpillars are called " geometers " or " loopers," but to our American con-frères they are known as " measuring worms " or " spanworms."

Most of the caterpillars feed openly on the foliage of trees, shrubs, or low-growing herbs, and the majority remain upon their respective plants during the day.

A large proportion of the moths may be obtained in the day-time, either by beating or otherwise disturbing the foliage or herbage among which they hide ; several kinds rest on tree trunks, palings, rocks, walls, etc., where they are sometimes conspicuous, but more frequently not easy to distinguish from their surroundings. On the whole, members of this family are more available to the day collector than are those of the Noctuidae. Although several species occasionally visit the sugar patch, such species are, as a rule, obtained more readily and in larger numbers by other methods. Brilliant light has a great attraction for many of the moths, some are more often captured at gas or electric lamps than in any other way, and among these are the migratory species.

The family is here divided into the following sub-families :—

Archiearinae.	Sterrhinae.
Oenochrominae.	Larentiinae.
Geometrinae.	Ennominae.

ARCHIEARINAE

The Orange Underwing (*Archiearis parthenias* Linn.)

The white markings of the fore wings vary a good deal in size ; in some specimens, chiefly males, they are very small and confined to the front margin (ab. *dilutior* Heinrich) ; in others, mainly females, they are much enlarged, and the central one is continued as a band across the wings. On the orange hind wings the blackish central band is usually more or less complete, but sometimes it is nearly **or** quite absent above the blackish triangular patch on the inner margin. Occasionally, there is a yellow blotch at the anal angle, and frequently another on the costal area. Still more rarely in ab. *luteata* Hennin the whole ground colour is yellow. (Figured on Pl. **38,** 1 ♂ and 2 ♀). The caterpillar is green, with six white lines along the back, and white stripes along the sides. When young it feeds on the catkins of birch, and afterwards on the foliage. April to early June (Pl. **46,** 1).

The moth is out in March and April, and on sunny days the males may be seen flying, generally pretty high up, on the lee side of the birch trees growing on heaths ; also in open spaces in or around birch woods. The females rest on the twigs, as also do the males when the sun is obscured. Both sexes have been found sitting on the ground in sunny glades.

The species is widely distributed over the southern and eastern counties, common in many parts ; but its range extends through England to Durham, and it has been recorded from Wales. Although it does not seem to have been noted in Scotland south of Kincardineshire, it occurs on the east to Moray. Westmeath is the only Irish locality that has so far been mentioned.

Its distribution abroad extends to Algeria, eastern Siberia, and Amurland.

White Ermine: *caterpillar, chrysalis and cocoon.*

1. **Ruby Tiger.** 2. **Ruby Tiger (ssp.** *borealis*).
3, 4, 5, 6, 7. **Wood Tiger.**

The Light Orange Underwing (*Archiearis notha* Hübn.)

Very similar to the last species, but rather smaller in size, and the fore wings are much less variegated. The antennae of the male of this species are bipectinate, whilst those of *parthenias* are finely serrate (Pl. **38,** 3 ♂ and 4 ♀).

The caterpillar feeds in May and June on aspen, eating the foliage and hiding between two leaves drawn together. The head is greenish or greenish brown, with three conspicuous black spots. Body, green, olive green, or reddish ; line along middle of the back darker green edged with white ; two thin white lines on each side, and a whitish stripe along the spiracles. When mature it burrows into decayed bark or wood (virgin cork in confinement), and before changing to a reddish brown chrysalis, it spins a thin covering of silk and woody particles over the mouth of the chamber. The caterpillar and the chrysalis are shown on Pl. **46,** 2 and 2*a*. Although the bulk of the moths emerge the following April, some have been known to remain until the following or even the third year. The males fly about aspen, but only in the sunshine ; in other respects its habits are pretty much those of the last species.

The distribution of the species in England seems confined to two areas : a western one represented by Worcestershire, Gloucestershire, with Monmouth, Wales, Wiltshire, and Dorset ; and an eastern one by Norfolk, Cambridgeshire, Suffolk, Essex, Middlesex, Hertfordshire, Kent, Surrey, and Sussex. In Scotland only recorded from Moray.

The range abroad extends to Amurland.

OENOCHROMINAE

The March Moth (*Alsophila aescularia* Schiff.)

Examples of each sex are shown on Pl. **109,** and 6 ♂, 7 ♀. The male varies in the general colour from pale to dark grey ; the central area being sometimes smoky tinged. In the north of England, chiefly in Yorkshire, blackish specimens occur in which the markings are more or less obscured (ab. *brunnea* Hannemann).

The caterpillar is pale green with a rather darker line along the back, and yellowish lines along the sides. Readily distinguished from other similar looking Geometrid larvae by the presence of an extra, but much reduced pair of prolegs

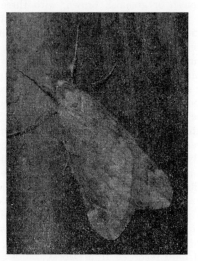

FIG. 3.—MARCH MOTH, MALE, AT REST (× 2).

on the fifth abdominal segment. It feeds on hawthorn, sloe, privet, lilac, currant, plum, cherry, rose, etc., also on oak, hornbeam, and some other trees : April to June. The figure of the caterpillar on Pl. **114**, 4, is from a coloured drawing by the late A. Sich.

The moth is out in the spring, and may be found on palings, tree-trunks, etc., in the daytime, and more freely flying about, or sitting on hedges, at night, when the spider-like wingless

1, 2. **Clouded Buff,** *male and female.*
3, 4. **Garden Tiger,** *male and female.*

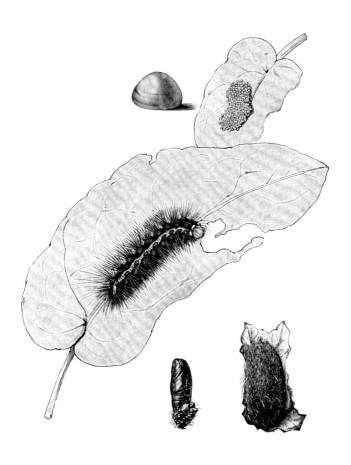

Buff Ermine: *eggs, natural size and enlarged, caterpillar, chrysalis and cocoon.*

female is more frequently obtained. The male is attracted by light, and sometimes is not uncommon on lamps.

Except that it seems not to have been noted north of Perthshire in Scotland, the species is generally distributed over the British Isles. The range abroad extends through Europe to Russian Transcaucasia.

GEOMETRINAE

The Rest Harrow (*Aplasta ononaria* Fuessly)

This greyish brown moth has two darker, sometimes reddish, cross-lines on the fore wings and one such line on the hind wings. The first record of this species occurring in Britain was of a specimen captured in the Warren at Folkestone in August, 1867, and three further specimens were taken there during the following ten years. From 1877 there were no further records from the Folkestone locality until specimens were again noted there in 1937. The colony gained in strength during the war years and it still exists. There is a larger and more flourishing colony in the same county, near Sandwich (Cockayne). In addition there are records of single specimens being taken, one at Westerham in Kent, one in " the South of England " in 1923, one in the New Forest in 1924, two in the Romney Marsh, one in 1932 and one in 1934, and one in Tilgate Forest in 1947. Mr. R. Hayward took a specimen at Portsmouth on August 15, 1959. The species is figured on Pl. 38, 5, 6).

The larva, sluggish in habit, is short and stout. The head and each segment bear small dark tubercles from which arise short stiff hairs. When fully fed it is usually green with a darker medio-dorsal stripe and yellow spiracular stripes.

It feeds solely on restharrow (*Ononis spinosa* and *repens*) and hibernates from September until mid-May. The cocoon is spun amongst the leaves of the food plant. The pupa is greenish, the vestigial tubercles bearing rather stiff setae, distinctly marked in black. The cremaster is strong, bearing eight well-developed hooks.

The moth flies in late June and in warm years there is a second emergence in late August and early September.

Abroad, the range includes central and southern Europe, Asia Minor, Syria, and Armenia.

The Grass Emerald (*Pseudoterpna pruinata* subsp. *atropunctaria* Walker)

When freshly emerged from the chrysalis, the species represented on Pl. **38**, 7, 8, is of a beautiful blue-green colour but in course of time a greyish shade creeps over the wings. The dark cross lines vary in intensity ; in some specimens well defined and blackish, in others very faint, and hardly discernible ; occasionally, the space between the lines on the fore wings is dark-shaded (ab. *fasciata* Prout) ; the whitish submarginal line is not always present. This species is the *cythisaria* of Schiffermüller, and the *cytisaria* of other authors.

The caterpillar (figured on Pl. **51**, 1, from a coloured drawing by the late A. Sich) is green, with three lines along the back, the central one dark green, the others whitish ; a pinkish stripe low down along the sides, the points on the head and the first and last rings of the body are often pink also. It feeds on petty whin (*Genista anglica*), also on broom (*Cytisus scoparius*) and gorse (*Ulex*) ; in captivity it seems to thrive on laburnum. Most frequently obtained in the springtime after hibernation.

The moth is to be found in June and July on moorlands and commons pretty well throughout the British Isles, but it seems not to have been noted north of Perthshire, in Scotland.

Odd specimens have been known to occur in late August or early September, but this is quite exceptional.

Abroad, the range extends to central and south-eastern Europe and Asia Minor.

The Large Emerald (*Geometra papilionaria* Linn.)

This charming green species (Pl. **41,** 5) varies in tint and in the distinctness of the whitish wavy cross lines. In some examples, one or other of the lines is absent, and far more rarely there is but little trace of any of these markings. Occasionally, the discal mark is preceded by a whitish wedge-shaped spot on the fore wings (ab. *cuneata* Burrows).

When newly laid the eggs are whitish, but soon change to greenish yellow, and finally to pinkish.

The caterpillar hatches in late summer, and feeds on birch, hazel, and beech, until the leaves begin to fall in the autumn ; it then constructs a carpet of silk on a twig, and near a bud, upon which it takes up its position for the winter. When thus seen, its reddish brown colour, variegated more or less with green, assimilates so closely with its surroundings that the creature is not easy to detect. In the spring, when it awakens, the green colour increases in extent as the buds open and the leaves unfold ; when they are fully expanded, the caterpillar sits among the foliage towards the tip of a twig, and is then almost entirely green, the reddish brown only showing on the head, slightly on the warts, and more distinctly on the hinder parts which are in touch with the twig. The chrysalis, enclosed in a flimsy silken web among the dead leaves, usually on the ground, is of a delicate green colour, dotted with buff on the back, and shaded with buff on the wing cases. The early stages are figured on Pl. **48,** 1–1*c*.

The moth is out in June and July, and may occasionally be beaten out of a hedge or bush, but is most frequently obtained late at night, when it is active on the wing, and is attracted by a brilliant light.

The species occurs in woods, on heaths and moors, and in fens, throughout the British Isles, except the most northern parts of Scotland and the isles ; it has, however, been recently recorded from the Isle of Canna.

Abroad, the range extends to Amurland and Japan.

The Blotched Emerald (*Comibaena pustulata* Hufn.)

When quite fresh, this moth (Pl. **38,** 9) is exceedingly pretty ; the pale blotches vary a little in size, as also do the reddish marks upon them.

The caterpillar adorns itself with particles of its food as soon as it leaves the egg in July ; after hibernation it uses the scales or husks of the oak buds for the same purpose. When stripped of its trappings it is found to be reddish brown in colour, with three slightly darker lines along the back ; hooded bristles arising from raised brownish spots afford means for the attachment of the masquerading outfit, each moiety of which is covered with silk on one side before being placed in the required position. When beating oaks for larvae in May and June, the contents of the umbrella or beating tray should not be too hastily thrown away, but allowed to remain therein for awhile, and closely watched for any movement among the litter. The spectacle of a cluster of oak bracts suddenly becoming active will certainly arouse curiosity, and on examination the cause of the commotion will frequently be found to be the caterpillar of this species (Pl. **51,** 2 ; after Auld).

The moth is out in June and July, and flies at dusk in and around oak woods. In the daytime it may be jarred from its perch in oak trees, and once I found a specimen on a fence in the Esher district. It comes freely to light, and examples of a September emergence have been recorded.

As a British species it only inhabits England; it has been noted from Staffordshire and Leicestershire, but seems to be rare in the midland counties generally. It is more frequently found in the southern and eastern counties.

Abroad, the range extends through central Europe to southern Sweden, South Russia, northern Asia Minor, and Andalusia.

The Common Emerald (*Hemithea aestivaria* Hübn.)

When freshly emerged from the chrysalis, this species (Pl. **41,** 1, 2) is darkish green, but it soon fades to a greyish tint.

1, 2. **Cream-spot Tiger,** *male and female.*
3, 4, 5, 6. **Speckled Footman.**

1, 1*a*. **Wood Tiger:** *eggs, natural size and enlarged, and caterpillars.*
2, 2*a*. **Ruby Tiger:** *caterpillar and cocoon.*

Easily distinguished by its shape, and by the chequered fringes. It is the *strigata* of Müller, and *thymiaria* of Schiff. The long, thin, green caterpillar is ornamented with reddish brown, the V-shaped marks on rings 5 to 8 are sometimes whitish; head, deeply notched, brown; the first ring of the body is also notched. It hatches from the egg in August, when it is said to feed on mugwort (*Artemisia vulgaris*), and other low plants; after hibernation it feeds on the foliage of oak, birch, hawthorn, rose, etc., and attains full growth in May or June. In late June and in July the moth may be put up from the undergrowth in woods, or from bushes in well-timbered hedgerows bordering lanes and fields. Specimens so obtained are poor in colour as a rule, and it is well, therefore, to rear the species from the caterpillar (Pl. **51,** 3 ; after Hofmann). This remark applies to all " Emeralds."

The species is often common in the south and east of England, and along the western side, including Wales, up to Cheshire and Lancashire, but it becomes local in Worcestershire and northwards. There are few records of it from Yorkshire, and its occurrence in Durham, Northumberland and Scotland is doubtful. In Ireland it appears to be widely distributed and is often common.

The range abroad extends to Amurland, Korea, and Japan.

The Small Grass Emerald (*Chlorissa viridata* Linn.)

This species, represented on Pl. **41,** 6 and 8, is readily distinguished by its small size and the well-defined white cross line on each wing. In most examples there is a more or less distinct whitish inner line on the fore wings. Ab. *mathewi* Bankes, has all the wings dusted with orange scales, more especially on the outer marginal areas. A few examples of this form were reared in 1905, with a number of normal specimens, from eggs laid by a female captured in South Devon.

The caterpillar (figured from a skin on Pl. **53,** 1) is green, roughened with whitish points ; a dusky line along the middle of the back, marked on the front and end rings, also between the rings, with purplish red. Head and first ring of the body notched, the points reddish ; last ring of the body pointed. When at rest on a twig it assumes a rigid posture, and the legs are tightly drawn together. It feeds on heather, sallow, and birch, but the general experience appears to be that in captivity it thrives best on a diet of hawthorn, and is especially partial to the young shoots. It may be obtained in July and August, and the moth comes out in the following May or June. In 1905, the late A. J. Scollick reared some caterpillars from eggs laid June 2nd, and hatched June 16th ; all duly pupated, and a moth came up on December 20th of that year. Four others appeared in January and February, 1906.

The late Rev. F. E. Lowe stated that in Guernsey the species occurred exclusively among furze on cliffs by the sea, and chiefly where the plant is cut down from time to time. In Britain it inhabits heaths and mosses, but is very local. It is found in the English counties of Surrey, Hampshire (New Forest, etc.), Dorset (Poole Heath, etc.), Devon (Woodbury, Exeter district, etc.), Norfolk (Horning), Worcester (Malvern district, rare) ; also at Methop, Witherslack, and other localities in Westmorland and Cumberland. Only doubtfully recorded from Scotland and Ireland.

Abroad, the range extends to Asia Minor and Armenia.

The Essex Emerald (*Thetidia smaragdaria* subsp. *maritima* Prout)

In some examples of this species (Pl. **38**, 10) the green colour is brighter than in others, and very occasionally it is tinged with bluish (ab. *caeruleoviridis* Burrows) ; typically, there are white cross lines on the fore wings, but the inner one is not infrequently absent (ab. *unilinea* Burrows), and more rarely both are missing (ab. *alinea* Burrows). The white central spot is very rarely absent, and the edges of the fore wings are yellowish.

The caterpillar feeds on the sea wormwood (*Artemisia maritima*), and adorns itself with fragments of its food plant in much the same manner as that of the species last referred to. Although obtained in the autumn in some numbers from its food plant, it seems to have been rarely met with in the spring after hibernation. It is, therefore, advisable to collect the caterpillars about September, and transfer them to plants of the garden, *Artemisia abrotanum*, locally known as " Southernwood," " Old man," or " Lad's love," or, where available, wormwood (*A. absinthium*) will suit it admirably. Upon either of these plants the larvae will hibernate, feed up in the spring, and become full grown about May. The early stages are figured on Pl. **48**, 2–2*b*, larva and pupa from photos by the late H. Main.

The moth is out in June and early July, but it is rarely seen in the open, although over ninety years ago a few specimens were put up from among grass and netted at St. Osyth ; in later years an example or two have been taken at Sheerness in Kent. Possibly, others may also have been captured in one or other of the insect's haunts, but records are silent on the matter. Barrett mentions a specimen emerging in September, and the Rev. C. R. N. Burrows noted that part of a brood of caterpillars reared from eggs, and fed on *A. absinthium*, attained the moth state during the autumn. So far as concerns the British Isles it seems to be almost exclusively an inhabitant of the salterns, or sea marshes of Essex.

Abroad, the species occurs inland, and is not confined to the coast ; its range extends eastwards to Siberia and Amurland.

The Sussex Emerald (*Thalera fimbrialis* Scop.)

The first example of this species was taken at Beachy Head in Sussex on August 7, 1902. During the next forty-four years only three other specimens were recorded, all being taken at light ; one at Swanage on August 11, 1936, one at Bournemouth on July 30, 1946, and one at Bradwell-on-Sea,

Essex, on August 8 of the same year.   In the years 1950 and 1951 and subsequently, however, several specimens were recorded from the Kent coast and a colony is now established at Dungeness.

The species is somewhat similar to *H. aestivaria* but is larger and of a lighter tone of green ; the margin of the hind wing is excurved above the angle and the fringes of the wings are chequered with red. The antennae of the male are strongly pectinate ; in *aestivaria* the pectinations are quite short. The female antennae of *fimbrialis* are shortly pectinate ; those of *aestivaria* are minutely ciliate. (Pl. **41**, 3, 4).

The larva is yellowish green with a red medio-dorsal line, which often appears merely as a row of red spots. The head is produced to sharp points, deeply cleft between. Two red-tipped points arise from the first segment and project over the head ; the anal flap is red. It feeds in August and September and again after hibernation in May and June on yarrow.

An account of the discovery of the larvae of this species in the wild has been published by Dr. H. B. D. Kettlewell (1953, *Ent. Rec.*, 65 : 305) and his paper is followed by a full description of the larva by Dr. E. A. Cockayne and of the pupa by Mr. C. N. Hawkins. An account of rearing the species has been published by Mr. G. Haggett (1954, *Ent. Gazette*, 5 : 95–102).

The moth appears in July and throughout August and is distributed through central Europe eastwards to central Asia.

The Small Emerald (*Hemistola immaculata* Thunb.)

This species (Pl. **41**, 9, 10) is smaller than *papilionaria*, the green colour is of a softer tint, and the lines crossing the wings, two on the fore wings and one on the hind wings, are whitish, and not waved.

The caterpillar hatches from the egg in August, and after hibernation is to be found in May and June on Traveller's Joy or Old Man's Beard (*Clematis vitalba*).   It is then green, with white dots arranged in lines along the back and sides ; the head is deep reddish brown, and this, and also the first and last rings of the body, have raised points. Transformation to the greenish chrysalis is effected among the leaves, drawn together with silk (Pl. **53,** 3, 3*a*).

The moth flies in the evening in July and August, and in the daytime may be disturbed, by beating, from its retreats in hedges, etc., where the food plant flourishes. Found in most of the southern and eastern counties of England, most frequently on the chalk ; its range extends to Worcestershire. One specimen has been reported from Argyllshire, 1913 ; very rare and local in Ireland. The distribution abroad extends to Amurland.

The Little Emerald (*Jodis lactearia* Linn.)

The green tint in this species (Pl. **41,** 7) is even more unstable than in others of the group. When quite fresh the wings can often only be described as whitish with a delicate green tinge, but even when the greatest care is taken to preserve it, the colour is apt to fade.

The caterpillar (Pl. **53,** 2, from a coloured drawing by the late A. Sich) is long and thin, with two points on the edge of the first ring, and one on the last ring, of a bright green colour, paler between the rings ; the spots along the back are reddish, as also is the whitish-fronted deeply notched head. It feeds on the leaves of various trees and bushes, such as birch, oak, hawthorn, sallow, etc. It may be obtained by beating or searching from August to September.

The moth is out in May and June, in some seasons later, and may be beaten out of hedges, as well as from trees in woods. Generally distributed, and often common, throughout England, Wales, and Ireland. In Scotland it is locally common in Clydesdale, and occurs in other southern parts of that country.

Abroad, the range extends to Amurland, Korea, China, and Japan.

STERRHINAE

The Blood-vein (*Calothysanis amata* Linn.)

The stripe across the wings of this pretty species (Pl. **44**, 3), extending from the apex of the fore wings to near the middle of the inner margin of the hind wings, is normally pinkish red, but it may be of a more crimson or purplish hue ; it also varies in width. The fringes are usually pinkish red, and occasionally the margins of the wings are tinged with the same colour. The whitish ochreous ground colour is normally finely powdered with grey, but sometimes so thickly that a greyish tinge is imparted to the wings. Barrett mentions a specimen with pale smoky brown wings, and, excepting that the tips of the fringes are tinged with pink, the usual markings are absent (ab. *nigra* Rebel). In another example, " the space between the central and second lines is filled up with purple brown."

The caterpillar is brownish grey, with three whitish lines on the back, the central one intersecting a series of four dark lozenges. When at rest, the third and fourth segments are distended, giving the larva somewhat the appearance of a small cobra. It feeds on various low-growing plants, such as persicaria, orache, sorrel, etc., but dock seems to be the most frequently selected pabulum. July to May, sometimes feeding up and appearing as a second generation of the moth in August.

Weedy ditches, hedge banks, or moist waste places, are the favourite resorts of the moth ; and when one example is flushed from its lurking place, others are almost certain to be hiding in the immediate vicinity.

Widely distributed throughout England, but most common in the south ; found also in North and South Wales ; and sparingly in Scotland to Aberdeenshire, also recorded from Arran. Apparently rare in Ireland, as it is only noted from Kerry, Cork, Galway, Louth, and Sligo.

Abroad, the range extends to North Africa, central Asia, Korea, and Japan.

The Birch Mocha (*Cosymbia albipunctata* Hüfn.)

The general colour of this species (Pl. **42**, 1, 2) is whitish, more or less powdered or suffused with grey ; all the wings have two blackish dotted cross lines and a greyish, sometimes reddish, central shade ; not infrequently there is an interrupted grey or dark greyish band on the outer marginal area, and this margin itself is always dotted with black ; the rings enclosing white dots on all the wings are usually black, but sometimes reddish. In some specimens having a reddish central shade, the general colour, especially of the fore wings, is delicately tinged with reddish. Ab. *subroseata* Woodforde, a form of this species occurring in North Staffordshire, is slaty grey with the space between the inner and outer cross lines of fore wings rosy pink or reddish. A somewhat darker form, ab. *decoraria* Newman, occurs in Kent and Surrey.

The caterpillar is of a green colour with slender yellowish lines along the back and sides ; between the rings the colour inclines to yellowish, and the head, legs, and prolegs are reddish brown. In another form the general colour is greyish, inclining to reddish, and the lines paler grey. It feeds on birch in June and July, and again in August and September. It is said to eat alder and oak.

The moth, which appears in May and June, and in some seasons in August, frequents woodlands and heaths where birch flourishes. Although fairly plentiful in most of the southern English counties, it appears to be rare in Dorset and Devon, and more or less so in the eastern counties. It is very local in Nottinghamshire and Yorkshire, but not uncommon at Strensall in the latter county ; and although it has been recorded from Cumberland it seems to be absent from Lancashire and Cheshire. Doubtfully reported from North Northumberland, but found in Wells Wood, Roxburghshire, and appears to be widely distributed in Scotland, although generally scarce in that country.   In Ireland it is local, but not uncommon sometimes.

Abroad the range extends through northern and central Europe to Siberia.

The Dingy Mocha (*Cosymbia pendularia* Cl.)

The wings are greyish, thickly striped with darker grey ; the markings similar to those of the preceding species, but the rings are nearly always reddish or purplish, and the central line is wavy.   (Pl. **42,** 3, 6).

The egg (which, together with the caterpillar and chrysalis, is figured on Pl. **54,** 1–15) is at first bone-coloured ; later, pink dots and patches appear.

The caterpillar is bright green with three lines along the back, the central one edged on each side with dark green and the others wavy ; the sides are blotched with pink or pale purple, or sometimes whitish and unmarked ; head slightly notched on the crown, pale brown, marked with darker ; fore legs tipped with pink.   (Porritt, abridged).   In another form of the green coloration, the sides are pinkish with dark-brown oblique stripes ; in a third the general colour is pale brown. The first brood of caterpillars feeds in June on sallow and alder and a second in August and September.

The moth appears in May and June, and again in July and August ; sometimes a third brood has been reared in captivity. It is less frequently met with than the other species of *Cosymbia*, even in its most favourite haunts, such as the New Forest, in Hampshire.   Other localities for it are Abbots Wood, St. Leonards and Tilgate Forests, and elsewhere in Sussex ; Redstone, Haslemere, and the Croydon districts, in Surrey ; and in some Kentish woods.   It has also been taken rarely in Dorset, Devon (Tiverton), South Wales, and Suffolk (Lowestoft).   Doubtfully recorded from Ireland (Galway).

Abroad the range extends through central Europe to southern Russia.

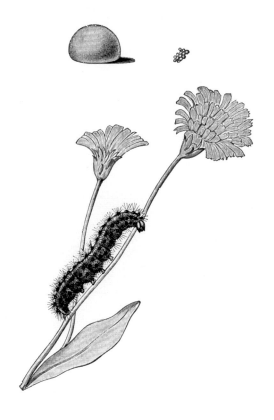

Clouded Buff: *eggs, natural size and enlarged, and caterpillar.*

1, 2. The Cinnabar, *male and female*.
3. Feathered Footman.
4, 5. Crimson Speckled.
6. Beautiful Utetheisa.

The Mocha (*Cosymbia annulata* Schulze)

Normally, the wings of this species (Pl. **42**, 9, 12) are yellowish white, inclining to ochreous yellow with the blackish central shade near to and sometimes united with the blackish irregular and outwardly toothed second cross line on both fore and hind wings ; the rings are deep brown or blackish. There is variation in the width and intensity of the central shade, and the rings sometimes are absent on the fore wings (ab. *obsoleta* Riding), and occasionally all the wings are devoid of the annular mark (ab. *biobsoleta* Riding). Examples of a second generation reared in captivity are rather deeper coloured, and have a sprinkling of black scales, chiefly on the fore wings (gen. aest. *aestiva* Prout).

The caterpillar (Pl. **54**, 2, after Hofmann) is dark green, yellow between the rings ; there are three yellow lines along the back, the outer ones waved ; head reddish brown, paler marked. (Adapted from Porritt.) There is also a pale ochreous brown form.

It feeds on maple in June, and as a second generation in August and September. It may be reared on sycamore. The moth frequents lanes, woods, and thickets, especially those in which maple is plentiful ; it flies at dusk, and in the daytime may be beaten from hedgerows in which the food plant grows. It has also been found among hornbeam. The species is most frequent from Kent to Hampshire, but widely distributed over England up to Worcester and Herefordshire, and eastward to Norfolk, occurring also in Northamptonshire and Yorkshire.

The colour and ornamentation of this charming little insect seem to have struck Haworth, who named the species in the vernacular, as bearing some resemblance to the Mocha stone from Arabia, a kind of transparent agate in which are seen brownish moss-like markings.

Abroad the range extends to Russia, western Asia Minor and Armenia.

Blair's Mocha (*Cosymbia puppillaria* Hübn.)

The first known British specimen of this species was captured by Dr. K. G. Blair on the Isle of Wight on October 2, 1946. It was a female and from fertile ova laid several further specimens were successfully reared. More fertile ova were obtained from this generation, but owing to difficulties in obtaining food for the larvae early in the year, only a single female was reared.

Subsequent records are : one at Swanage in Dorset on August 3, 1947, one near Torquay in Devon in 1951, one in N.W. Kent on August 22, 1955, a female on the Isle of Portland in Dorset on September 25, 1956, one at Eastbourne in the same year and a female at Chalfont St. Peter in Buckinghamshire on September 25, 1957. Known also from the Scilly Isles.

Superficially this variable species most nearly resembles *porata* but the acute and somewhat produced apex distinguishes it quite readily (Pl. **42**, 4, 5). The genitalia, however, show that it is more closely related to *annulata*, *albipunctata*, and *orbicularia*.

The larva has the head as broad as the prothorax, yellowish, and on the vertex, red ; the body is usually green but sometimes yellowish, brown or red ; lines yellow, the subdorsal ones narrow ; intersegmental rings yellow ; legs and anal flap red. It feed on evergreen oak, *Cistus*, *Myrtus*, *Phillyrea*, and *Arbutus* (*Quercus ilex*) (Millière).

A full account of the early stages of this species has been published by Mr. G. Haggett (1958, *Ent. Gazette*, 9 : 103–5) and an account of rearing the species by Mr. R. Mere and Mr. G. Haggett has also appeared (1959, *Ent. Gazette*, 10 : 45–50).

Probably double brooded. Abroad its range includes southern Europe, Asia Minor, North Africa, and Madeira.

The False Mocha (*Cosymbia porata* Linn.)

The wings are pale ochreous brown, finely flecked with purplish grey, and more or less tinged with reddish ; the cross lines are indicated by blackish dots, the central shade is greyish inclining to reddish, and the rings enclosing white dots are blackish or dark brown, but sometimes indistinct on the fore wings ; occasionally there are some purplish grey clouds on the outer marginal area, and this is more frequent in examples of a second generation. Sometimes the wings are entirely suffused with dull reddish brown, and all the markings, except the white dot on the hind wings, are obscured (Pl. **42,** 7, 8).

The caterpillar is pale pinkish ochreous, with inconspicuous wavy white lines, and brownish dots, on the back ; dark oblique marks on the sides ; the head is pencilled with darker brown. It feeds on oak and birch in June and July, and individuals of a second brood sometimes occur in September or October.

The moth is out in May and June, and rests in the daytime among the foliage of trees and bushes in or around woods. Like others of the genus, it is attracted by light, and is said to visit the sugar patch. Specimens of a second generation sometimes appear in August and September, but, I believe, more frequently in the breeding cage than in the open. Although it has been recorded from several of the northern counties from Staffordshire to Cumberland, this is more especially an inhabitant of the south and west of England, and of Wales. In Scotland, it is known to occur singly and rarely in Clydesdale and Arran, and has been found in Perthshire.

Abroad the range extends through southern and central Europe to Armenia.

The Maiden's Blush (*Cosymbia punctaria* Linn.)

In a general way, this moth (Pl. **42,** 10, 11) is not unlike the last mentioned. Apart, however, from the absence of ringed dots on all the wings, the central line is more prominent. Certain vagaries occur in connection with this line, which is generally reddish, or purplish brown. Occasionally, it may be visible on the fore wings, but absent on the hind wings ; or it may change its course mid-way, and turn inwards to the base of the fore wing. South has a specimen from Surrey in which this line is double the normal width, and dark purplish in colour. Examples of the second generation, gen. aest. *naevata* Bast., have brownish clouds on the outer margin.

The caterpillar is pale reddish ochreous or bright green ; a black line along the middle of the back, and a brownish one along the sides ; a black horse-shoe mark, edged below with yellow, on the back of rings four to nine.

It feeds, in June and July, on oak, but may be reared on birch ; also found in September as a second brood.

The moth is out in May and June, and specimens of a second generation are often not uncommon in August. It occurs in woodlands throughout England, but is most plentiful in the south. In Scotland, it appears to be local in Clydesdale, but is found thence up to Moray. In Ireland, only recorded from Galway, Cork and Wicklow.

The range abroad extends through Europe, Asia Minor, and northern Persia.

The Clay Triple-Lines (*Cosymbia linearia* Hübn.)

This species (Pl. **42**, 13, 14) varies in the general colour from yellowish to pale reddish ochreous ; the cross lines are also variable, often the first is missing, and not infrequently the dark central line is the only visible marking, but very exceptionally the central line is very little, if at all, more distinct than the normal first and second. A very rare form, ab. *fasciata* Prout, has a smoky band on all the wings. The ringed white dots are rarely very conspicuous, and may be absent.

The caterpillar is pale brownish, with a brown-edged yellowish line along the middle of the back, and some yellowedged dark-brown streaks on the sides. In another form, the head is brown and the body green.

Speckled Footman, *eggs and caterpillar.*

1, 2. Scarlet Tiger.
3, 4. Jersey Tiger.

It feeds in June, July, and again in September, on beech. The moth is out in May and June, and again in August and September. Beech woods are its favourite haunts, and it seldom strays far from them. It is generally common in the south, and its range apparently extends to Northumberland ; but it is local and infrequent in the north. Three specimens have been recorded from Co. Galway, a few from Co. Cork, and one from Co. Wicklow in Ireland.

Abroad the range extends through central Europe, North Italy to North Persia.

NOTE.—In 1859, at Brighton, a single specimen was reared from one of eight larvae that hatched from the same number of eggs deposited by a female *C. linearia* that had paired with a male *C. pendularia* Cl. This hybrid has been named *brightoni* Tutt. (*Brit. Lep.*, v. pp. 29–30 and 541–2).

The Smoky Wave (*Scopula ternata* Schrank)

The sexes of this greyish white moth are figured on Pl. **44,** 6. It will be seen that the female is smaller than the male. The caterpillar is very slender, and finely wrinkled ; pale ochreous brown, with three pale lines along the back, each of which is shaded on both sides with brown. Beneath the ridge, low down along the sides, is a dark stripe, and the under surface is pale. It feeds on bilberry, sallow, and heather, and will eat knotgrass, chickweed, and dandelion. Hatching in August, it hibernates when nearly mature, but it resumes feeding in the spring. The moth is out in June and July, and frequents moors and mosses. Plentiful in Scotland and in the north of England, its range extends through Wales and the west of England to Devonshire, where it occurs on Exmoor and is common in some parts of that extensive area. In Ireland, recorded by Birchall as widely distributed ; Kane notes it from counties Kerry, Waterford, and Galway. Donovan says, " Very rare, south only."

The range abroad extends to Amurland and Japan.

The Lewes Wave (*Scopula immorata* Linn.)

Although the late Mr. S. Stevens exhibited a British specimen of this species, as a curious variety of *Chiasmia clathrata*,
at a meeting of the Entomological Society of London in 1868,
it was not until the year 1887, when the late C. H. Morris
captured two specimens in Sussex, that the insect became
recognised as a native. It is probable that the earlier example, taken some years before it was shown at the meeting
referred to, may have come from the same locality in the
Lewes district where the later specimens were captured. Anyway, the species has, so far, not been recorded from any other
part of our islands, but it continues to be found in its original
haunts, described as " some heathy ground," up to the present
day (Pl. **44**, 10).

The long, slender, and roughened caterpillar is pale greyish
brown ; the central line along the back is greyish white, each
side edged on the hinder half with brown, having at the beginning of each ring after the third a black dot on either side ;
side stripes dark brown, inclining to black above ; a slender
brown line below the black spiracles. (Adapted from Barrett.)
It feeds from August to May on ling (*Calluna vulgaris*), marjoram, thyme, knotgrass, etc.

From eggs laid on July 1 and 2 caterpillars hatched on
July 17 and 18. These were placed on leaves of ribwort
plantain (*Plantago lanceolata*), and as soon as large enough
transferred to a potted plant, and kept out of doors. Two
of the caterpillars grew up quickly, and on August 24 were taken
indoors, where they spun up for pupation, one on August
28, and the other on September 1. A female moth emerged
September 14 from the first chrysalis (F. C. Woodbridge, 1906).

The range abroad extends to eastern Siberia and Amurland.

The Tawny Wave (*Scopula rubiginata* Hufn.)

This attractive little moth (Pl. **44**, 12), known also as
rubricata Schiff., varies in colour from ochreous brown with

a purplish or reddish tinge, to purplish brown or crimson ; the first line of the fore wings is curved, and the second is parallel with the central shade. Sometimes the space between the last two lines and between the first and second lines of the hind wings is paler than the general colour. A dusky brown form has been recorded from boggy heaths in Norfolk.

The roughish caterpillar, which gradually tapers to the notched head, is greyish inclining to yellowish or greenish ; three blackish lines on the back, the central one widened on the middle rings, and the others only distinct on the front rings ; a black-edged pale line above the black spiracles, and a dusky stripe below them (Barrett). It feeds from August to May on clover, trefoil, knotgrass, etc. Sometimes as a second generation in June and July.

According to Stephens, who figured this species in 1831, a specimen was taken near Dover, about 1825 ; he also refers to Yorkshire specimens, one of which he had in his collection. Since that time the species has been obtained in Lancashire (Ashton-on-Mersey) and it was noted, not uncommon from the first to third week in July, 1875, on low heathery ground at Winch Bridge, Upper Teesdale, Durham. Casual specimens have also been recorded from Folkestone, Kent ; Arundel and Hastings, Sussex ; and Newton Abbot, South Devon. What may be termed the British home of the species is, however, the Breck sand district in the eastern counties, where, since 1860, it has been found in greater or lesser plenty, in June, each year up to the present time. The best known localities are Tuddenham, Brandon, Thetford, and Bury St. Edmunds.

Abroad, its range extends to Amurland and Korea.

The Mullein Wave (*Scopula conjugata* Borkh.)

This species exhibits more variation than is usual in this group. Typically, the moth is greyish white, but in some specimens the grey is most in evidence, and in others the white. A practically black form, with white fringes, has been noted from North Cornwall (ab. *orphnaeata* F. Fuchs), and at Eastbourne and Portland many of the specimens have a clear, bone-coloured ground, with fine but very distinct cross-markings (ab. *mundata* Prout). The cross lines in both dark and light forms are sometimes very indistinct, but occasionally the first and second of the fore wings are united, and so form an irregular dusky band; the greyish clouding on the outer marginal area is also variable. Two specimens are shown on Pl. **44,** 7, 8.

The long caterpillar is very pale slaty-olive, with three paler lines along the back, the central one edged on each side with olive, darkest on the last three rings; spiracles black, and under surface of the body pale slate blue (adapted from Porritt). It feeds on various low-growing plants, among which yarrow, mugwort, chickweed, cinquefoil, and knotgrass have been mentioned; also, it is said, on sallow. There are certainly two broods in the south, one feeding up in the summer, and the other hatching in September, and after hibernation attaining full growth in May or June. Moths of the first generation are on the wing in June and July, and of the second in August and September. Although sometimes found inland, the species is more especially attached to the coast, and is found in nearly all the seaboard counties of England, Wales, and Ireland. It has been recorded from the Isle of Man. In Scotland, it occurs in Wigtownshire, and very dark specimens have been obtained on rocks in dry pastures at Ardrossan; June to end of July.

Abroad the range extends to Mongolia.

The Lace Border (*Scopula ornata* Scop.)

The conspicuously marked white moth depicted on Pl. **44,** 13 and 14, is unlikely to escape the notice of the collector who visits rough fields and hillsides in some of the chalk districts of southern England, especially in the counties of

1, 2. **Orange Underwing**, *male and female*.
3, 4. **Light Orange Underwing**, *male and female*.
5, 6. **Rest Harrow**, *male and female*.
7, 8. **Grass Emerald**, *male and female*.
9. **Blotched Emerald**.
10. **Essex Emerald**.

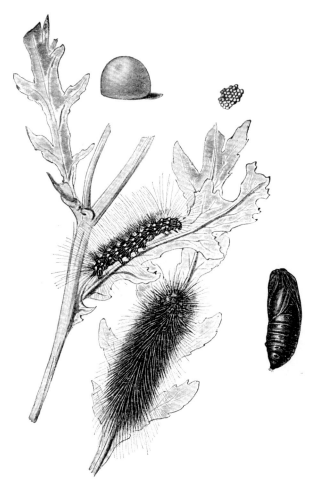

Garden Tiger: *eggs, natural size and enlarged, caterpillars and chrysalis.*

Kent, Surrey, and Sussex. Usually there are two generations
of the moth during the year ; one is on the wing in May and
June, and the other flies in August and September.

The caterpillar is of long and slender build, the head is
notched, and the skin of the body is roughened. In colour it
is ochreous brown above and greyish beneath ; there are three
lines along the back, the central one pale, except towards the
head, edged with dusky, the others dark brown. On each
ring, from four to eight, are two dark V-shaped marks ; low
down along the sides there is a dusky-edged and mottled,
pale ochreous stripe. It feeds, from October to May, and in
July and August, on thyme, marjoram, and may be reared on
garden mint. Abroad, the species ranges over central and
southern Europe, and through central Asia.

According to Prout (*Entom.*, xxxix. 267), this species is the
type of the genus *Scopula* Schrank.

The Small Blood-vein (*Scopula imitaria* Hübn.)

All the wings of this pale reddish brown species are angulated
(Pl. **44**, 15). A conspicuous character is the reddish or
purplish red stripe crossing both the wings, and to which
its English name no doubt refers. It varies somewhat in
the amount of reddish in the general coloration, also in the
tint and the width of the prominent oblique cross stripe.

The early stages are shown on Pl. **59**, 2–2*b*. The eggs
when laid on June 18 and 19, were whitish green, but soon
turned pinkish, inclining to coral red. The caterpillars hatched
July 3 to 6, and were reared on a diet of privet leaves—a food
that South had always found they preferred to any other that
had been offered to them, and upon which he had found them
in the open. They are exceedingly easy to rear, and if, as
sometimes happens, they refuse to feed up and get through to
the moth state in September of the same year, they do not die
off during the winter or early spring, as do so many larvae
of other hibernating species. Enclosed in a suitable receptacle,

such as a roomy glass cylinder, with some twigs of privet plugged in a bottle of water, the caterpillars may be left in any odd corner until spring, when fresh twigs should be introduced from time to time. Other food plants are dock, groundsel, dandelion, knotgrass, bedstraw, etc. In colour the caterpillar is pale ochreous brown, with three darker brown lines on the back, the central one broken on the front rings, and the others edged above with whitish ; the spiracles are black, and the stripe along the side pale drab.

The moth affects hedgerows, banks, bushy places on rough sloping ground, and sandhills by the sea. It flies in the evening, and may be met with in July and August, sometimes in September, in most English and Welsh counties, and in the south of Ireland. It is local and somewhat rare in northern England, and seems not to occur in Scotland.

Abroad, the range extends through central and southern Europe, North Africa, and Asia Minor.

The Rosy Wave (*Scopula emutaria* Hübn.)

Pl. **44**, 11, shows an example of this species, which also has angled hind wings. In coloration it is whiter and more silky than the last, and when fresh is delicately tinged with pink ; the first and second lines are dotted or represented by dots, and the greyish central shade is obliquely inclined in the direction of the tips of the wings. In the marshes on the Essex and Kentish coasts the species is generally rather more rosy (ab. *subroseata* Haworth), but this form occurs occasionally in the New Forest also. The long, slender caterpillar is whitish ochreous, inclining to pinkish ; on the back of each ring is a broad grey shade enclosing a white spot, and a faint grey line on each side. Spiracles black, with black spots below them on rings four to eight ; undersurface bluish grey with a central white stripe. (Adapted from Fenn.) When reared from the egg, the caterpillar will feed on knotgrass, chickweed, bird's-foot trefoil, etc. The moths sometimes appear in August or September, but the more usual habit of the larva is to hibernate when small and complete growth in the following spring.

The moth, which is out in July and early August, conceals itself by day among the vegetation growing in its somewhat restricted haunts. These are chiefly the marshes on the east coast, and similar spots in Kent and Sussex; also the bogs of Hampshire and Dorset, but especially those between Lynd-hurst and Brockenhurst in the former county. It is not readily put up during the day, but towards evening it becomes active on the wing, and after its flight may be found sitting about upon the herbage.

Abroad, it occurs in Holland, southern Europe, and North Africa.

The Sub-angled Wave (*Scopula nigropunctata* Hufn.)

This species is greyish white, sometimes brownish-tinged; dusky cross markings, of which the oblique shade following the central black dot of the fore wings, and that before the central black dot of the hind wings, are usually most distinct, forming a narrow band across both pairs of wings; the outer margin of the hind wings is angled.

The long, slender caterpillar has a roughened appearance; the colour is greenish grey, and the markings comprise a dull green line along the middle of the back, spotted with black on each side; the grey head is variegated with very pale brown. (Adapted from Porritt.)

This species (Pl. **44,** 9) was known to Haworth, who gave it the English name which it bears to-day. Stephens, writing of it in 1831, states that it was very rare, and that specimens in his collection were from a lane near Darenth, in Kent. The best known locality in the British Isles for the species is the Warren, near Folkestone, Kent, where it was discovered in 1859. Here it occurred more or less freely for several years, then it became scarce, and finally, about 1890, seemed to be practically extinct. In 1906, however, Mr. G. H. Conquest netted a female specimen in the Warren on July 24, and as she laid a few eggs, it may be presumed that others had been deposited before capture. From the eggs obtained by Mr. Conquest, nine moths were reared in July, 1907. The caterpillars thrived on traveller's joy (*Clematis vitalba*), which is probably the natural food ; but they will also eat dandelion, knotgrass, etc., and like the withered leaves. By keeping in a warm place, it is possible to get moths out the same year, but as a rule, the caterpillars prefer to hibernate. It was recorded from the Warren again in 1946. The species is also recorded from Sussex (Hastings, 1876) and mid-Kent (July 6, 1951).

The range abroad extends to Amurland, China, Korea, and Japan.

The Lesser Cream Wave (*Scopula immutata* Linn.)

White, more or less tinged with ochreous or ochreous grey in the male, is the general colour of this moth ; the wings are crossed by several ochreous lines, the third line of the fore wings and the second line of the hind wings rather wavy. All the wings with central black dots, most distinct on the hind pair, occasionally absent from the fore wings (Pl. **44**, 4 ♂, 5 ♀).

The long caterpillar is pale greyish brown, with three dusky lines on the back ; the black spiracles are set in a pale stripe, and below this is a dusky line ; head small and round (Barrett). August to May. The natural food appears to be *Valeriana officinalis*, and *Spiraea*, but it has been reared from the egg on groundsel, knotgrass, etc., also hawthorn, and moths obtained the same year, about September.

In the open the moth is to be found in fens, bogs, and marshy places in fields and woods, during June and July. It is not uncommon, in suitable spots, in most of the southern and eastern counties of England. In the west, including Wales, and through the Midlands, it is local to Yorkshire, but is widely distributed in the south of the latter county ; it occurs, rarely, in Durham. In Scotland it has only been definitely noted from Arran. Widely distributed, and common, in many parts of Ireland.

Abroad, the range extends to Amurland.

The Cream Wave (*Scopula lactata* Haw.)

This species, which has also gone under the names of *floslactata* Haw. and *remutata* Schiff (Pl. **44**, 1, 2), has the wings white or ochreous white, becoming rather smoky grey on the front edge of the fore wings, and sometimes this tinge spreads all over the wings. In well-marked specimens there are two dark, wavy, cross lines, a dusky central shade, and a dusky shade-like stripe along the outer area beyond the second line ; the first line of the fore wings is often placed close to the central shade, and sometimes it is merged in it (ab. *conjunctiva* Prout). Not infrequently the lines are barely traceable ; almost as often the wings appear to have a pair of lines only, and these distinctly darker than usual (ab. *sublactata* Haw.)

The caterpillar is rough, long and slender ; grey-brown with irregular darker marks, a pale line along the middle of the back, and a dark cross on the back of ring ten. The notched head is pale brown with a black V-mark. It feeds, from July to September, on bedstraw (*Galium*), woodruff (*Asperula*), dock, sallow, etc., and hibernates fully grown, pupating in the spring.

The moth is out in May and June, and often is plentiful in woods throughout the greater part of England and Wales ; in Yorkshire and northwards through Scotland up to Moray it is rather local. In Ireland it has been found in Wicklow and Louth, but more commonly in the south and west.

The range abroad extends to Amurland and Japan.

The Bright Wave (*Sterrha ochrata* subsp. *cantiata* Prout)

At one time this ochreous brown species (Pl. **47**, 19) was an inhabitant of the Essex coast, and was found commonly at Southend among other places. Deal and other parts of the Kentish coast are more frequently mentioned in connection with later records of the species. In the present day it is far less plentiful at Deal than formerly, but it is still to be found there. Specimens have been taken in the Isle of Wight (Barrett), and one has been noted from Suffolk (Aldeburgh).

The pale ochreous brown or greyish ochreous caterpillar has three broken greyish lines on the back ; it tapers towards the small head, and the skin of the body is closely wrinkled. It feeds from August to May, or a little later, on the flowers of hawk's-beard (*Crepis*), dandelion, coltsfoot, golden-rod, etc., and in confinement it seems to accept most kinds of flowers that are offered, even when widely different. Thus, Mr. Conquest, in 1907, had some caterpillars which hatched during the first week in August from eggs laid on July 25 ; these were at first supplied with flowering sprays of yellow bedstraw (*Galium verum*), and later on with the flowers of golden-rod (*Solidago*). Instead of hibernating, which is no doubt the normal habit in the species, some larvae reared from the egg in confinement and subjected to fostering warmth will grow very quickly and produce moths the same year.

Abroad, this species ranges through Spain, North Africa, central and southern Europe, Transcaspia, and northern Persia.

The Least Carpet (*Sterrha vulpinaria* H.-Sch.)

The whitish fore wings of this species (Pl. **47**, 3, 6) are crossed by a blackish central band, and there is a blackish patch at the base of the wings, with an extension along the front margin, almost or quite to the central band ; the hind wings have a central dot, and three or four dark grey wavy lines, the space between the first and second darkened, and appearing to be a continuation of the fore wing band. The thick-set, pale ochreous brown, or grey brown, caterpillar (Pl. **59**, 1, drawn from a skin) has three more or less distinct pale lines along the back, and a series of darker diamonds along the central area ; head, brown. In the open, its food probably consists of decaying or withered leaves, but when treated in captivity it will eat and thrive upon growing knot-grass, groundsel, dandelion, etc. August to May. The late Mr. Mera mentioned that some caterpillars he reared on dandelion produced moths that were larger in size than most captured specimens.

The moth is out in July, and specimens have been bred in September from eggs laid in July of the same year. Its present distribution extends along both banks of the Thames east of London, though it is found more commonly on the Kentish side ; it occurs also in Sussex, on the Isle of Portland in Dorset and at Torquay in Devon. In the past it has been recorded from Kingsdown, Dover, Folkestone (Kent) ; Brighton, Lewes, West Horsham (Sussex) ; single specimens have been reported from Cornwall and from Stowmarket and Felixstowe (Suffolk). C. M. Gordon Hewitt records it as common on the island of St. Kilda (*Ann. Scot. Nat. Hist.*, 1907 : 220).

Abroad, the range extends through Europe to central Asia and North Africa.

The Dwarf Cream Wave (*Sterrha interjectaria* Boisd.)

This moth (Pl. **47**, 13, 15) was for many years known in England as *fuscovenosa* Goeze. It is also the *dilutaria* of some authors, but not of Hübner. Hübner's *dilutaria* is the *holo-sericata* of Duponchel, and therefore an earlier name for the species generally known by the latter name.

The present species, to which Haworth gave the English name here used, is whitish straw-coloured, and silky in appear-ance ; the wings have a central black dot and four or five dusky cross lines, some of which are more distinct than others ; the front edge of the fore wings is tinged with reddish brown, in which is often a dark dot at the ends of the first and central lines ; a series of linear blackish dots at the base of the fringes, most distinct on the fore wings.

The somewhat stumpy caterpillar is dull smoky brown, marbled and variegated with ochreous, the darker colour most in evidence in front, and the ochreous behind ; an ochreous line along the middle of the back, and one along the region of the spiracles ; white spots on rings 5–7. (Adapted from Porritt.) It feeds from August to April on dandelion and other low-growing plants, and especially on the withered leaves. The moth occurs among weeds growing on banks, and hedgerows, and the outskirts of woods, in greater or lesser plenty throughout the South of England ; but it becomes local, and more or less rare in the north of the country. In Scotland it is said to occur locally, in Clydesdale, but has not been noted from Ireland, or from Wales.

Abroad, the range extends through central and southern Europe, North Africa, and Transcaucasia.

The Isle of Wight Wave (*Sterrha humiliata* Hufn.)

This species (Pl. **47,** 18) is the *osseata* of Fabricus, but not of Haworth and other British authors. It is very similar in general appearance to the species last considered, but the wings are somewhat less ample, and rather yellower in tint. It is most readily recognised, however, by the distinctly reddish stripe on the front edge of the fore wings. Previous to 1891, when specimens were obtained by Mr. A. J. Hodges in the Isle of Wight, the species was not certainly known to be an inhabitant of the British Isles, although it seems to have been represented in many collections. The insect is still found by those who know where to look for it on the sea cliffs of its island home, but so far as appears to be known at present, it does not occur in any other part of Britain, though there is a single record of the species being taken at Portsmouth. For this reason, it does not seem desirable to indicate

Cream-spot Tiger: *caterpillars, chrysalis and cocoon.*

1, 2. **Common Emerald,** *male and female.*
3, 4. **Sussex Emerald,** *male and female.*
5. **Large Emerald.**
6, 8. **Small Grass Emerald.**
7. **Little Emerald.**
9, 10. **Small Emerald,** *male and female.*

the exact locality more definitely ; but it may be added that the moth flies in July.

Abroad, the range is similar to that of the preceding species.

The Silky Wave (*Sterrha dilutaria* Hübn.)

Somewhat similar to *S. interjectaria*, but tinged with pale brown, and even more glossy ; the front edge of the fore wings is of the general coloration, and the only markings on the wings are darker cross lines, the third on the fore wings, and the second on the hind wings, being the most distinct (Pl. **47,** 16).

The rough and rather stumpy caterpillar tapers towards the small notched head ; general colour dusky reddish brown, a pale line along the middle of the back, finely edged with black. It feeds from August to May on rock rose (*Helianthemum*), eating the withered and even mouldy leaves. Will eat knotgrass, and, no doubt, dandelion also.

Here, again, we have an ancient name brought forward to supplant that which the species has borne for years, and by which it is well known to entolmogiosts (*holosericata* Dup.). As it is now established that Hübner's (Fig. 100) *dilutaria* does represent this species his name is therefore used.

As a British insect, it has only been known since 1851, when the capture of a specimen in the neighbourhood of Bristol was recorded in *The Zoologist*. Subsequently it transpired that the scene of capture was Durdham Down, Gloucestershire, and here it has been found annually, and in some plenty, among the bushes and low vegetation covering the ground in that rugged locality. Specimens have also been noted from Berkshire (Newbury), Buckinghamshire (Chalfont St. Peter), Dorset (Halstock), Norfolk (Thetford), and Denbighshire. Possibly there are other localities in England, more especially in the west, where this species may be awaiting discovery.

Abroad, the range extends through central and southern Europe, Asia Minor, and Transcaucasia.

The Ochraceous Wave (*Sterrha serpentata* Hufn.)

How far there may have been confusion in the records of this species and *S. ochrata* Scop., South had no means of ascertaining, but probably all but two should properly have referred to *ochrata*. Only two then known British specimens of *serpentata* therefore appear to have been captured in the Redhill district of Surrey, one in 1865 and one in 1869. Three further male specimens have recently been found in the collection of the National Museum of Wales ; two are simply labelled " 27 July 1868, ex collection Dr. J. C. Melville " and the other is labelled " Gravel Pit, Brent, 1899, ex collection A. B. Farn." As will be seen on reference to Pl. **47,** where a portrait of a Continental specimen will be found (Fig. 20), the general colour is much brighter than that of *ochrata*. It will be noted, also, that there are four darker cross lines on the fore wings, and three on the hind wings. The antennae of the male are toothed, and therefore differ from those of *ochrata*.

Abroad, the range extends through Europe, and Asia to East Siberia.

The Purple-bordered Gold (*Sterrha muricata* Hufn.)

Two forms of this pretty little species (known also as *auroraria* Borkh.) are shown on Pl. **47.** Fig. 1 represents the more usual form, but between this and the almost entirely purple variety, ab. *totarubra* Lambill. (Fig. 4), which occurs chiefly in the north, there are various modifications. Then again, especially in the south of England, there is a tendency to become entirely yellow, the purple, inclining to crimson in such specimens, being confined to the front margin and cross lines on the fore wings, and a narrow band on the outer margin of all the wings (ab. *lutescens* Prout).

The caterpillar is pale brownish, inclining to ochreous at

each end, marked with irregular blackish lines on the back, and dots and streaks on the sides. The late Hon. N. C. Rothschild recorded *Comarum palustre* as its natural food plant, but when reared from the egg the caterpillar will eat knotgrass, and sometimes a few will feed up and attain the moth state the same year. August to May.

The moth occurs in late June and in July, and frequents fens, boggy heaths, and mosses. Although odd specimens may, occasionally, be flushed during the day, the collector will need to be up early in the morning if he would see this species on the wing, as it seems to fly most freely about sunrise. The New Forest in Hampshire is a noted district for it, as also are Ranworth, Horning, etc., in Norfolk, and Witherslack in Westmorland. In Ireland, it is found in counties Galway, Mayo, Kerry, Cork, and Offaly.

Abroad, the range extends to Amurland, China, Korea, and Japan.

The Single-dotted Wave (*Sterrha dimidiata* Hufn.)

The most noticeable feature in this whity brown moth (Pl. **49,** 12, 15), sometimes known as *scutulata* Schiff., are the larger dots at the costal end of the dotted cross lines, and the blackish or dark-brown chain-like mark on the lower part of the outer marginal area of the fore wings ; the latter is sometimes obscured in a cloud of its own colour.

Eggs (Pl. **56,** 1*a*), laid in a batch on a dried leaf of dandelion, were whitish at first, but turned reddish later.

The elongated and somewhat flattened caterpillar (figured on Pl. **57,** 1, from a coloured drawing by the late Mr. Sich) is ochreous, with brown lines on the back, the central one double, and interrupted on the middle rings, upon which are oblique pale brown dashes. It feeds, from September to April, on beaked parsley (*Anthriscus sylvestris*), burnet saxifrage (*Pimpinella*), etc., and may be reared on withered leaves of dandelion and other weeds. The moth is out in June and

July, and in northern localities in August. Generally distributed, and often common.

Abroad, the range extends through Europe, Asia Minor to Transcaspia.

Weaver's Wave (*Sterrha eburnata* subsp. *brittaniae* L. Müll.)

The earliest known British specimen of this species (Pl. **47,** 2, 5) was taken in North Wales by Weaver, in 1855, and was figured and described in *The Entomologist's Annual* for 1856 as *Dosithea eburnata* Wocke. About seven years later Greening captured a female specimen, and he subsequently reared the insect, when it became known as " Greening's Pug." Still later, about 1875, the English name was changed to " Capper's Acidalia."

Fortunately, the species seems not difficult to rear from the egg, otherwise specimens in collections would be not only very limited in number, but frequently very indifferent in condition.

Dr. L. Müller (1936, *Mitt. münzhen. ent. Ges.*, 26 : 1–32, Pl. I) deals very fully with this species, under the preoccupied name *contiguaria* Hübn., describing its races and their aberrations.

In colour the moth is whity brown, more or less dusted or clouded with dark grey ; except in the darker forms, three irregular black lines on the fore wings, and two on the hind wings, are clearly seen. It flies at dusk in June and July, and sits by day on lichen-covered rocks.

The caterpillar is pale ochreous brown, with irregular dark brown lines. It feeds on ling (*Calluna*) and crowberry (*Empetrum*) from September to May ; but when eggs are obtained, the caterpillar hatching from them may be kept on chickweed, knotgrass, etc., and the moth be reared the same year.

Mr. R. Tait recorded the finding of ten caterpillars on navelwort (*Cotyledon*) growing among heather in a very sheltered

1. Birch Mocha.

2. Birch Mocha.

3. Dingy Mocha.

4. Blair's Mocha.

5. Blair's Mocha.

6. Dingy Mocha.

7. False Mocha.

8. False Mocha.

9. The Mocha.

10. Maiden's Blush.

11. Maiden's Blush.

12. The Mocha.

13. Clay Triple-lines.

14. Clay Triple-lines.

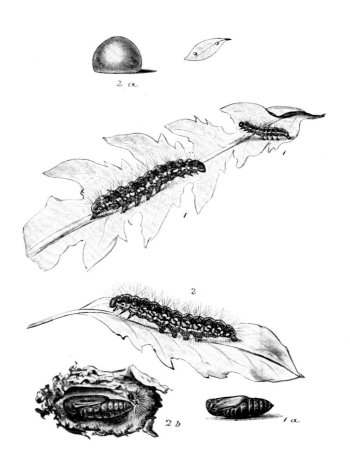

1, 1a. **Jersey Tiger**: *caterpillars and chrysalis.*
2, 2a, 2b. **Scarlet Tiger**: *eggs, caterpillar, chrysalis and cocoon.*

corner among rocks in North Wales, at Easter, 1906. He also noted that moths reared in captivity pair readily.

The British localities, all in North Wales, are Aber, Bangor, Barmouth, Bettws-y-coed, Conway, Dolgelly, Llanfairfechan, and Penmaenmawr.

Abroad, the range extends through central and southern Europe.

The Small Dusty Wave (*Sterrha seriata* Schrank)

In most parts of the southern half of England this species, of which two specimens are shown on Pl. **47, 11, 14,** is more or less common, and is often to be seen on garden walls, pales, and other kinds of fences. Although apparently infrequent in the Midlands, it has been recorded as common at Rugeley in Staffordshire ; in several parts of Cheshire it is not uncommon, and its distribution is known to extend to Northumberland. Possibly the species is more widely spread over England than the records show it to be. In Wales, it has been found in the North ; in Scotland, it occurs locally from Berwick to Aberdeen ; and it is doubtfully recorded from Ireland. The long, thin caterpillar is ochreous brown, with a pale stripe on each side. It feeds on the leaves of various low plants, and seems, at times, to like its food best when withered. Some that South reared from eggs deposited in September, 1904, fed for a time on fresh dandelion, but on the approach of winter they apparently ceased feeding, and were allowed to remain in the box with the food last supplied. In March it was found that they had been, and were then, eating the old provender. Some fresh dandelion was added, but this was not touched until all the old had been consumed. The same thing was repeated until the caterpillars were nearly full grown, when the fresh food was eaten as well as the stale. The moths resulting from them emerged during the last week in April, 1905, and were all well above the average size, and considerably larger than the female parent. From eggs deposited by a melanic female captured in south-east London, Mr. Bauman reared some twenty-three specimens, many of which agreed with the parent female in tint, others were grey, but none were of the typical coloration of *seriata*. The blackish specimens are referable to *cubicularia* Peyrhff.

There are certainly two generations of the moth during the year ; in some years possibly more.

Abroad, the range extends through Europe and reaches North Africa.

The Satin Wave (*Sterrha subsericeata* Haw.)

The wings of this species (Pl. **47,** 17) are glossy whitish, with a faint greyish, or sometimes yellow greyish tinge ; the cross lines are grey, oblique and straight on the fore wings, but the outer two on the hind wings are curved or bent.

Ab. *mancuniata* Knaggs, found locally in Lancashire, Yorkshire, and elsewhere, is rather more tinged with yellowish, the lines being distinct, and some more or less distinct dusky dots on the outer margin of the fore wings.

A blackish form, with white fringes (ab. *obscura* Rebel), has been recorded from North Cornwall, where the species, in its usual form, has been noted as abundant.

The rough-looking caterpillar is pale greyish, inclining to reddish above ; three black lines along the back, the central one slender, and the outer ones widening out towards each end. It feeds on knotgrass, dandelion, chickweed, and other kinds of weeds, and will eat plum. Hatching in August, it hibernates, as a rule, and attains full growth in the following spring ; but sometimes caterpillars feed up quickly, and produce moths the same year.

The moth, which is out in June and July, is partial to heathy ground, but not confined to heaths, as it has been met with in lanes bordered by pasture fields and on chalk downs. Widely distributed throughout England and Wales, rare in Scotland, where it has only been recorded from the Solway. In Ireland it has been found commonly at Howth, near Dublin; and in the counties Tipperary, Cork, Down, and Waterford. The only record for the north is, according to Donovan, Kilkeal, Co. Down.

Abroad, the range extends through central and southern Europe, North Africa, Asia Minor, and northern Persia.

The Dotted Border Wave (*Sterrha sylvestraria* Hübn.)

In its ordinary form this moth (Pl. **47**, 9, 12) is greyish white, sometimes with a tinge of brown, especially on the fore wings; the darker cross lines are slightly wavy; each wing has a central black dot, and there is a more or less distinct series of black dots on their outer margins. Ab. *circellata* Guenée, has the first and second lines of the fore wings strongly defined and deep brown, and the first is united with the central shade above the inner margin; the corresponding lines on the hind wings are also deep brown. This form, which occurs on the Lancashire and Cheshire mosses and occurs as a race in places abroad, and is known as the Obscure Wave, has been considered a distinct species, but it is connected with typical *sylvestraria* by intermediate aberrations which occur together with *circellata* and the ordinary form on the same ground. Similar intergrades also occur in the New Forest, Hampshire, the Dover district of Kent, and probably elsewhere.

The rough-looking, long and slender caterpillar is pale greyish, with a black-edged pale line along the middle of the back, the black edging interrupted on rings 4–9; on each side of the central line, and lower down along the sides, are other black streaks; head, notched on the crown, and marked with brown.

Some eggs laid on August 8, hatched on September 1; the infant caterpillars were long and thread-like, the colour was

black, and there was a whitish stripe low down along the sides.
They would not feed on knotgrass and other plants offered to
them, and South failed to rear them. Moths have, however,
been bred, as a second generation, in the autumn from caterpillars reared from the egg, on bramble and knotgrass.

The moth occurs in July and August on bush-sprinkled
heaths, or heathy ground, where it may be disturbed from the
herbage in the daytime, or netted as it flies in the evening.
South of England from Kent to Dorset; also in Berkshire;
Cheshire (one specimen, Whitegate Heath, 1901, one ab.
circellata in Delamere Forest, July, 1903); Yorkshire (Thorne
Moor, and rather plentiful on Skipwith Common in 1900 and
subsequent years; ab. *circellata* also occurred).

Abroad, its range extends through northern and central
Europe; it occurs in southern France, Dalmatia, and the
Caucasus.

Sterrha lævigata Scop.

Four larvae of this central European species were discovered
among coconut fibre at Durham in 1927 and were successfully reared on the shrivelled leaves of dandelion and *Salix
phylicifoliae* (*Entom.*, lx. 222). The moth is figured on Pl. **47,** 8.

The range of this insect extends through southern and
central Europe and Asia Minor to Persia.

The Rusty Wave (*Sterrha inquinata* Scop.)

In *The Entomologist's Annual* for 1856, two species of *Sterrhinae* were brought forward as new to the British list. One
of these has been referred to under *S. eburnata*, the other
was the present species, which at the time was wrongly referred
to *circuitaria* Hübn. The specimens depicted on Pl. **47,** 7 and
10 are of Continental origin.

Although other specimens were then known to exist in at
east two British collections, the first recorded example was that
mentioned above. This was captured in Bloomsbury **Street,**

1. Cream Wave.

2. Cream Wave.

3. The Blood-vein.

4. Lesser
Cream Wave.

5. Lesser
Cream Wave.

6. Smoky
Wave.

7. Mullein
Wave.

8. Mullein
Wave

9. Sub-angled
Wave

10. Lewes
Wave.

11. Rosy
Wave.

12. Tawny
Wave.

13. Lace
Border.

14. Lace
Border.

15. Small
Blood-vein.

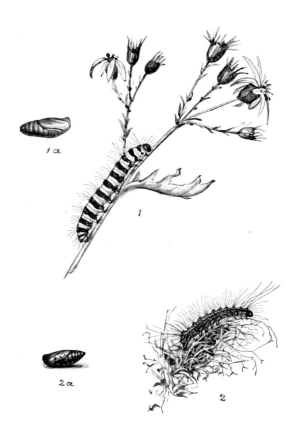

1, 1a. **The Cinnabar:** *caterpillar and chrysalis.*
2, 2a. **Red-necked Footman:** *caterpillar and chrysalis.*

London. In June, 1868, three or four examples were found in a herbalist's shop in Holborn ; one occurred on a shop window in Oxford Street in 1873 ; one example was taken from a door-post in Cannon Street, July 21, 1879 ; and two others have been noted from the same street, but dates were not given. The later records are that of a specimen on July 21, 1898, in a shop in Southampton Row, Bloomsbury, one at Stroud, Gloucestershire, July, 1910 and two were taken in the basement of the museum at Tring, no doubt introduced with packing from the Continent (Cockayne) ; it thus appears that almost all the British specimens known to us have been taken in London.

The eggs are laid on dry or withered plants, upon which the long brownish or greenish caterpillars feed throughout the autumn, winter, and following spring. They pupate towards mid-May, and the moths appear in June and July. According to Guenée, caterpillars seem to have been found only in herb or drug stores, and the moths occur in gardens and houses in July and August.

Abroad, this species ranges through central and southern Europe, and Asia Minor reaching Transcaucasia. It occurs also in North Africa and the Canary Islands.

The Portland Ribbon Wave (*Sterrha degeneraria* Hübn.)

This reddish-banded species (Pl. **49**, 1) is only found, in Britain, at Torquay, Devon, and in the Isle of Portland, Dorset, where it was first noted on June 24, 1831. It will be seen that apart from its different colour, the bands in this moth are placed nearer the base of the wings than in *S. aversata* ; on the fore wings the band is limited by the first and central lines, but sometimes it encroaches on the basal area ; on the hind wings, it occupies more or less of the basal area, from the first line inwards ; the front edge of the fore wings is also reddish.

The caterpillar is ridged along the sides of the roughened

body, and tapers towards the slightly notched, blackish-marked head ; the general colour is reddish ochreous, darker on the back of the middle rings, along which are three inter-rupted pale greyish ochreous lines, and dark V-shaped marks. The natural food plant is not known, but it may be reared from the egg on bramble, traveller's joy (*Clematis*), and, of course, knotgrass and dandelion, both of these plants being generally acceptable to larvae of the *Sterrhinae*, as well as to those of many other species of Geometridae.

The moth is out in June and July in the open, but has been bred as early as June 2. Some of the caterpillars from eggs laid in June will feed up quickly, and produce moths in September ; from these, other eggs may be obtained, the caterpillars from which will feed for a time and then hiber-nate ; as also do the slow-growing individuals of the earlier hatching.

Abroad, this seems to be a Mediterranean species, ranging eastward through Asia Minor to parts of central Asia ; and northwards to Austria, Hungary, west-central Germany, France and Castile.

The Plain Wave (*Sterrha straminata* Borkh.)

Somewhat similar to the last in appearance, but without reddish bands, and front edging to the fore wings ; the second or outer line of the fore wings is generally distinct, but the others, especially the central, are often obscure. This species, one example of which is shown on Pl. **49**, 2, may be dis-tinguished from the plain form of *S. aversata* by its generally smaller size and more silky appearance ; the cross lines are less distinct, and the outer one of the fore wings is not indented below the front margin. The eggs (Pl. **56**, 3*a*) are laid in strings of from 6–20 ; at least this is so in captivity. Like the eggs of other species in this genus that South had seen, they were at first whitish bone colour, changing to reddish. They were laid in July, and most of the caterpillars that hatched from them attained the moth state in September; about one-third hibernated, but died off during the winter.

The much-wrinkled and rough-looking caterpillar is pale reddish brown, varying to greyish; the back with V-shaped marks, and a light coloured spot on rings 5 and 6. It feeds, from August to June, on dandelion, dock, and other weeds, also on sallow, bramble, heather, etc.

The moth is out in July, earlier or later in some seasons; it affects woods in which there is plenty of heather or bilberry, and may often be seen resting on tree-trunks, especially those of the pine. It is on the wing in the evening, and is said to visit the sugar patch, as well as flowers growing in its haunts. Widely distributed over England and Scotland to Moray, but does not appear to have been noted in Wales. Rare and very local in Ireland.

Abroad, the range extends through Europe eastwards to central Asia and southwards to North Africa.

The Riband Wave (*Sterrha aversata* Linn.)

There are two distinct colour forms, one is greyish white (ab. *remutata* Linn.), and the other decidedly ochreous; the former is sometimes tinged with ochreous, and sometimes heavily sprinkled with dark grey. In the type form of *aversata*, the general colour is greyish white, and the space between the central and outer lines of the fore wings, and that enclosed by the first and central of the hind wings, is more or less entirely filled up with dark grey inclining to blackish; occasionally the dark colour spreads beyond the outer line, and covers a large portion of the outer area. These bands also occur in the ochreous and intermediate colour forms. A specimen, bred in June by the late W. G. Sheldon, from a caterpillar found on a fence at West Wickham in May, had the wings and abdomen black, but the head, thorax, anal tuft, and fringes of the wings were normal (Pl. **49,** 3–5).

The caterpillar (Pl. **56,** 2; from coloured drawing by the late Mr. Sich) is much wrinkled, rather thickened behind, and tapers gradually towards the small, black-flecked head ; the general colour is brownish, merging into ochreous on the hinder rings ; a darker brown shade along the back, interrupted on the middle rings by V-shaped marks, encloses a slender whitish line, and there is a whitish spot on ring eight ; a wavy pale ochreous line low down along the sides. (Adapted from Fenn.) It feeds on dandelion, dock, primrose, bedstraw, knotgrass, and many other low-growing plants ; after hibernation, from April to May, it will thrive on the young growth of sallow, birch, hawthorn, etc. It will sometimes feed up and reach the moth state in August or September.

The moth flies in June and July, and is generally distributed ; but in Scotland does not seem to have been observed north of Moray. Common in Ireland.

Abroad, the range extends through Europe to Asia Minor, Sicily, and North Africa.

The Treble Brown Spot (*Sterrha trigeminata* Haw.)

This species (Pl. **49**, 8, 11) is similar to *dimidiata* Hufn., but generally rather larger and somewhat paler ; the front edge of the fore wings is marked with blackish or dark purplish grey, and there is a band of the same colour on the outer marginal area ; the inner edge of this band is formed by the second line, and the outer edge is wavy, interrupted above the middle, and sometimes below also.

The rough and rather flattened caterpillar tapers towards the head ; in colour it is dusky brown. The markings comprise interrupted black lines and V-shaped blackish marks on the back. Buckler states that this caterpillar may be distinguished from those of its nearest allies by having a rather long, dingy ochreous bristle from each of the raised dots ; these bristles, which are of the same thickness throughout, curve forwards on all rings to the ninth, and on the other three backwards. It feeds, from September to April, on various low-growing plants, ivy, birch, etc. If kept warm it is said that whole broods will attain the moth state in July or August ; this may happen sometimes, but in South's experience only a few individuals have obliged in this way. The moth is another inhabitant of the hedgerow and the bushy wood-border, where it may be disturbed in the day-time during late May and June. It flies in the evening, and will visit light, and occasionally the sugar patch. Always a local species, but not uncommon in its special haunts in Kent, Surrey, Berkshire, Wiltshire, Essex, and Suffolk ; it is also found more or less frequently in Sussex, Hampshire, Dorset, Gloucestershire, Herefordshire, and Worcestershire. In Scotland, it is reported in Renfrew, scarce ; and Kane notes that it does not occur in Ireland.

Abroad, it occurs in central and southern Europe, Asia Minor and the Mediterranean islands.

The Small Fan-footed Wave (*Sterrha biselata* Hufn.)

One form has whitish wings, with a deep, dark-grey border on the outer area of all the wings ; this border is traversed by a whitish wavy line (ab. *fimbriolata* Stephens). In the more or less typical form the marginal borders are much paler, and are broken up into bandlets. Between these two forms there are modifications, and sometimes a greyish shade spreads over all the wings (Pl. **49**, 7, 10).

The caterpillar is long and slender, with a somewhat flat-tened appearance, and gradually tapered towards the notched head ; the general colour of the roughened body is greyish brown, the middle ring divisions, and V-shaped marks on the back, are blackish or dark brown ; there is also a double dark-brown line along the back, not always distinct. It feeds, from August to May, on a variety of low-growing plants, and is partial to withered leaves, especially those of bramble and dandelion. The moth is out in June and July, and is often common, and pretty generally distributed throughout our islands, except that it seems not to have been noted north of Moray, in Scotland.

Abroad, the range extends to eastern Siberia and Amurland.

The Small Scallop (*Sterrha emarginata* Linn.)

As will be noted on turning to Pl. **49,** 6, 9, the male of this pale ochreous brown species is generally rather larger than the female, and the more ample wings are less acutely angled in outline ; the latter sex is also more clouded with reddish brown.

The caterpillar is variable in colour ; one form is of a dusky ochreous colour with a pale line along the middle of the back, edged on each side with a darker tint, and most conspicuously so on the hinder rings ; the back is also dotted with black, and has some dark V- or X-shaped marks upon it ; the body tapers to the notched dark-brown head. It feeds on bedstraw (*Galium*), convolvulus, etc., and, like others of its tribe, has a taste for withered leaves. August to May or June, according to the season. In confinement it has been induced by warmth to feed up quickly, and appear as a moth the same year. Only a short time is passed in the chrysalis stage. July is perhaps the best month for the moth, but it may be seen at any time from late June to early August. Its haunts are fens, marshes, and moist woodlands, etc., and although it is more frequent in the south, it is widely spread throughout England, but in the north it is rare, and its occurrence more or less casual.

In Wales it has been recorded from Glamorgan and Flintshire ; but it is apparently unknown in Scotland and Ireland.

Abroad, the range extends through Europe to central Asia.

The Vestal (*Rhodometra sacraria* Linn.)

The fore wings are pale yellow inclining to ochreous, and the front edge is more or less tinged with the same colour as that of the oblique stripe from the tips of the wings to the middle of the inner margin. In the type, this stripe is crimson, but in ab. *labda* Cramer, it is more brown, while in ab. *atrifasciaria* Stefan, it is blackish. In ab. *sanguinaria* Esper, the ground colour is pinkish. The hind wings are always white (Pl. **49,** 13 14).

From 1857, in which year the first specimen recorded as British was captured in September at Plymouth, one or more examples of this interesting migrant seem to have occurred during the autumns of most years, in some part of the British Isles, but chiefly in the south of England. Occasionally larger numbers have occurred, as in 1867 when nearly thirty were secured, and of these four were taken in May in the Isle of Wight, where also two females were captured on August 14 and 16, and one specimen on September 3. Six or seven occurred during August in Lancashire, and three in Perthshire, also in August. The late E. R. Bankes took a specimen in the Isle of Purbeck on September 6, 1905, and eight in Cornwall and two in South Devon during September and October, 1906, from which he bred his long series. In 1947 it occurred in large numbers all over the southern half of England, particularly in stubble fields where knotgrass was growing. In that year it was also recorded from the counties of Cork and Killarney in southern Ireland, the Isle of Man, North Wales, and Scotland. It has subsequently been recorded from Argyll and Inverness-shire. A concise account of its history in Britain, its habits and life history have been published by Mr. G. Haggett (1954, *Entom.*, lxxxv : 49).

The long caterpillar is variable, but is usually some shade of green above, inclining to whitish beneath, and yellowish between the rings ; the lines along the back are paler green, reddish, and olive green. It feeds on low-growing plants, such as knotgrass and dock, and has been reared from the egg in August and September. If eggs were obtained in May it would be possible to raise two generations of moths, or, perhaps, even three, during the year.

The species is an inhabitant of southern Europe and North Africa, and its range extends to India, Madeira, and the Canaries. In central Europe, including the British Isles, its occurrence is always a more or less casual event.

LARENTIINAE

Lythria purpuraria Linn.

This species has long been reported as a British one, but there does not appear to be any very convincing record of its capture in the British Isles. It is widely distributed in Europe, and generally common. As it is a sun-loving insect, it could hardly escape detection if it occurred in any part of our isles. A note by Mr. V. R. Perkins, in *The Zoologist* for 1861, p. 7449, should, however, not be overlooked. This refers to the capture, on June 18, of two male specimens that were disturbed from broom, " not far from the city of Perth, by Mr. D. P. Morrison " (Pl. **50**, 3, 6).

The Silver-Ground Carpet (*Xanthorhoë montanata* Schiff.)

Figs. 3 and 6 on Pl. **52** represent the most usual form of this species, which is variable in the amount of clouding on the fore wings and in the intensity of the cross marking. In some specimens, chiefly from southern localities, the fore wings are almost clear white, and the central band is broadly blackish (Fig. 7). Shetland specimens, on the other hand, are much clouded or suffused with ochreous brown, and the central band is greyish brown (subsp. *shetlandica* Weir (Fig. 5)). Then there is variation in the central band, which is often entire, but more frequently broken up by bandlets ; or it may be considerably narrowed, especially from the middle to the inner margin. Not altogether rarely it is completely severed below the middle (ab. *degenerata* Prout), and sometimes the lower part is absent (ab. *costimaculata* Rebel). A specimen with all the wings smoky leaden-grey, and the central bar

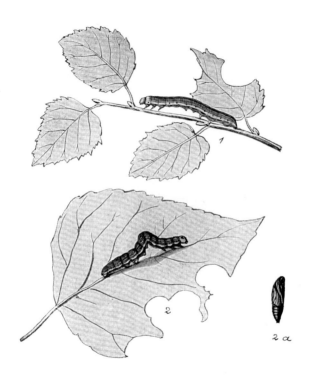

1. **Orange Underwing:** *caterpillar.*
2, 2a. **Light Orange Underwing:** *caterpillar and chrysalis.*

1. Purple-bordered
Gold.

2. Weaver's
Wave.

3. Least
Carpet.

4. Purple-bordered
Gold.

5. Weaver's
Wave.

6. Least
Carpet.

7. Rusty
Wave.

8. *Sterrha
laevigata.*

9. Dotted
Border
Wave.

10. Rusty
Wave.

11. Small
Dusty
Wave.

12. Dotted
Border
Wave.

13. Dwarf
Cream
Wave.

14. Small
Dusty
Wave.

15. Dwarf
Cream
Wave.

16. Silky
Wave.

17. Satin
Wave.

18. Isle of
Wight
Wave.

19. Bright
Wave.

20. Ochraceous
Wave.

of the fore wings pale grey-brown, was taken near Longfleet in Wiltshire, in the summer of 1881 (ab. *unicolor* Rebel).

The caterpillar is wrinkled, with a ridge along the sides ; in colour it is pale brown, inclining to purplish with blackish dots ; three lines along the back, the central one dark greyish, the others paler and broader ; below the latter the sides are greyish tinted with a lower edging of pale yellowish brown. It feeds at night on bedstraw, and various low-growing herbage, including grass. August to April.

The moth is out in June and July, sometimes earlier in the south. It is generally distributed, and, as a rule, common, in woodlands, lanes, etc., throughout the British Isles.

Abroad, it occurs throughout the greater part of Europe ; it is also recorded from Siberia, southern Russia, and Afghanistan.

The Red Carpet (*Xanthorhoë munitata* Hübn.)

The typical form (Pl. **50,** 4) has pale greyish fore wings, and these are crossed by a black-edged purplish central band. In the form from the Shetlands, subsp. *hethlandica* Prout Fig. 5), the ground colour is ochreous and the band is reddish.

The caterpillar is yellowish green, with greyish clouds around white dots, tinged with pink between the rings ; three lines along the back, the central one grey inclining to blackish, broken on three of the hinder rings, and edged with whitish ; the others are double, wavy, brownish, a whitish stripe bordered above with grey along the area of the spiracles ; head, ochreous, dotted with dark brown (adapted from Fenn). It feeds on lady's mantle (*Alchemilla*), chickweed, groundsel, etc., from September to May.

The moth is out in July and August, and in England is only found in the mountain districts of Yorkshire and the more northern counties. It has been reported from the high-lying district on the border of Cheshire, between Macclesfield and Buxton (Day), and from Llantrissant, Glamorganshire, South Wales (Evan John). Generally distributed through

Scotland and the Isles. Widely spread, but local, in the northern half of Ireland.

Abroad, the range extends to eastern Siberia, Amurland, and North America.

The Garden Carpet (*Xanthorhoë fluctuata* Linn.)

Of this common frequenter of our gardens four examples are depicted on Pl. **52.** Figs. 8–10 are the more frequent forms, but specimens with the central band complete, are not un-common. Chiefly, but by no means exclusively, in southern

FIG. 4.—GARDEN CARPET AT REST (× 1½).

localities, some examples have the ground colour almost pure white ; often the wings are more or less suffused with dark grey and this is especially the case in Scotland, where, in Aberdeen-shire and in Shetland, the blackish subsp. *thules* Prout, occurs. Fig. 12 represents a specimen of this form from Aberdeen. Somewhat rarely, the central band is only indicated by a small spot on the front area of the wing (ab. *costovata* Haworth), and more often the band is much narrowed or otherwise modified in the direction of that aberration. Specimens vary in size from rather under one inch to one inch and a half in expanse.

The caterpillar varies in colour from dark grey through yellowish green to obscure green, but the underside is always paler ; on the back there is a series of pale blotches, and some black spots on the middle rings; the head is rather paler than the general colour, and marked with black. It feeds, at night, on cabbage, horseradish, wallflower, white arabis, and many other kinds of Cruciferae; and it is said to eat the foliage of gooseberry and currant. June–October.

There are certainly two broods, and possibly more, as the moths occur in greater or lesser numbers throughout the year, from late April to October, but it seems to be most plentiful in May and June, and in August and September.

Generally distributed over the British Isles.

Abroad, the range extends through Europe to Syria and Asia Minor, central Asia, and Siberia.

The Large Twin-spot Carpet (*Xanthorhoë quadrifasiata* Cl.)

The ground colour of the fore wings of this species is most often of a pale reddish brown, but sometimes it inclines to grey brown; the outwardly-angled central band is often black, but more frequently perhaps the middle area is pretty much of the ground colour or greyish, with a black dot in the upper portion, and limited by two black lines which approach, or join, in the lower half. A dusky basal blotch is not always present, but it is sometimes well in evidence, as also is a dusky shade before the whitish submarginal line; frequently there are two blackish or brownish dots on the upper part of this line, and a third dot above them, but nearer the outer margin (Pl. **50**, 1, 2).

The caterpillar is pale yellowish brown, finely freckled with grey, and with greyish V-shaped marks on the back; three greyish lines along the back, the central one broken, and the others most distinct at each end. It feeds on bedstraw (*Galium*), violet, chickweed and other plants, such as primrose, groundsel, etc., from August to April. The moth is out in June and July, and should be looked for on tree-trunks growing around the borders of woods or in lanes near by. It may also be beaten out of hedgerows in the vicinity of woods.

A very local species and only found with us in the southern
half of England.   Its chief haunts appear to be in the counties
of Kent, Surrey, Hampshire, Essex, Suffolk, Cambridge, and
Norfolk (the Breck sand district) ;   thence its range extends
through Hertfordshire, Buckinghamshire, and Berkshire to
Gloucestershire, where, however, it is scarce, as it is also in
Lincolnshire.   Abroad, the range extends through northern
and central Europe to eastern Siberia, Amurland, Korea,
and Japan.

The Dark-barred Twin-spot Carpet (*Xanthorhoë ferrugata* Cl.)

Portraits of three examples of this species will be found on
Pl. **50**, 10–12.   The ground colour of the fore wings is whitish
tinged with pale ochreous or greyish ;   the central band in
the typical form is reddish or purplish with darker wavy lines
running through it near the edges ;   a narrow patch at the
base of the wings is of the same colour as the central band,
and is followed by a reddish brown streak ;   as a rule, there
is an irregular reddish brown line, commencing in a cloud on
the front margin, and sometimes stripe-like, beyond the pale
edging of the central band ;   in ab. *unidentaria* Haw., which
is the commonest form, the basal and central bands are black ;
in ab. *coarctata* Prout, the central band is much narrowed ;
the two black dots on upper part of the outer margin, generally
well in evidence, are occasionally united, but sometimes they
are very small.   The hind wings are whitish, more or less
sprinkled with dusky scales, chiefly on the basal two-thirds,
and crossed by dark grey wavy lines.

The caterpillar is very similar to that of the next species, it
feeds on the same kinds of plants, and during the same months
of the year (Pl. **61,** 2).   The first generation of moths is on
the wing in May and June, and the second in August.

The species is widely distributed in England and Wales,
often plentiful in some districts in the southern half of the

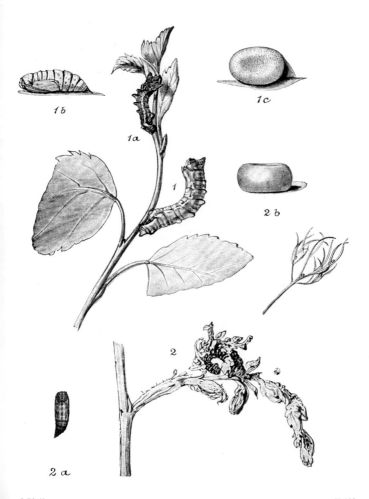

1, 1a, 1b, 1c. **Large Emerald:** *egg, enlarged, caterpillars and chrysalis.*
2, 2a, 2b. **Essex Emerald:** *eggs, natural size and enlarged, caterpillar and chrysalis.*

1. Portland
Ribbon Wave.

2. Plain
Wave.

3. Riband
Wave.

4. Riband
Wave.

5. Riband
Wave.

6. Small
Scallop.

7. Small
Fan-footed
Wave.

8. Treble
Brown-spot.

9. Small
Scallop.

10. Small
Fan-footed
Wave.

11. Treble
Brown-spot.

12. Single-dotted
Wave.

13. The
Vestal.

14. The
Vestal.

15. Single-dotted
Wave.

former country, scarce and more local northwards from York-shire. Widely spread in Roxburghshire and Clydesdale in Scotland, but less frequent than *spadicearia* ; this also seems to be the case in Ireland. The range abroad extends through Europe, Siberia, and North America.

NOTE.—It is to be regretted that the names by which this and the following species were known for many years have had to be changed. It has been claimed that the reddish-banded form of *unidentaria* Haw. is identical with *ferrugata* as figured by Clerck, *Icones*, Plate XI, Fig. 14. Thus the red form referred to has been adopted as the *ferrugata* of Clerck, and that name will supersede *unidentaria* Haw., and the species formerly known as *ferrugata* Auct., has become *spadicearia*.

The Red Twin-spot Carpet (*Xanthorhoë spadicearia* Schiff.)

Three examples of this variable species are shown on Pl. **50** 7–9. The ground colour of the fore wings is usually greyish, more or less ochreous tinted, but sometimes inclining to whitish ; the basal patch and the central band are reddish brown, the latter usually entire in southern specimens, but frequently broken up (ab. *tromsoensis* Fuchs), especially in northern examples. A bright, ochreous form, with the central band much streaked, occurs in Scotland and elsewhere. Occasion-ally the central band is dark purplish. The hind wings are whitish, more or less suffused with smoky grey, and lined with the same ; the outer margin is bordered with smoky grey.

The caterpillar is ochreous brown, mottled with greyish, and marked with pale diamonds and black spots on the back of the middle rings ; there are wavy lines along the sides. It feeds in June and July, and also in September and October, on various low plants : knotgrass, dandelion, bedstraw, garden marigold, and ground ivy (*Nepeta*) being especially useful in captivity. The moth is usually double-brooded, at least in

the southern half of England, the first flight occurring in May
and June, and the second in July and August.

The species is generally distributed, and often common, over
the greater part of England and Wales, but somewhat local
north of the Midlands and through Scotland to Aberdeen ;
widely spread in Ireland. Abroad, it is widely distributed
throughout Europe.

The Balsam Carpet (*Xanthoroë biriviata* Borkh.)

The Balsam Carpet was first recorded as a British species in
1956 by Mr. W. E. Minnion and Mr. B. S. Goodban (*Ent. Gazette*,
7 : 3–6) ; specimens had been taken in the Home Counties on
May 31, 1955, and subsequently. A previously unidentified
British specimen has since been found dated late April, 1951.

The species is double-brooded ; the first brood flies from late
April or early May until June (Pl. **52,** 1). The second brood
(Pl. **52,** 2), sometimes only partial, flies during July and
August ; it is darker and of a smoky appearance and is referable to gen. aest. *aestiva* Fuchs. The moth appears to be
partially diurnal in habit, flying freely in the late afternoon and
evening sunshine, as well as at dusk and shortly afterwards.

The ova are green and are laid on the foliage of *Impatiens
fulva*, *I. parviflora*, and *I. noli-me-tangere*. During the first
three instars the larva is green or light brown and is without
pattern ; a full description of the variable pattern of the later
instars and a description of the pupa have been published by
Mr. G. Haggett (1957, *Ent. Gazette*, 8 : 167–70).

In Britain the species is now known to occur widely in two
of the Home Counties and is thought to occur in two more.
Abroad the range includes S. Scandinavia, Holland, Belgium,
France, and extends through C. and E. Europe to E. Siberia.

The Flame Carpet (*Xanthorhoë designata* Hufn.)

The ground colour of this rather common woodland species
(Pl. **50,** 13–15) is pale grey, varying to whitish, or sometimes

1. Large
Twin-spot
Carpet.

2. Large
Twin-spot
Carpet.

3. *Lythria
purpuraria.*

4. Red
Carpet.

5. Red
Carpet
(**ssp.** *hethlandica*).

6. *Lythria
purpuraria.*

7. Red
Twin-spot
Carpet.

8. Red
Twin-spot
Carpet.

9. Red
Twin-spot
Carpet.

10. Dark-barred
Twin-spot
Carpet.

11. Dark-barred
Twin-spot
Carpet.

12. Dark-barred
Twin-spot
Carpet.

13. Flame
Carpet.

14. Flame
Carpet.

15. Flame
Carpet.

1. **Grass Emerald:** *caterpillar.*
2. **Blotched Emerald:** *caterpillar.*
3. **Common Emerald:** *caterpillar.*

faintly brownish tinged. The purple band on the fore wings is always broadly edged in front with black, but the black outer edging is irregular, and sometimes only distinct towards the front margin of the wings ; it varies in width, and in tint, being, in some specimens, faint purplish grey.

The caterpillar is ochreous, inclining to greyish on the back, which is marked with whitish lines on the front rings, and with ochreous diamonds and black dots on the other rings ; there is also a row of black spots low down along the sides ; head, brownish, freckled with black. It feeds, in June and July, probably, in a wild state, on some kind of " cress," growing in the moister parts of woods ; in confinement, it will eat cabbage, horseradish, and wallflower, among other kinds of Cruciferae. There is a second brood in August and September (Pl. **61,** 3, after Hofmann).

The moth is out in May and June, and again in August. It is fond of resting on tree-trunks in woods, especially where the ground is moist, but it may also be beaten out of hedges and bushes. It is most plentiful in the southern half of England, but is spread over the greater part of the British Isles, including the Orkneys.

Abroad, its range extends to Iceland, the Faeroe Isles, eastern Siberia and Amurland.

The Gem (*Nycterosea obstipata* Fab.)

Also known in the vulgar tongue as " The Narrow-barred Carpet." As will be seen on reference to Pl. **52,** the male (Fig. 4) is pale brown with a dark central band ; and the female (Fig. 11) is purplish brown, the central band rather blackish, and on it is the discal mark, a black-centred white spot. The specimens figured are rather small.

The following are three of the aberrations that have been named—ab. *albicinctaria* Haw. (*marginata* Mathew), with the fringes of all the wings conspicuously pinky grey ; ab. *olivacea* Mathew, a form of the female with olive brown fore wings ;

ab. *obsoleta* Mathew, a form of the male with the dark central
band nearly or quite absent.

The caterpillar is greyish, sometimes tinged with pink, and
sometimes with green; three dusky lines on the head and
first three rings of the body, a series of blackish outlined,
whitish marks on the middle rings, and blackish marks on
the other rings, which are pale in colour; a blackish line above
the black-edged spiracles is broken up into dashes on the
middle rings. Several other forms of the caterpillar, which is
a variable one, have been described by Hellins. The food
comprises groundsel, knotgrass, chrysanthemum, and various
other plants. There are several generations during the year,
and in hot weather the caterpillars feed up rapidly, so quickly
indeed that in about a month the whole round of changes
from egg to moth is effected. The species is migratory in
habit, and there is little doubt that the specimens taken in
this country in late spring or early summer are immigrants;
those examples obtained later in the year are probably the
descendants of such aliens. It is more frequently noted from
southern England, chiefly from the seaboard counties, but
it has been recorded from Lancashire and Yorkshire; also
from Wales, the Isle of Man, and from several parts of Ireland :
April to November.

Abroad, this species has an immense range, occurring
throughout Europe, Asia, including North India, Africa, North
and South America.

The Oblique Carpet (*Orthonama lignata* Hübn.)

This species, also known as *vittata* Bork., is usually pale
brown in ground colour, tinged with ochreous or pinkish; the
darker oblique stripes vary in width and in intensity (Pl. **52**,
13, 14).

The caterpillar is of a yellow green colour, inclining to
ochreous brown on the upper portions of the middle rings; a
darker irregular line along the back, and a whitish line on

1. Balsam
Carpet
(*1st brood*).

2. Balsam
Carpet
(*2nd brood*)

3. Silver-ground
Carpet.

5. Silver Ground
Carpet
(ssp. *Shetlandica*).

4. The Gem.

6. Silver-ground
Carpet.

7. Silver-ground
Carpet.

8. Garden
Carpet.

9. Garden
Carpet.

10. Garden
Carpet.

12. Garden
Carpet
(ssp. *thules*)

11. The Gem

13. Oblique
Carpet.

14. Oblique
Carpet.

15. *Ortholitha
moeniata*.

16. *Ortholitha
peribolata*.

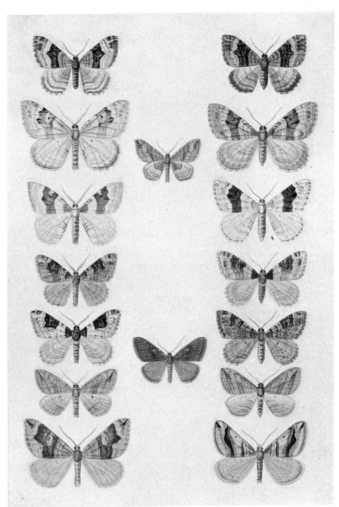

1. **Small Grass Emerald:** *caterpillar.*
2. **Little Emerald:** *caterpillar.*
3, 3*a*. **Small Emerald:** *caterpillar, chrysalis and cocoon.*

each side, the latter edged above and below with a fine black line ; below the spiracles is a pale pinkish brown stripe. Varies in the tint of ground colour and in the markings. It feeds, after hibernation, on bedstraw (*Galium palustre, G. saxatile*, etc.), and caterpillars from eggs laid in June may be reared on clematis, wild or cultivated.

The moth is out in May and June, sometimes later, and a second generation appears in August and September ; the individuals of the later brood are often smaller than those of the first brood. Its haunts are fens, marshes, and water-meads, but in Middlesex South had taken a specimen or two flying along a weedy ditch. Widely distributed throughout the British Isles, but not noted in Scotland north of Moray.

Abroad, it occurs in north and north-central Europe.

The Lead Belle (*Ortholitha mucronata* Scop.)

In a well-illustrated article in the *Stett. ent. Zeit.*, 102 : 1–28 (1941), Dr. Heydemann gives an account of the differences between the two species *O. mucronata* Scop. and *O. plumbaria* F. and separates the races and aberrations which have been variously described under the two names.

Superficially, *mucronata* of which we have two subspecies in Britain, *umbrifera* Prout and *scotica* Cockayne, tends to display very much more clearly a lighter, often whitish outer shading to the subterminal line and to have a dark inner shading to the wavy transverse lines. On the underside the black cell spots show up clearly. *O. plumbaria* tends to have the ante-median line lying usually nearer the cell spot, so that the latter does not always lie in the middle of the median band and on the underside, the cell spots are weakly marked and often absent. The shape of the lines is not regarded as of any value in separating the two species and the shape of the cell spot is little better, though it is more often streak-shaped in *mucronata* than in *plumbaria*. Structurally, the genitalia show good differences, particularly in the females, and excellent figures are given in the above-mentioned paper. The dates of emergence offer some assistance in separation, *mucronata* usually flying in May and the first half of June and *plumbaria* in the latter part of June, during July and occasionally in August. In some seasons and localities, however, the two species overlap and fly together.

O. mucronata subsp. *umbrifera* Prout (Pl. **55**, 1, 2) is a pale grey with the median lines suffused distally with fuscous. It was founded on a female taken in Epping Forest on May 9, 1896, and appears to be widely distributed in the western half of southern England and in southern Ireland.

O. mucronata subsp. *scotica* Cockayne (Pl. **55,** 3, 4) is a darker, more fuscous coloured form described from Braemar. It has since been recorded from other Scottish localities including Rannoch and Aviemore.

The long stick-like larva is pale ochreous brown, often striped with darker brown or blackish ; the larva of *scotica* is said to be usually darker. It feeds on broom (*Cytisus*) and furze (*Ulex*) from late June to September and probably pupates immediately after hibernation.

Abroad, the range extends through northern and central Europe and the mountains of southern and south-eastern Europe.

The July Belle (*Ortholitha plumbaria* Fab.)

Specimens of this species are shown on Pl. **55,** 5, 6. Details of the differences between this and *O. mucronata* Scop. are given under the preceding species.

The larvae feed in August and September and again in May on broom (*Cytisus*) and furze (*Ulex*) and have not yet been found to be distinguishable from *mucronata*.

O. plumbaria is widely distributed throughout the British Isles and abroad the range is similar to that of *mucronata*.

The Shaded Broad-bar (*Ortholitha chenopodiata* Linn.)

To the earliest British entomologists this species (Pl. **55,** 7, 8) was known by the English name given to it by Moses Harris, which is here revived. Haworth's popular name for the insect is the " Small Mallow," but this seems less suitable.

The fore wings are usually ochreous brown in colour, with a darker brown band, the inner area of which is often paler. The ground colour, however, varies considerably, in some examples tending to whity brown, and in others to a smoky hue with the median band very dark, the latter form is referable to ab. *monodii* Th.-Mieg. The whitish hind wings are generally more or less dusky clouded, chiefly from the base of the wing to the dark brown or blackish cross shade ; but sometimes these wings are entirely blackish, with just a trace of a pale cross stripe.

The caterpillar is greyish, with a pinkish tinge and black dots ; there are three lines along the back, the central one slaty blue, and the others ochreous, shaded on each side with pale brown ; a pinkish irregular ridge runs low down along the sides. It feeds on clover, vetch, grass, etc., from September to June (Pl. **62**, 2, after Hofmann).

The moth is out in July and August, and is often common in fields and grassy places, generally throughout the greater part of the British Isles. In ancient times it was dubbed the " Aurelian's Plague." The range abroad extends to Amurland.

Ortholitha moeniata Scop.

Except that one specimen was said to have been taken near Baron Wood, Carlisle, some years prior to 1855, and another, in 1866, near York, there is no evidence that this species is an inhabitant of the British Isles (Pl. **52**, 15).

Ortholitha peribolata Hübn.

A single specimen of this species was taken at Westward Ho, North Devon, in 1890. A second specimen was taken at Frenhurst, Sussex, on August 26, 1951 (Pl. **52**, 16). Abroad, the range includes the Channel Islands, France, Spain, and

North Africa, where the moth flies in July and August. The larva feeds on *Genista*, *Ulex* and *Calycotome* in the autumn and again in April and the beginning of May.

The Chalk Carpet (*Ortholitha bipunctaria* subsp. *cretata* Prout)

In this species (Pl. **55,** 9, 10) the ground colour of the fore wings is white (inclining to bluish white in some specimens), more or less stippled and scored with greyish brown ; the cross band is darker grey brown, and there are two black dots placed :-wise (sometimes united as in ab. *confluens* Wehrli) in the paler central space of the band. Hind wings, smoky grey, with a darker shade across the middle, and a pale one parallel with the outer margin. In some rare instances, the ground colour of the fore wings is entirely white, and the band exceedingly dark (ab. *fasciata* Prout) ; but specimens with the general colour, slaty black and the band and basal patch grey (ab. *reversa* Prout), are extremely rare ; Barrett mentions one such example, from Box Hill, Surrey, in the late R. Adkin's collection.

The caterpillar is whity brown, more or less tinged with pink, dotted with black, and lined with grey along the back, the sides, and the under surface. It feeds, at night, on clover and trefoils, from September to June (Pl. **62,** 3, after Hofmann). The moth is out in July and August, and in suitable localities, such as chalk downs, limestone hills, etc., is generally plentiful throughout England and South Wales ; it is also recorded from Denbighshire and Caernarvonshire in N. Wales. It does not appear to have been noted in Ireland, or in Scotland, except that it has been recorded from the Isle of Arran.

Abroad, its range extends through central and southern Europe to Asia Minor.

The Mallow (*Larentia clavaria* Haw.)

The fore wings of this species are normally ochreous brown, inclining to reddish, but sometimes the general colour is of a light chocolate tint, and in such specimens the slender white lines edging the dark markings, and the white wavy sub-marginal line, are more distinct ; the central band-like marking occasionally tapers towards the inner margin (Pl. **55, 11**).

The long caterpillar (figured from a coloured drawing by the late A. Sich, Pl. **62, 1**) is of a greenish colour, inclining to yellowish between the rings ; there are indications of darker lines on the middle of the back and along the sides ; the usual dots are whitish and the spiracles black ; in some specimens the central line on the back is pinkish. It hatches from the egg in March or April, and feeds until June on mallow (*Malva sylvestris*) ; will also eat hollyhock.

The moth appears in September and October, and is sometimes seen in November. It hides under the mallow, and other plants around, and is not much inclined to move during the day, but it becomes active in the evening, and then flies pretty briskly. The occurrence of this species in any locality will, of course, largely depend upon the presence of the food plant, but it seems to be widely distributed throughout the greater part of the British Isles. It is, however, most frequent in the southern half of England.

Abroad, the range extends throughout Europe, except in the extreme North and South, Asia Minor and occurs in southern Russia and the Altai.

The Beech-Green Carpet (*Colostygia olivata* Schiff.)

The species, depicted on Pl. **57, 4, 6**, when quite fresh has the fore wings greenish, and the central band more or less tinged with brown, in some specimens with blackish ; the inner edge of the band is not so clearly defined as the outer, the latter being followed by a narrow whitish wavy band ; a series of black dots edged with white represent the sub-marginal line. Hind wings, smoky grey, with a pale band beyond the middle, and a pale line nearer the outer margin.

The roughened caterpillar (Pl. **64, 1**) is ochreous brown, mottled with darker brown, and lined with grey ; the raised dots are black, each with a short bristle. It feeds at night on bedstraw (*Galium*), in the spring to May, after hibernation.

The moth is out, as a rule, in July and August, but sometimes much earlier. South reared specimens during the last week in May, 1907, from caterpillars sent from Torquay by Mr. Walker. It lurks among the vegetation growing on banks, and the hedgerows of lanes, etc.

In the south of England the species chiefly affects the coasts of Dorset, Devon, and Cornwall ; but it occurs locally in and around beech woods of Kent, and is more frequent in those of Berkshire, Oxfordshire, and Buckinghamshire. From Somerset it spreads through the western counties, including part of Wales, to Lancashire. It is, however, most common among the hills from Yorkshire northwards. In Scotland it is local in Roxburgh, widely distributed, and sometimes abundant in Clydesdale and throughout the Highlands to Sutherland. It has also been noted from Arran. Local in Ireland, but apparently abundant in some parts.

Abroad, the range is similar to that of the preceding species, but is found also in southern Europe.

The Green Carpet (*Colostygia pectinataria* Knoch)

This species (Pl. **57**, 1, 2), also, has green fore wings, with a rather deeper green central band and basal patch. The former is limited by white lines marked with black, conspicuously so on the front and inner margins ; there are also black marks on the front edge of the basal patch, and at the tips of the wings. The green colour quickly fades to a yellowish or sandy tint.

The wrinkled caterpillar is olive brown, with bristle-bearing black dots ; the back has a dark central line, and is adorned with reddish V-shaped marks except on the end rings. It feeds in the spring, after hibernation, on bedstraw (*Galium*), but it is said to eat sorrel, dead-nettle (*Lamium*), etc.

The moth is out in June, earlier in the south, and later in

the north. It hides among herbage during the day, and may occasionally be seen resting on tree-trunks, etc., then flying just before dark about hedges, and on commons and heaths. Specimens have been noted in some years in September.

Except that it has not been detected in the Shetlands, the species seems to be found in all parts of the British Isles.

Abroad, the range extends through northern and central Europe to southern Russia and the Altai.

The Striped Twin-spot Carpet (*Colostygia salicata* subsp. *latentaria* Curtis)

Portraits of a male and a female of this species will be found on Pl. **57**, 7 ♂ and 9 ♀. The fore wings are greyish white, crossed by several darker grey wavy lines ; the central band is rather darker, and in some specimens there is also a darker basal patch. In an almost unicolorous form the fore wings are wholly suffused with darker ; Kane, who stated that such specimens occur with the paler form in Ireland, referred the aberration to *unicolorata* Kane.

The caterpillar is brownish, with three whitish lines along the back, and a pinkish line low down along the sides. It feeds, at night, on bedstraw (*Galium*), in September and October, but may be found on the plants in the daytime (Pl. **64**, 2, after Hofmann). It remains as a larva in its cocoon through the winter (Cockayne).

The moth is out in May and June, and in some localities again in August and September. It is fond of sitting on rocks, and also on tree-trunks.

Except that it has been found, not infrequently, on Dartmoor and Exmoor, in Devon, and has also been once noted from Dorset, the species in England is chiefly an inhabitant of the northern counties. It occurs in Wales, but almost exclusively in the north and on the Isle of Man. In Scotland it appears to be widely distributed throughout ; and in Ireland it occurs locally in all four provinces.

Abroad, this species occurs in north-central and central Europe.

The Mottled Grey (*Colostygia multistrigaria* Haw.)

The fore wings in the typical form of this species are grey with a slight brownish tinge ; basal patch, central band, and shade before the whitish submarginal line, sometimes darker (Pl. **57,** 10 ♂, 12 ♀). In some specimens the central band is very much darker (ab. *virgata* Tutt) ; and in some parts of south-west Yorkshire a blackish form (ab. *nubilata* Tutt) is not uncommon (Pl. **65,** 3).

The caterpillar is ochreous grey, with three brownish lines along the back, and two other lines on each side, the upper one yellowish, wavy, and edged above with dusky. It feeds on bedstraw (*Galium*) in May and June (Pl. **64,** 3).

The moth is out in March and April, and keeps pretty much to the shelter afforded by its food plant or other herbage around in its favourite haunts, which are damp woodlands, heaths, and mosses. Occasionally, however, it may be seen on the lower parts of fences, tree-trunks, rocks, etc. About dusk it may be found sitting on grass and other vegetation, and at such times is not much disposed to fly away from the collector.

Pretty generally distributed throughout the British Isles, including the Orkneys.

Abroad, the range extends to western and central Europe and North Africa.

The Twin-spot Carpet (*Colostygia didymata* Linn.)

The fore wings in the male are pale greyish, more or less tinged with ochreous brown, and crossed by a dark grey, inclining to blackish, central band ; the base of the wings is often banded with dark grey, as also is the outer marginal area ; on the latter, above the middle, are twin black spots, and there is a black spot or streak above nearer the tip of the

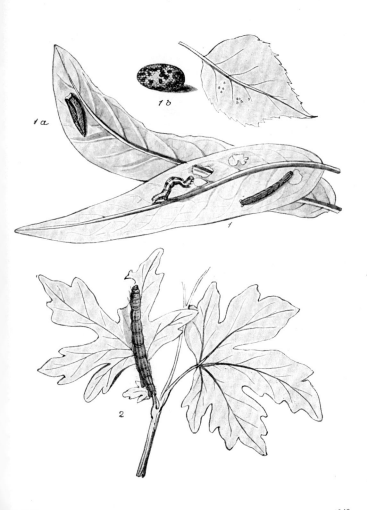

1, 1a, 1b. **Dingy Mocha**: *eggs, natural size and enlarged, caterpillars and chrysalis.*
2. **Mocha**: *caterpillar.*

1. Lead
Belle
(ssp. *umbrifera*).

2. Lead
Belle
(ssp. *umbrifera*).

3. Lead
Belle
(ssp. *scotica*).

4. Lead
Belle
(ssp. *scotica*).

5. July
Belle.

6. July
Belle.

7. Shaded
Broad-bar.

8. Shaded
Broad-bar.

9. Chalk
Carpet.

10. Chalk
Carpet.

11. The Mallow.

wing. The female is smaller, paler, often whitish and the central band is the most distinct cross marking in this sex. A blackish form of the male occurs (ab. *nigra* Prout), and this is very similar to ab. *nubilata* of the previous species; ab. *ochroleucata* Aurivillius is uniformly greyish brown, with a white submarginal line, and South had a specimen near this from Durham. In the Shetland subsp. *hethlandica* Rebel, the ground colour of the wing is orange brown in the male and lighter ochreous brown or fawn in the female.

The caterpillar is green, inclining to yellowish on the back, and to pinkish on the sides; three lines along the side, the central one dark green, and the others whitish. It feeds on primrose, red campion (*Lychnis diurna*), bilberry, etc., as well as on the flowers of coarse grasses; in North Devon South found it in profusion at night, on the blossoms of a wood-rush (*Luzula*), growing in a sheltered wood near the sea. April and May, later perhaps in the north (Pl. **57**, 35 ♂, 8, 11, 14 ♀).

The moth is out in July and August, and is common in almost every part of the British Isles.

Abroad, its range extends to north and central Europe. It is also found further south and in central Asia, but there appears to be confined to the mountains.

The Barberry Carpet (*Pareulype berberata* Schiff.)

The fore wings are greyish or whitish, tinged with grey; there are two dark-edged black lines on the basal half, and a black line beyond the middle of the wings; the latter has a conspicuous tooth in its upper half, but the lower wavy half is indistinct; there is a black streak in the tip of the wing (Pl. **57**, 13, 15).

The stout and roughened caterpillar is brown, with indistinct darker stripes along the back; the head is brown, checkered with darker brown. It feeds, in June and July, on barberry (*Berberis vulgaris*); there is a second brood in late August and September.

The moth is out in May and early June, and again in August. Although it certainly has been noted from other parts of England, the species seems at present to be confined to the eastern counties. Barrett gives Somerset also.

Abroad, the range extends through Europe to central Asia.

The Shoulder Stripe (*Earophila badiata* Schiff.)

The ground colour of the fore wings is pale ochreous brown, inclining to whitish ; there are three dark-edged black cross-lines, the first of them sharply bent below the front margin, the second is rather oblique, and the third is wavy and often not clearly defined towards the inner margin ; the outer marginal area is broadly bordered with pale reddish brown or dark purplish brown, there is a black streak from the more or less indistinct, whitish submarginal line to the tips of the wings, and a white mark about the middle of the line ; the ground colour is most in evidence on the central area of the wings, but even here it is frequently reduced to a slender band, or occasionally only a patch near the front margin of the wing (Pl. **57,** 16, 17).

The caterpillar (Pl. **67,** 1) is green, inclining to yellow between the rings ; the spiracles are black, and there is sometimes a pinkish brown or purplish stripe along their area. Varies in general colour, and also in marking. It feeds, at night, on wild rose, and may be beaten from the bushes from May to July. When full grown it forms an oval cocoon in the earth, and therein changes to a chrysalis (Pl. **67,** 1*a*), which is dark reddish brown, inclining to blackish on the thorax, wing-cases, and the front edges of the body rings.

The moth appears in March and April, and may be obtained from almost any hedgerow, where wild rose is plentiful, throughout the British Isles, except that it seems not to extend north of Moray in Scotland.

Abroad, the range extends through central and eastern Europe to central Asia.

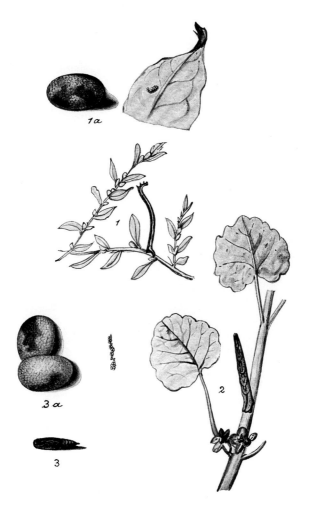

1, 1a. **Single-dotted Wave**: *eggs, natural size and enlarged, and caterpillar.*
2. **Riband Wave**: *caterpillar.*
3, 3a. **Plain Wave**: *eggs, natural size and enlarged, and chrysalis.*

1. Green
Carpet.

2. Green
Carpet.

3. Twin-spot
Carpet, *male*.

4. Beech-green
Carpet.

6. Beech-green
Carpet.

5. Twin-spot
Carpet, *male*.

7. Striped
Twin-spot
Carpet.

9. Striped
Twin-spot
Carpet.

8. Twin-spot
Carpet,
female.

10. Mottled
Grey,
male.

12. Mottled
Grey,
female.

11. Twin-spot
Carpet,
female.

13. Barberry
Carpet.

15. Barberry
Carpet.

14. Twin-spot
Carpet,
female.

16. Shoulder
Stripe.

17. Shoulder
Stripe.

The Streamer (*Anticlea derivata* Schiff.)

Two examples of this species are depicted on Pl. **58**, 1, 2.

The long caterpillar is green, inclining to yellowish between the rings ; a purplish, or reddish brown stripe along the back is broken up into spots on the middle rings. It feeds on the flowers and leaves of wild rose and will also eat honeysuckle, and can be found or beaten out in May and June (Pl. **67**, 2, larva, 2*a*, ova).

The moth is out in April and early May, and is often seen at rest on palings, etc., but it occurs chiefly in hedgerows, along which it flies at dusk.

This species (also known as *nigrofasciaria* Goeze) is pretty well distributed over England, Wales, and Scotland up to Sutherlandshire. In Ireland it seems to be local.

Abroad, the range is similar to that of the preceding species.

The Beautiful Carpet (*Mesoleuca albicillata* Linn.)

The English name of this species (Pl. **58**, 3) is exceedingly appropriate ; few of our native moths exhibit such a pleasing combination of colour and marking. It varies but very little in a general way, but a specimen taken in York some years ago has the fore wings dark leaden grey instead of creamy white (ab. *suffusa* Carrington), and very rarely the ground colour inclines to yellow.

The stoutish caterpillar (Pl. **91**, 2) is green with reddish marks along the back ; a white line low down along the sides is edged below with purplish red on the first three rings ; the last ring, and the claspers, tinged with purplish red. It feeds at night on bramble, raspberry, and wild strawberry in August and September, occasionally earlier or later. In the daytime it rests on the underside of a leaf. When full grown it forms a cocoon just under the surface of the soil, or among rubbish (in the cage), and therein changes to a dark reddish brown chrysalis (Pl. **91**, 2*a*).

The moth is out in June, sometimes in late May, and occasionally there seem to be a few individuals about in August. The species is a denizen of the woodlands, and is generally to be found in the more open parts of woods where its food plants are well established. It is widely distributed over England and Wales, but most frequent in the south of the former country. In Scotland, it is local in Roxburghshire and Wigtownshire ; it occurs in the Hebrides and in many parts of Ireland. The range abroad extends to Amurland.

The Grey Mountain Carpet (*Entephria caesiata* Schiff.)

The typical greyish form, with blackish wavy cross lines and dark central band, is shown on Pl. **58**, 4, 5. Fig. 6 represents an interesting blackish suffused form from the Isle of Arran (ab. *nigricans* Prout). Ab. *prospicuata* Prout (var. *A.* of Guenée), is a form with the fore wings whitish, and the base and the central band thereof blackish ; some Shetland specimens closely approach this pretty variety.

The caterpillar is green, with a brownish line along the middle of the back, and a series of pinkish or purplish red oblique streaks which nearly meet at the central line and so form V-shaped marks ; a whitish or yellowish stripe low down along the sides, sometimes edged above with reddish. In some examples the general colour is reddish brown. It feeds in April and May, after hibernation, on bilberry, ling, and heath in a wild state, but may be reared on knotgrass or sallow.

The moth is out from June until early August, and may be found resting, often in numbers, on rocks and stone walls in mountain and moorland districts, from Herefordshire, northwards through England, North Wales, and over the whole of Scotland, including the isles, and Ireland. Kane states that in the latter country melanic forms, such as those from Yorkshire, etc., are nowhere met with.

Abroad, the range extends to Iceland, northern and central

1. The Streamer.

2. The Streamer.

3. Beautiful
Carpet.

4. Grey Mountain
Carpet.

5. Grey Mountain
Carpet.

6. Grey Mountain
Carpet.

7. Yellow-ringed
Carpet.

8. Yellow-ringed
Carpet.
(ssp. *ruficinctata*).

9. Royal
Mantle.

10. Royal
Mantle.

11. Ruddy
Carpet.

12. Ruddy
Carpet.

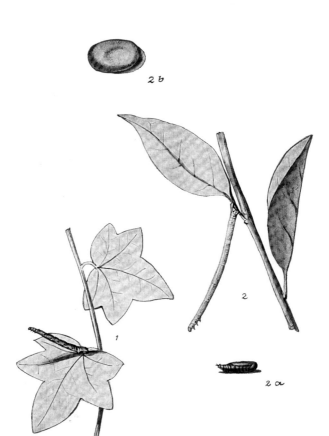

1. **Least Carpet:** *caterpillar.*
2, 2a, 2b. **Small Blood-vein:** *egg, enlarged, caterpillar and chrysalis.*

Europe, the mountains of northern and central Italy, the
Caucasus and eastwards to Japan.

The Yellow-ringed Carpet (*Entephria flavicinctata* Hübn.)

The typical form of this species (Pl. **58, 7**) is pale grey with
a dusting of bright yellow scales on the basal, central, and
outer marginal cross-bands of the fore wing and it is this
feature that at once separates this species from the preceding
one. The English and Irish specimens are referable to this
form.

Subspecies *ruficinctata* Guenée from Scotland and the isles
has both wings much darker grey and the median band of the
fore wing, as a consequence, not very distinctly differentiated
from the rest of the wing (Pl. **58, 8**).

The bristly caterpillar is green, chocolate, or red brown, but
always of a dull shade ; on the back is a series of black V-
shaped marks, and a central dark, slender line ; the front part
of each V-mark filled up with pink or lilac, forming a triangle,
the apex of which is yellow ; a yellowish stripe low down
along the side (adapted from Fenn). It feeds in the spring
till April, after hibernation, on saxifrage (*Saxifraga aizoides,
S. hypnoides*, etc.), and also on stonecrop (*Sedum*), and is most
partial to the flowers of these plants.

The moth flies throughout the summer, possibly in two
generations, as, when reared in confinement, moths appear in
May, and from eggs obtained from these, caterpillars feed in
June and July, and attain the perfect state in August. Like
the last species, its chief resting-places are the rocks, in its
favourite haunts, in gorges among the hills and moorlands.
It has been recorded from few parts of northern England, but
one specimen is said to have been taken in Dovedale, Derbyshire. In Lancashire it has been noted as scarce about
Clougha ; and in Yorkshire one example was taken on Malham
Moor in August, 1876, near Scarborough, July 16, 1891 ; and
also Grassington, August, 1916. It is more plentiful in Scotland;

in Clydesdale it is local, but not uncommon, the localities mentioned being Lochgoilhead, and watercourses above Arden-tinny ; more frequent in Perthshire, thence to Sutherland, and it occurs also in the Hebrides and the Orkneys. In Ire-land it is found in Co. Antrim ; and the late T. Greer stated that it is common at Murlough Bay, Fair Head ; Fermanagh (Donovan).

Abroad, the range extends to northern and central Europe and to the mountains of southern Europe.

The Marsh Carpet (*Perizoma sagittata* Fab.)

The fore wings of this very distinct species are brown, with white-edged black bands at base and across the central area, the latter with a strong projection on its outer edge, almost reaching a white spot on the outer margin ; submarginal line whitish, often only traceable on the front edge. The central band is always narrowed below the middle, sometimes divided (ab. *interrupta* Hirschke), and occasionally this part of the band is finely cut off from both upper and lower portions (Pl. **60**, 8).

The moth is out in July, occasionally at the end of June, and occurs locally in " Fenland."

The caterpillar is yellowish green, merging into pinkish on the sides ; the pink is edged below with black, and this is followed by a dark olive stripe ; rings 1–3 and 10–12 are along the sides ; ridges olive green, paler anteriorly, black at sides ; hind segments blackish green on back and suffused with pink. It feeds, in August and September, on the unripe seeds of meadow-rue (*Thalictrum flavum*), also on *T. minus*, and, according to Barrett, on old withered leaves of columbine.

Doubleday recorded it as British in the *Zoologist* for 1848. He there states, " A single example of this pretty species was obtained last season near Peterborough, but I believe it was not in very good condition. A splendid female was sent to me from the same neighbourhood this week (July 15, 1848)."

In 1853 and 1854 the species was discovered in the fens of Huntingdonshire and Cambridgeshire. Later it was found to inhabit the fens of Norfolk and Suffolk. It is still obtained in

FIG. 5.—CATERPILLAR OF MARSH CARPET FEEDING ON MEADOW-RUE.
(ENLARGED ×2).

the Cambridge fens from Bottisham to Chatteris. Outside "Fenland" it has been recorded from Worcestershire (Bewdley Forest), Warwickshire (Rugby), and Kent (Dover).

The range abroad extends to Amurland and Japan.

The Barred Carpet (*Perizoma taeniata* Steph.)

This species is shown on Pl. **60**, 18. There are two forms of the central band of the fore wings, which in the type as figured by Stephens is broad, but is narrower in the aberration *angustifasciata* Strand. The colour of the bands may be greyer or browner than in the specimen figured, and the ochreous general colour of the fore wings is more tinged with brown in some specimens than in others.

The rather bristly caterpillar is light brown with a pinkish tinge ; the back is marked with browner diamonds and some black dots, and there is a yellow stripe along the sides. It feeds on moss (Hodgkinson, *Entom.*, xxviii. 141) growing in damp places, hibernates when quite small, and reappears about April, when it seems to prefer the fruit of the moss, but will also thrive on chickweed, self-heal, *Linaria*, and will sometimes eat wild strawberry and knotgrass. The moths appear from the end of June, and may be found, but in wasted condition, up to early September.

The species is extremely local, and in its secluded haunts may be found on the trunks or branches of holly and yew trees, or it may be disturbed from hedgerows, etc.

In Britain, the species seems to have been first noted in Castle Eden Dene, Durham (1825), and subsequently in Cumberland (Flimby, near Maryport), Westmorland, Lancashire (Arnside and Silverdale), Yorkshire (Scarborough), Derbyshire (Dovedale), Arthog in North Wales, and Tintern in Monmouthshire. The only English localities for it south of Monmouth are Watersmeet, near Lynton, in North Devon, and Torbay, in South Devon. It has been noted from Rannoch and Pitlochry, in Perthshire, from Laggan in Inverness-shire, and from Dalmallin, in Argyllshire. It has a wide distribution in Ireland, and is common in some parts of that country, as at Killarney, Co. Kerry, and Rockwood, in Sligo.

Abroad, the range extends to Amurland and Japan.

The Small Rivulet (*Perizoma alchemillata* Linn.)

This species (Pl. **60,** 3, 6) is exceedingly close to the one following, but in a general way it is to be distinguished by its greyish brown coloration. A stippled whitish stripe before the central band, usually only faintly indicated in *affinitata*, is fairly distinct as a rule. Although the outer edge of the central band is rather more irregular, the middle tooth is not so prominent as in *affinitata*.

1. Barred
Rivulet
(ab. *unifasciata*).

2. The Rivulet.

3. Small
Rivulet.

4. Barred
Rivulet.

5. The Rivulet.

6. Small
Rivulet.

7. Heath
Rivulet.

8. Marsh
Carpet.

9. Heath
Rivulet.

10. Pretty
Pinion.

11. Grass
Rivulet.

12. Grass
Rivulet
(ssp. *subfasciaria*).

13. Pretty
Pinion.

14. Grass
Rivulet.

15. Grass
Rivulet
(ssp. *subfasciaria*).

16. Sandy
Carpet.

17. Sandy
Carpet.

18. Barred
Carpet.

1. **Water Carpet:** *caterpillar.*
2. **Dark-barred Twin-spot Carpet:** *caterpillar.*
3. **Flame Carpet:** *caterpillar.*

The rather plump caterpillar is purplish above and yellowish green below ; three yellow lines on the back, the central one broad ; the spiracles are black, and a little above them is another yellow line ; head, black and glossy, and there are black shining plates on the first and last rings of the body, that on the first ring divided by the yellow central line (adapted from Porritt). It feeds, in August and September, in the seed capsules of hemp nettle (*Galeopsis tetrahit*), sometimes on the rarer *G. ladanum*, and is said to eat woundwort (*Stachys*) occasionally.

The moth is out in June and July, and, as in the case of the last species, may be stirred up from among its food plant or the surrounding vegetation, in lanes, and around wood borders. The species is widely distributed over the British Isles, except that it seems not to have been noticed in Scotland, north of Moray, although it occurs in the Hebrides.

Abroad, its range extends through the greater part of Europe, to Asia Minor and central Asia.

The Rivulet (*Perizoma affinitata* Steph.)

The whitish band crossing the brownish fore wings is generally fairly wide, sometimes broad, but occasionally it is very narrow ; the reduction in width is mainly the result of brownish suffusion of the outer half of the band, leaving the inner half white. Kane mentions a smoky form from Co. Derry, in which the band is absent, and refers this to ab. *unicolorata* Kane. In a specimen which South had from Sligo, the band is tinged with brownish throughout. The hind wings are usually smoky brown, with a paler central band, but in some specimens, referable to form *rivinata* Fisch.–R., the basal two-thirds are whitish. The moths vary in size (Pl. **61**, 2, 5).

The caterpillar is pinkish ochreous inclining to brown ; three pinkish lines along the back, and a similar line along the blackish spiracles ; a dark plate on the first and last rings. It feeds in the capsules, on the seeds, of red campion (*Lychnis*

dioica), and will eat those of the white *L. alba* and ragged
robin (*L. floscuculi*) : July to September. When eggs can be
obtained early, it is possible to rear moths from them in August
of the same year.

The moth is out in June and July, in some southern districts
in late May.

As it conceals itself during the day among its food plant, or
other vegetation around, it may be put up therefrom by gently
stirring the herbage ; but it flies freely about sundown, and is
then easily netted.

The species is widely distributed over England, Wales,
and Scotland, up to Moray. In Ireland it occurs locally in
the north, and the same is the case in the North of England.

Abroad, the range extends to northern and central Europe.

The Barred Rivulet (*Perizoma bifaciata* Haw.)

Haworth described two forms of this species, and a specimen
of each is shown on our Pl. **60.** Fig. 4 represents his type
(*bifaciata*, the Double-barred Rivulet), and Fig. 1 depicts ab.
unifasciata (the Single-barred Rivulet). The chief difference
appears to be that in the type (*bifaciata*) the " rivulets " are
white and distinct, thus bringing out a dark band between the
central one and the base of the wing.

The stoutish caterpillar is pale brown, inclining to ochreous
on the back, along which are three lines, the central one
greyish, and the others whitish shaded with greyish ; a whitish
stripe low down along the sides ; the usual dots are black, and
the spiracles are black, margined with ochreous (adapted from
Fenn). In September and October it feeds in the seed capsules
of *Bartsia odontites*, and is often plentiful ; the late G. F.
Mathew recorded obtaining nearly five hundred from three
small bundles of the food plant gathered in the Harwich
district. Dr. E. A. Cockayne has found larvae on eyebright
(*Euphrasia officinalis*).

The moth is out in July and August, but is not often seen in the daytime, and is not taken very frequently, even when flying at night, but it comes to light, and visits flowers.

From chrysalids obtained from caterpillars reared in 1900, the late Robert Adkin bred ten moths in 1901, eleven in 1902, two in 1903, five in 1904, and two in 1905.

The species is widely distributed over England, Wales, and the south of Scotland, but it is most frequent in the south of England. In Ireland it is scarce and sporadically distributed (Donovan).

Abroad, the range extends to central and southern Europe.

The Heath Rivulet (*Perizoma minorata* subsp. *ericetata* Steph.)

The British form of this species (Pl. **60**, 7, 9) is rather smaller and darker than typical *minorata* Treitschke, and as Stephens has figured and described it as *ericetata*, this name should be adopted for our native race.

The white fore wings have a greyish basal patch and three bands of the same colour ; the outer one is traversed by a more or less distinct wavy whitish line ; the band nearest the basal patch is sometimes very faint ; more rarely the markings are absent from the central area of the wings (ab. *monticola* Strand), and a specimen approaching this form has been taken in Perthshire.

The caterpillar is pale green with a dark green-edged ochreous brown stripe along the middle of the back, and green stripes on each side ; the usual dots are black, and the plates on first and last rings are brown, as also is the head. It feeds, in September, on the seeds of eyebright (*Euphrasia officinalis*).

The moth is out in July and August, and is found very locally, flying in the late afternoon among its food plant, on the moorlands and pasture-grounds of Northumberland, Cumberland, Durham, and Westmorland ; and has been reported from Hawkshead, in Lancashire. In Scotland, it is common in suitable parts of Roxburghshire and several localities in Clydesdale ; it occurs in the Hebrides and is thence widely spread to the Orkneys. Only noted from the Mourne Mountains in the north-east of Ireland.

Abroad, this species occurs in Scandinavia and the mountains of northern and central Europe as far south as the Abruzzi.

The Pretty Pinion (*Perizoma blandiata* Schiff.)

This species (Pl. **60**, 10, 13) is also known as *adaequata* Borkhausen, the name under which it is catalogued by Staudinger. As a rule the central band on the whitish fore wings is only represented by a round, or sometimes triangular, blackish spot on the front margin, a smaller blackish mark on the inner margin, and some dusky clouding between these two portions. In specimens from the Hebrides the band is more or less complete and the black markings are emphasised. These specimens are referable to subspecies *perfasciata* Prout.

The caterpillar is green, with three crimson lines, the outer ones bent inwards to the central one on the middle of each ring ; two lines above and one below the yellowish spiracular line are pink ; head green, tinged and freckled with pink. It feeds in September on the flowers and seeds of the eyebright (*Euphrasia officinalis*).

The moth is out from late May to July, and its habits are similar to those of the last species. In Scotland it appears to be commoner than in other parts of the British Isles, its range extending from Clydesdale to the Hebrides, Orkneys, and Shetland ; but it has been recorded from Cumberland, once from Durham and from Gloucestershire. In Wales it has been taken at Dolgelly, in Merionethshire. Prout states that in 1902 he secured two specimens near Cwm Bychan, and that the species has since been captured regularly in the locality. It is widely distributed in the north-west and south-west of Ireland.

Abroad the range extends through northern and central Europe to central Asia.

The Grass Rivulet (*Perizoma albulata* Schiff.)

Although some English specimens approach the larger and whiter typical form, the species as it occurs in the British Isles is generally greyer, ab. *griseata* Staud. ; two examples of this form are shown on Pl. **60**, 11, 14. In the Shetland Isles, the species assumes a darker coloration, and is either well marked on the fore wings, as in Pl. **60**, 12, or almost plain, as in Pl. **60**, 15 (ab. *thules* Weir), which is an extreme aberration of the subspecies *subfasciaria* Boheman. In other examples of a deep leaden grey, or brown tint, the central area is no darker than the rest of the wing. In the Isle of Lewis a white form with faint markings is prevalent, and this leads up to a clear white aberration devoid of markings, ab. *hebudium* Weir (*niveata* Stephens =).

The wrinkled caterpillar, which feeds, in July and August, on the seeds of the yellow rattle (*Rhinanthus crista-galli*), and lives in the capsule, is whitish, inclining to greenish, dotted with black, and striped with dark green on the back and sides ; head, black and glossy ; plates and first and last rings of the body dusky (Pl. **71**, 1).

The moth is out in May and June, sometimes later. It occurs chiefly in meadows where the yellow rattle flourishes, and is to be seen on the wing, often in large numbers, in the late afternoon about sundown. Generally abundant in suitable places, throughout the British Isles.

Abroad, its range extends through Europe to Transcaucasia.

The Sandy Carpet (*Perizoma flavofasciata* Thunb.)

The pale ochreous brown, or sandy, markings on the white fore wings of this species readily distinguish it from either of its allies. Variable in size, and also in the brownish tint of the markings ; the central band is usually contracted below the middle, and not infrequently it is completely severed at this point. It is also known as *decolorata* of Hübner (Pl. **60**, 16, 17).

The stoutish caterpillar is pale reddish ochreous with browner lines ; head, brown and shining, plate on first and last rings of the body brown. It feeds on the flower buds and on the immature seeds of red campion (*Lychnis dioica*), white campion (*L. alba*), and bladder campion (*Silene inflata*) but seems to favour more the first-named plant.

From May until August, or even later, the moth may be beaten out of hedgerows, sandy banks, and borders of woods and sometimes disturbed from patches of the campion growing in thickets ; in such places it is on the wing about sundown. The species may be double brooded or it may have an extended emergence period, for there is no clearly defined time during the four months from May to August when it is not to be found.

Although local to some extent, it appears to be common enough in most of the counties of England and Wales. In Scotland it is fairly common in Roxburghshire, Kirkcudbrightshire, and Clydesdale, and it is said to have occurred in Perthshire (Montcrieffe Hill). It also occurs in the Hebrides. It appears to be local in Ireland, but is recorded from Antrim, Tyrone, Down, Fermanagh, Derry, and Kerry, and noted as common at Larne in the first-named county.

Abroad, it occurs in most parts of Europe and it has been recorded from North Africa.

The Royal Mantle (*Euphyia cuculata* Hufn.)

This species (Pl. **58**, 9, 10) is also known as *sinuata* Schiff. The white fore wings have a blackish patch at the base and a blackish mark on the front margins beyond the middle ; the former is separated into two parts by a pale reddish brown band, and there is a reddish band, most distinct on the front area, beyond the black mark ; in some specimens these bands are greyish.

The caterpillar is green, sometimes inclining to yellowish, with two black or purplish stripes, enclosing a broader pale yellow one, along the back ; head, green, freckled with black. It feeds on the flowers of bedstraw (*Galium mollugo*, and *G. verum*), in July and August, or later in some seasons.

The moth is out in late June and in July, and occasionally may be disturbed from its food plant or the surrounding herbage. About dusk it is on the wing, and later is attracted by light. It seems to occur in most of the English counties from Kent to Cornwall ; also in Berkshire, Oxfordshire, Hertfordshire, and the eastern counties. Always local, and except in the east, where it is found in the Breck sand area, most frequent in chalky localities. Barrett notes a specimen from Knowle, Warwickshire, and there are at least three records from Scotland, two from Perthshire and one from Angus. In Ireland, a few specimens have been recorded from Co. Clare and another recorded from Galway.

The range of the species abroad extends to Siberia and Amurland.

The Sharp-angled Carpet (*Euphyia unangulata* Haw.)

This species (Pl. **63**, 1, 2) may be recognised by the distinctly angled outer edge of the blackish central band, which is thrown into strong relief by the usually broad white stripe following it. Wilkes, who figured the moth in 1742, called it the " White Stripe." By some authors the species has been called *amniculata* Hübner.

The caterpillar is pale whity brown, with a slightly darker but indistinct line along the centre of the back, and a black spot on the middle rings ; a pale line on the sides is edged with dark grey ; head, brown, marked with black. It feeds, in July and early August, on chickweed (*Stellaria media*).

The moth, which is partial to hedges and easily disturbed therefrom, is out in June and July, and even later in some seasons. The earliest hatched caterpillars reared in confinement sometimes attain the moth state in August of the same year. Although certainly local, the species has a wide distribution in the southern half of England, and is not uncommon in some localities. Its range extends into Wales, and also northwards to Cumberland and Westmorland, but it is generally very much scarcer in the north than in the south. In Ireland it is known to occur locally in counties Antrim, Tyrone, Fermanagh, Waterford, Kerry, and Galway, but, as a rule, only sparingly, also in Derry, Wicklow, and Cork (Donovan).

Abroad, the distribution includes North Amurland and North America.

The Cloaked Carpet (*Euphyia picata* Hübn.)

An older English name for this species (Pl. **63,** 3, 4) is " The Short Cloak Carpet," Harris (1782), but that given to it by Haworth is here adopted. It is also the *biangulata* of Haworth.

As will be observed on referring to the figures, the outer edge of the blackish central band of the fore wings is twice angled just above the middle ; the basal area and the outer marginal border are dark greyish brown, more or less tinged with olive ; the whitish ground colour only shows distinctly as a strip immediately beyond the central band, and from this an irregular streak runs to the tips of the wings ; some white wavy cross lines through the outer border are often obscure.

The stoutish caterpillar is yellowish brown, or sometimes reddish brown ; there is a series of blackish or dark brown spots along the back, and a stripe of dusky freckles along each side ; lower down are two slender wavy lines enclosing a dusky stripe ; head, yellowish brown mottled with darker brown. It feeds, at night, on chickweed and other kinds of *Stellaria*, in August and September. One of the mouse-ear chickweeds (*Cerastium glomeratum*) has also been mentioned as a food plant, and for rearing the caterpillars this would perhaps be useful, as common chickweed, unless in a growing state, is

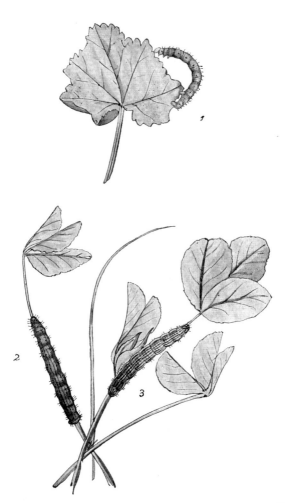

1. **Mallow:** *caterpillar.*
2. **Shaded Broad-bar:** *caterpillar.*
3. **Chalk Carpet:** *caterpillar.*

1. Sharp-angled
   Carpet.

2. Sharp-angled
   Carpet.

3. Cloaked
   Carpet.

4. Cloaked
   Carpet.

5. White-banded
   Carpet.

6. White-banded
   Carpet.

7. Yellow
   Shell.

8. Yellow
   Shell.

10. Yellow
    Shell.

9. Yellow
   Shell
   (ssp. *atlantica*).

11. Yellow
    Shell
    (ssp. *atlantica*).

13. Yellow
    Shell
    (ssp. *atlantica*).

12. Yellow
    Shell
    (ssp. *hibernica*).

14. Yellow
    Shell
    (ssp. *hibernica*).

difficult to keep in a suitable condition for larval requirements.

The moth, which is partial to a hedgerow as a hiding-place, is out in June and July, and may be sometimes reared as a second generation in September.

The species is somewhat local, but it is not scarce in many parts of England ; its range does not appear to extend north-wards beyond Worcestershire on the western side, although it has been recorded from North Wales ; on the eastern side it is found up to Norfolk. In Ireland it is very local, being recorded from Mayo, Tipperary, Cork, Wicklow, and Dublin.

Abroad, the range extends through central and parts of southern Europe, and central Asia.

The Ruddy Carpet (*Euphyia rubidata* Schiff.)

The markings on the reddish fore wings of this species (Pl. **58**, 11, 12) recall somewhat those of *Pareulype berberata*, but there is no black streak in the tips of the wings, and the upper part of the outer black line is not toothed. The lower central area is often greyish, and the reddish ground colour is sometimes obscured.

The caterpillar is pale brown, sometimes greyish or greenish tinged, with obscure darker diamond-shaped marks on the back ; a black central line, indistinct on the middle rings ; underside striped and lined with pale and dark brown ; head, with a black V-shaped mark. It feeds, in July and early August, on bedstraw (*Galium mollugo* and *G. verum*), and will eat cleavers or goosegrass (*G. aparine*) in confinement.

The moth flies in June and July, and in the daytime may be readily disturbed from hedges in localities on the chalk in the southern half of England and Wales, especially in the seaboard counties from Kent to Cornwall. It has been recorded from Derbyshire and Yorkshire, and once from the Isle of Arran (*Entom.*, xv. 250).

Abroad the range extends through central Europe, Asia Minor, and central Asia.

The White-banded Carpet (*Euphyia luctuata* Schiff.)

Until recently this species was known in Britain from only two specimens, one taken in North Kent on June 2, 1924, and the other at Woodham Ferrers, Essex. On August 6, 1950, however, another Kentish specimen was taken, a female, and from ova which she laid another female was reared. In the same year two other specimens were taken on the coast of Sussex, both in August, and in 1951 between August 1 and early September four more specimens were taken in three different localities in Kent. The species is now known to be established in both Kent and Sussex. The moth is on the wing from June to August, suggesting either two slightly over-lapping broods or a protracted emergence period (Pl. **63**, 5, 6).

According to Mr. G. Haggett, who has bred the species and described the early stages (*Ent. Gazette*, 1952, 3 : 27), the egg is dull pale green, flattened and broadly oval with very blunt ends, about twice as long as broad. The surface is shallowly pitted with irregularly sized but regularly shaped hexagonal depressions that give the appearance of beaten copper. This stage lasts about seven to eight days.

When fully fed the body colour of the larva is a clear sap green, but this colour is prominent only along the sides ; the dorsal and subdorsal lines are rich golden yellow and the whole of the dorsal area is thickly dusted with the same hue, extending to just beyond the subdorsals where it disintegrates into green. There are a few fine hairs scattered over the thoracic segments. In form the larva is stout and thickset. It feeds on *Epilobium angustifolium*, *E. montanum*, and *Galium*, the larval stage lasting about three and a half weeks.

The pupa is a uniform shining brown with the leg, antennal and proboscis sheaths a paler colour. Its last segment terminates in a well-formed, dome-shaped cremastral head, sharply pointed and bearing two simple spines. Mr. Haggett records the pupal stage as lasting sixteen days.

The range of the species extends through Europe to central Asia.

The Yellow Shell (*Euphyia bilineata* Linn.)

This very common and generally distributed species is subject to a good deal of variation in the tint of ground colour, and also in the greater or lesser amount of black marking. On Pl. **63** eight specimens are shown. Figs. 7, 8, represent the more frequent form in most localities, but in many districts ab. *infuscata* Gumppenberg (Fig. 10), is hardly less common ; in some specimens the central band is entirely blackish, and occasionally the middle area of the band is partly or wholly whitish. Sometimes the wings are uniformly yellow without markings, but such aberrations are scarce, or have not been noted often. A small form occurring in the Hebrides and the Shetlands, subsp. *atlantica* Staud., has the wings generally darkened ; Figs. 9, **11**, **13** depict three specimens from the Isle of Lewis. In western Ireland occurs the subsp. *hibernica* Prout (Figs. 12, 14) which has the forewings almost unicolorous fuscous brown and the hind wing ochreous brown. Subspecies *isolata* Kane has both wings fuscous black and is only recorded from the islands of Dursey and Tearaght off the coast of Cork.

The eggs, which are laid loosely, are yellowish or pale straw colour (Pl. **71**, 3*a*). Caterpillar, stoutish, green inclining to yellowish ; three lines on the back, the central one dark green, and the others yellowish, as also are the ring divisions ; a pale wavy line low down along the sides. In some examples the general colour is pale greyish-brown, inclining to reddish brown. It feeds on grass, dock, chickweed, and various low-growing plants from August to May, and is often abundant in hay meadows (Pl. **71**, 3, is from a coloured drawing by the late A. Sich). The moth occurs throughout the summer, and is very plentiful (often a pest) in almost every hedgerow and most bushy places.

Abroad, the range extends throughout Europe and Asia

Minor to Transcaucasia. It occurs also in the Mediterranean Islands and North Africa.

The Many-lined Moth (*Costaconvexa polygrammata* Borkh.)

The examples of this species, represented on Pl. **65,** 4, 5, are from Germany ; the male is somewhat paler and the central markings less distinct. This form, ab. *conjunctaria* Lederer, and most of the specimens formerly obtained in the Cambridgeshire fens, chiefly Burwell and Wicken, were referable to it. The species has not been seen in its old fenland haunts for very many years, and it is probably now extinct in Britain. Specimens have been in the past (and still continue to be) recorded from other British localities, but these on investigation are found to be cases of mistaken identity. *O. lignata* Hübner (*vittata* Borkh.=) bears a strong likeness to *P. polygrammata*, and is often confused with it, but in the latter the outer band does not run to the tips of the fore wings, as it does in the former species.

Abroad, the range includes central and southern Europe, North Africa, and central Asia.

The Pretty Chalk Carpet (*Melanthia procellata* Schiff.)

From almost any well-grown hedgerow, in which traveller's joy, or old-man's beard (*Clematis vitalba*) is plentiful, throughout the southern counties of England, this species (Pl. **65,** 3) may be disturbed by the beating stick. It is generally to be met with in July and early August, but may be obtained in forward seasons, or in sheltered localities, at the end of June.

On the fore wings the dark, slender and wavy cross lines are more distinct in some specimens than in others, and occasionally the blackish blotch on the front margin is traversed by a white line, sometimes by two lines.

The caterpillar is pale ochreous brown, with three darker brown lines along the back, the central one slender, spotted with black on the middle rings ; usual dots, black, encircled

1. **Beech-Green Carpet:** *caterpillar.*
2. **Striped Twin-spot Carpet:** *caterpillar.*
3. **Mottled Grey:** *caterpillar.*

1. Oblique
Striped.

2. Oblique
Striped.

3. Pretty Chalk
Carpet.

4. Many-lined
Moth.

5. Many-lined
Moth.

6. Purple
Bar.

7. Water
Carpet.

8. Water
Carpet
(ab. *porrittii*).

9. Devon
Carpet.

10. Water
Carpet
(ab. *piceata*).

11. Devon
Carpet.

12. Broken-barred
Carpet.

13. Broken-barred
Carpet
(ab. *albocrenata*).

14. Broken-barred
Carpet
(ab. *ruptata*).

15. Dark
Spinach.

16. Dark
Spinach.

with white ; head, marked with a reddish brown triangle. It
feeds on *Clematis* in August and September.

Distribution of the species abroad extends to Amurland, and
in Formosa, Japan, Korea, and China it is represented by the
darker *inquinata* Butler.

The Oblique Striped (*Mesotype virgata* Hufn.)

The sexes of this species are shown on Pl. **65,** 1 ♂, 2 ♀. The
fore wings are greyish, inclining to whitish or to brownish,
with two white-edged oblique bands, which in the lighter
coloured specimens are broad and show up conspicuously, but
in the darker are narrower and much less distinct.

The caterpillar is brownish, but varies in tint, in some cases
inclining to pink ; there are three lines along the back, the
central one dark green or brown, and the others more or less
yellowish ; a blackish or dark grey line low down along the
sides. It feeds on yellow bedstraw (*Galium verum*), and may
be reared on other kinds of *Galium*. There are two broods,
one in May and June, and the other in August and September.

The moth, which frequents sandhills and shelving banks by
the seaside, is found resting upon its food plant or other
vegetation around, in May and June, and again in July and
August.

The species has a wide distribution, and occurs in suitable
localities around the coasts of England (except the north-east),
and on the west coast of Wales. It also inhabits the Breck
sand district of Norfolk and Suffolk, and has been found on
chalk downs and hills in the south of England, and in Cambridgeshire and Berkshire. In Ireland, it has been recorded
from the counties of Down and Kerry.

Abroad, its distribution spreads to eastern Siberia and
Amurland.

The Purple Bar (*Lyncometra ocellata* Linn.)

The whitish fore wings of this species (Pl. **65,** 6) are often
tinged with pale ochreous brown on the lower two-thirds of

the outer marginal area, and this tint sometimes invades the central portion of the bluish black central band. Rarely the ground colour is almost entirely white, and the central band is very slender (ab. *coarctata* Prout), and perhaps rather more frequently the band is completely severed below the middle.

The caterpillar, which feeds at night on bedstraw (*Galium mollugo* and *G. verum*), is pale ochreous brown, or pale pinkish brown, netted with darker brown ; on the back are a reddish ochreous central line, and some reddish-edged pale, posteriorly pointing V-marks : June and July, and sometimes again in the autumn.

The moth is out in June and early July, occasionaly in late May in some southern localities. Individuals of a second emergence sometimes appear in August and September. It rests by day on tree-trunks or in hedges, and flies at night. Widely distributed over the British Isles, but, except perhaps in the highlands of Scotland, not very common.

Abroad, the range includes central Europe, Asia Minor, and central Asia.

The Water Carpet (*Lampropteryx suffumata* Schiff.)

The fore wings are whitish, more or less clouded with brownish, with dark brown, inclining to blackish, basal patch and central band. The variation tends in two opposite directions ; in the one the general colour is so clouded and suffused with blackish brown, that the entire fore wings become almost entirely of that colour (ab. *piceata* Stephens), northern England and Scotland ; the other extreme is ab. *porrittii* Robson (Pl. **65,** 8), in which the central band and basal patch are black, and the white ground colour is almost free of brown clouding ; the last named occurs at Huddersfield, Yorkshire, the Forest of Dean, and a modification of it at Dover. On Pl. **65,** Fig. 7 showr the typical form and Fig. 10 ab. *piceata*. The caterpillar varies from greyish, with pinkish or greenish tinge, to ochreous brown ; the upper surface is rather darker

than the under, and there is a series of dark V-shaped marks
and arrow-heads on the back of rings 4–8 ; there is a whitish
central stripe on 1–3 and a dark one on 9–12 ; head, brownish,
marked with black. It feeds on goosegrass (*Galium aparine*),
and other kinds of bedstraw, in May and early June. It seems
to thrive best, however, on the goosegrass (Pl. **61**, 1, after
Hofmann).

The moth may be found in weedy lanes and along hedgerows, pretty well throughout England, Wales, Scotland to
Moray, and Ireland. It cannot, however, be said to occur in
all suitable places, as although it may be found in some plenty
in one lane or hedgerow in a district, it may be quite absent in
similar spots just around. Wherever it is noted one year it
may be almost certainly obtained there in subsequent years.
April and May are the months in which it is usually seen, but it
has been taken in June in late seasons, and occasionally in
July.

Abroad, the range includes northern and central Europe.

The Devon Carpet (*Lampropteryx otregiata* Metcalfe)

In bringing this forward as an addition to our Geometridae,
the Rev. J. W. Metcalfe (*Entom.*, 1917, p. 73) states, " I first
captured the insect some ten years ago, flying in considerable
numbers, in a remote locality in North Devon. The striking
difference in the shape of the wings from those of *suffumata*,
the small size, and the shining, silvery ground colour, at once
attracted my attention. A subsequent visit led to further
captures, and on coming to live in East Devon I was delighted
to discover it again in a similar locality in this part of the
county. In addition to this, Mr. Newman has now found a
series in a collection made in Cornwall, where he reports that
it was taken under similar conditions.

" The species seems to be absolutely constant in form, and
in all specimens I have taken, well over a hundred, there has
not been the slightest variation nor any approach to any of

the known forms of *suffumata*. The general pattern and position of the wing markings correspond closely to those of *suffumata*, but the dark markings are much reduced, especially on the outer third of the wing, and are very delicately outlined with silvery white. The small size, the shining, silvery, ground-colour, and the shape of the fore wings, which are full and well rounded (very unlike those of *suffumata*), serve to separate it at a glance. The hind wings are devoid of markings, shining whitish grey. Seen in a series the general appearance is most striking, and somewhat suggests a cross between *suffumata* and *silaceata* " (Pl. **65**, 9, 11).

Cockayne has published a detailed life-history, with careful comparisons with *suffumata* (*Entom.*, 1936, lxix. 245–52). From eggs received on May 18 the larvae, which readily accepted *Galium aparine*, fed up very rapidly (18 days), moulting three times and pupating in moss on the earth about June 10–12 ; imagines emerged in numbers on July 1 and a few more up to the 5th, then five more in September, only one pupa going over the winter. The tubercles afford the best character for distinguishing the larvae. In both this species and *suffumata* each seta is set in a small ring of black chaetin at the apex of a conical tubercle ; the alpha, beta, rho, and many other tubercles are almost white in *suffumata*, whereas those of *otregiata* are blackish brown on the dorsum of the thoracic and the first five abdominal somites and are especially large and conspicuous on the fourth and fifth abdominals, alpha, beta, rho, the trapezoidals and the supraspiracular being the largest and blackest.

Since the first discovery of this species in North Devon, in 1907, it has been found in several other localities in that same county, also in Somerset, Cornwall, the New Forest, and four localities in Wales, at Mydrim and Pencader in Carmarthenshire, near Machynlleth on the Merioneth–Montgomeryshire border, and in Caernarvonshire. Abroad, it has been recorded from Germany, but its full distribution is not yet known.

1. Small
Phoenix.

2. Netted
Carpet.

3. Small
Phoenix

4. The Phoenix.

5. Blue-bordered
Carpet.

6. Barred
Straw.

7. The Spinach.

8. Blue-bordered
Carpet
(ssp. *plumbata*).

9. The Spinach.

10. The Chevron.

11. Blue-bordered
Carpet
(ab. *fumosa*).

12. The Chevron.

13. Northern
Spinach.

14. Barred
Yellow.

15. The Chevron.

16. Northern
Spinach.

17. Barred
Yellow.

18. Northern
Spinach
(ab. *fuscata*).

1, 1a. **Shoulder-stripe:** *caterpillar and chrysalis.*
2, 2a. **The Streamer:** *eggs, natural size and enlarged, and caterpillars.*

The Broken-barred Carpet (*Electrophaës corylata* Thund.)

The fore wings have an olive brown basal patch and central band, both are edged with white, wavy lines, and the band is contracted below the middle (Pl. **65,** 12), and often broken at this point, ab *ruptata* Hübn. (Fig. 14) ; the inner marginal portion sometimes very small ; the space between the basal patch and central band is pale brown, and so also is the outer marginal area ; but there are dark clouds and white marks beyond the white wavy submarginal line. Variable in tint and in marking, the variety generally known as *albocrenata* Curtis (Pl. **65,** 13) in which the median band is only represented by some indistinct grey dusting, is perhaps most frequent in Perthshire and Sutherland.

The caterpillar is green, inclining to yellowish ; three stripes on the back, the central one reddish brown and broad, but only distinct at each end, the other paler green ; spiracles, white, placed in a reddish brown stripe, which is sometimes broken up. An entirely red form has been recorded. It feeds on sloe, birch, oak, and the foliage of other trees, and may be found from July to September, and even later.

The moth is out in May and June, and is to be beaten from hedges, or may be found at rest on tree-trunks, palings, etc.

Generally distributed, but not extending to the Scottish Isles. Scarce but widely spread in Ireland.

Abroad, the range spreads to Amurland and Japan.

The Dark Spinach (*Pelurga comitata* Linn.)

The darker banded, pale ochreous species shown on Pl. **65,** 15, 16 varies in the colour of the band to brownish ; the central area of this band is almost always pale ochreous or whitish, to a greater or lesser extent. In ab *zonata* Wahlgren, the median band is entirely fuscous.

Caterpillar, stout and roughened ; ochreous inclining to reddish, and tinged above with greenish ; a series of V-shaped marks along the back, yellow oblique darker on the sides, and a greyish edged pale wavy line low down along the sides. The figures 2, 2a, on Pl. **86** are from coloured drawings by the late A. Sich.

It feeds in the autumn on the flowers and seeds of various kinds of goosefoot (*Chenopodium*), also on orache (*Atriplex*). The moth is out in July and August, and may be found among its food plants and other low herbage growing in waste places, more particularly those on sandy coasts. Around the borders of market gardens, especially those in the south of London, and in Kent and Surrey, it is often very common. The species probably occurs more or less freely in suitable places almost throughout the British Isles. It has been recorded from the Isle of Man.

Its range abroad extends to eastern Siberia, and northern China.

The Small Phoenix (*Ecliptopera silaceata* Schiff.)

In its typical form (Pl. **66, 1**) the blackish band of the fore wings is entire, but in ab. *insulata* Haworth (Fig. 3), this band is interrupted by two whitish lines along the median veins, and so divided into three or four portions, the smaller section placed between the lines ; occasionally, the dividing lines assume stripe-like proportions, and the main portions are consequently smaller in size and further from each other, but one " island " still remains. In another form, the lower outer corner is distinctly separate from the costal portion ; thus the band is broken into four parts.

The long caterpillar is green, with a reddish brown stripe along the back ; this is broken up into spots, except on the first three rings ; there are some reddish brown spots on the sides. It feeds on various kinds of willow herb (*Epilobium*), balsam (*Impatiens noli-me-tangere*), and enchanter's nightshade (*Circaea lutetiana*) in July, and sometimes in August and September.

The moth should be looked for in beech and other woods

amongst the food plants, from which, and the surrounding herbage, it is readily evicted. It flies at twilight, and also later, when it has been known to visit the sugar patch; it is also attracted by light. It is out in May and June, and specimens of a second generation sometimes occur in the south. The species occurs locally throughout England, probably Wales, and in Scotland up to Ross. In Ireland, it is widely distributed and locally common in the north and is also recorded from Clare, Westmeath, Kerry, and Cork.

Abroad, the range extends through northern and central Europe to eastern Siberia.

The Netted Carpet (*Eustroma reticulata* Schiff.)

The white veins and white lines passing through the blackish blotches at the base and on the front margin of the fore wings, give these wings a curious netted appearance; the hind wings are smoky grey, with two white lines which appear to be continuations of the white second line and submarginal of the fore wings (Pl. **66**, 2). The variation of this species is described fully by Mr. Prout (*Entom.*, xlv. 1-3, Pl. 1) and fourteen forms are figured.

The caterpillar is green, inclining to yellowish, and more or less tinged with pinkish, especially on the sides; three lines on the back, the central one reddish, the others whitish; a central line along the pinkish spiracles. It feeds at night on yellow balsam (*Impatiens noli-me-tangere*), preferring the flowers, seeds, and young foliage, and rests by day on the undersides of the leaves: September and October (Pl. **73**, 2, after Hofmann). The early stages of *E. reticulata* are described and illustrated by Mr. F. Littlewood (*Entom.*, xlv. 85-9).

The moth is out in July and August, and, of course, will only be found in localities where the balsam flourishes; these are very limited, and in Britain are confined to Westmorland and the northern border of Lancashire, and North Wales. The species was first recorded as British in 1861, when the late Henry Doubleday noted the capture of three specimens in August, 1856, on the border of one of the lakes in Westmorland, by his friend the late Thomas H. Allis. It seems that other specimens had been taken at the same time, but these passed into collections as the "second brood of *silaceata*." The caterpillar is said to have been found in North Wales, but has been more frequently obtained in the English Lake District.

The range abroad extends to eastern Siberia and western China.

The Barred Straw (*Lygris pyraliata* Schiff.)

In certain respects this species (Pl. **66, 6**) is not unlike the one following. The fore wings are yellowish straw-colour, the cross lines are brownish, but the central two are closer together, especially on the inner margin, than they are in *mellinata*, and are straightly oblique from the angle, or elbow, below the front margin ; there is often a line of brownish dots between the second line and the outer margin, and the fringes are brown, not chequered. Occasionally there are darker clouds on the second line, at the angle, and such clouds sometimes appear in the central space. Not infrequently the markings are very faint (ab. *deleta* Strand). Staudinger and others refer this species to *dotata* L., but this has now been found to be incorrect, *dotata* being an aberration of *populata* Linn.

The caterpillar feeds, in April and May, on the common cleavers or goosegrass (*Galium aparine*) of our hedgerows, etc., but it also eats *G. mollugo* and other kinds of bedstraw. It is to be found low down on the stems.

The moth may be disturbed from the herbage along hedges and ditches in lanes, and the borders of woods, but it seems most partial to the former.

The species is generally distributed, and often plentiful, in the southern half of England ; but although widely spread in the northern half, it is only common locally. It occurs in Wales, both North and South, and on the Isle of Man ; is common in Roxburghshire and Clydesdale, and is found in Aberdeenshire, Inverness-shire, and in West Ross ; it has been recorded from the Isle of Eigg. In Ireland it is widely distributed, and sometimes abundant ; but more frequent on the coast than inland.

The distribution abroad includes eastern Siberia and Amurland.

The Spinach (*Lygris mellinata* Fab.)

The fore wings are pale ochreous, more or less clouded with darker ; three brownish cross lines. Hind wings, paler, with indication of cross lines on the inner margin. Fringes of all the wings chequered with brown, most distinct on the fore wings (Pl. **66,** 7, 9).

The long caterpillar is green, inclining to yellowish ; three lines along the back, the central one dark green and the others whitish ; there is also a whitish line low down along the sides. It feeds at night, in May and June, on currant (*Ribes rubrum* and *R. nigrum*), and may be found on the underside of a leaf in the daytime. (Figured on Pl. **74,** 1, from a coloured drawing by the late A. Sich.)

During July and August the moth flies in the evening, and after dark it often comes to any bright illumination. It is essentially a garden insect, and where currant bushes are there also spinach is often grown ; hence it was probably connected with the vegetable rather than the fruit when Haworth named it *spinachiata*. The species seems to be found more or less frequently in suitable spots through England. In Wales it has been recorded from Glamorgan, and from Rhyl, Flintshire ; on the Isle of Man, it is found occasionally at Douglas ; in Scotland, Renton states that it is common in Roxburgh gardens ; and it is also noted from Paisley and from Inverness-shire. It has been recorded from Ireland.

The range abroad extends to Amurland.

The Phoenix (*Lygris prunata* Linn.)

The English name here retained was given to this species
(Pl. **66**, 4) by Harris, in 1775, but in 1782 he changed it to
" Clouded Carpet."

In ground colour the fore wings are pale brown, more or
less clouded with darker brown, or with reddish brown ; the
basal patch, central band, and blotch on outer margin below
the tip of the wing, are all chocolate brown clouded with
blackish and edged with white.   Hind wings, whitish, suffused
with smoky grey, except on front area ; three dusky whitish-
edged wavy lines, inclining to blackish on the inner margin.
The egg (Pl. **74**, 3) is yellowish when laid, and then changes
to purplish with a whitish bloom.

The caterpillar is green, varying to brownish ; along the
middle of the back is a series of purplish-edged, brown-
centred, whitish, triangular markings ;   the third ring is
swollen, and has a black collar.   It feeds at night on the foliage
of red and black currant, also on gooseberry, and may be
found in April and May, earlier or later according to season,
sitting by day upon the bushes.

The moth flies in July and August, and occurs in gardens,
but is said to be partial to sloe bushes and hedges.   It is
always more or less local, although it is distributed over the
greater part of the British Isles.

Abroad, this species occurs in central and northern Europe
and many parts of Arctic Russia.

The Northern Spinach (*Lygris populata* Linn.)

The fore wings are yellow, with a reddish or purplish brown
basal patch, central band, and small patch on outer margin
below tip of the wing, the central band more or less clouded
or mottled with yellow.   Hind wings, whitish, tinged with
yellow.   The female is usually smaller, the colour generally
paler, and the markings frequently only represented by cross
lines (Pl. **66**, 13, 16).   Specimens from the Isle of Arran have

the ground colour of fore wings more or less dappled with brown of the same tint as that of the central band and other markings ; the hind wings are tinged with a smoky hue. In other parts of Scotland the brown colour becomes more and more general, until the fore wings are uniformly brown, and the hind wings dusky. On the mountains in the north nearly black specimens occur, and these are referable to ab. *fuscata* Prout (Pl. **66**, 18).

The long caterpillar is variable in general colour, brown, mottled with greyish, pale grey, reddish brown, or yellowish green ; all have darker or whitish lines along the back, and whitish or pinkish triangles or X-marks. It feeds, in May and June (earlier in some localities, and later in others), on bilberry, crowberry, and sallow ; it may also be reared on willow.

The moth is out in July and August, and may be found on the leaves and among the sprays of *Vaccinium myrtillus* growing in woodlands (especially the more ancient), bogs, and moorlands.

The species is widely spread, and generally abundant in suitable districts, over the greater part of the British Isles ; but it seems to be more or less casual in England south of the Midlands, although its range runs through Gloucestershire and Somerset into Devon. In the last-named county it sometimes swarms at Martinhoe, on the edge of Exmoor.

The distribution abroad includes eastern Siberia and Amurland.

The Chevron (*Lygris testata* Linn.)

The fore wings of this rather variable species (Pl. **66**, 10, 12, 15) are yellowish or reddish grey with a darker basal patch and central band ; a reddish blotch below the tip of the wing is edged with white, and the central band is also outwardly edged with white. Hind wings, whitish, with two lines, and dusky hind marginal border, the latter sometimes inclining

to reddish. Occasionally, the fore wings are entirely pale
ochreous, and the basal patch and the central band only very
slightly darker, but the limiting lines are reddish, and the
patch under the tip of the wing is bright orange red. Ab.
insulicola Staud., from the isles of Scotland and elsewhere,
has the fore wings rather narrower, and suffused with purplish
brown or deep violet grey ; the hind wings are smoky grey.
The female is usually smaller than the male, and often more
yellow in colour.

Eggs, whitish brown, mottled with darker. The early stages
are shown on Pl. **74**, 2–2*b*.

The long caterpillar is pale yellowish brown, with three
lines along the back, the central one dark brown, and most
distinct at each end ; the others are white, irregularly shaded
above with reddish ; another white line along the region of
the spiracles. It feeds, in May or June (earlier or later in
some seasons), on sallow, aspen, and birch. The moth is out
in July and August, and frequents heaths and bogs more
especially, but is also found in or around woods, and South
captured male specimens as they flew along hedgerows bordering fields, at dusk, in Middlesex. The female is rarely seen
on the wing.

The species, which ranges through central and northern
Europe to the Ural and Altai, is generally distributed throughout the British Isles.

The Barred Yellow (*Cidaria fulvata* Forst.)

This very pretty, and most distinct, little species (Pl. **66**,
14, 17) does not vary very greatly ; there is certainly some
modification in the general colour, and in that of the markings,
but in both it is only a matter of tint.

The caterpillar is somewhat wrinkled, and in colour is green,
with three greyish lines along the back, the central one double ;
the ring divisions are yellow, and there is a yellow line low
down along the sides. It feeds at night, in May and June, on

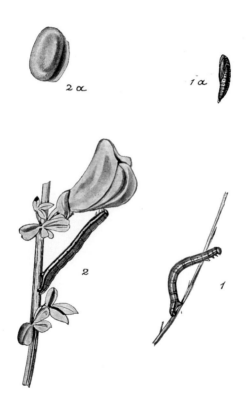

1, 1a. **Broom-tip:** *caterpillar and chrysalis.*
2, 2a. **The Streak:** *caterpillar and egg, enlarged.*

1. Common
Marbled
Carpet.

2. Common
Marbled
Carpet.

3. Common
Marbled
Carpet.

4. Common
Marbled
Carpet.

5. Dark
Marbled
Carpet.

6. Dark
Marbled
Carpet.

7. Dark
Marbled
Carpet.

8. Dark
Marbled
Carpet.

9. Arran
Carpet.

10. Arran
Carpet.

11. Arran
Carpet.

12. Arran
Carpet.

the leaves of wild rose, and does not object to the garden
kinds (Pl. **76,** 3, after Hofmann).

The moth is out in June and July. It hides by day under
leaves in hedges, and although not often induced to get on
the wing at that time, the male commences its evening flight
at an early hour. It is generally a common species in England and Wales ; it occurs here and there through Scotland,
in the Hebrides and up to the Orkneys ; and although somewhat local, it is common enough, where found, in Ireland.

Abroad, the range extends through the greater part of
Europe, Asia Minor, northern Persia, and central Asia.

The Blue-bordered Carpet (*Plemyria rubiginata* Schiff.)

The more usual form of this pretty little species is shown
on Pl. **66,** 5. In the type the central band is only represented by a spot on the front margin of the fore wings ; in
the aberration, ab. *parvula* Retz., there is also a portion of
the band showing on the inner margin. Subspecies *plumbata*
Curtis, from northern England and Scotland, has the median
band uninterrupted (Pl. **66,** 8) or only narrowly interrupted and
the smoky dark bordering is usually intensified. Sometimes
also, there are traces of a narrow smoky band midway between
the basal and median patches. Ab. *fumosa* Prout (Pl. **66,** 11),
not infrequent among this northern race, has the ground colour
of the fore wing partly or wholly suffused with smoky brown,
sometimes so deeply as to almost obscure the markings.
Barrett mentions a form with all the wings smoothly smoky
black ; markings of the fore wings olive brown, margined with
slender stripes of smoky white.

The long, thin, caterpillar is green, with a darker stripe
along the back, and a yellowish green stripe on each side ;
two points on the last ring. It feeds on alder, birch, sloe, and
crab ; also in orchards and gardens on plum and apple :
April to June.

The moth is out in July and August. It appears to occur

most freely in districts where alder is plentiful, but it is not uncommon in country lanes, especially where these are rather moist. It is one of the earliest Geometrid moths to get on the wing, as it is generally active well before dark. Decidedly more common in some districts than in others, but it may be said to be generally distributed throughout the British Isles.

The range abroad extends to eastern Siberia, Amurland and Japan.

The Red-green Carpet (*Chloroclysta siterata* Hufn.)

The general colour of the fore wings of this species (Pl. **70** 1–3) is greyish green, with more or less of rosy suffusion ; the basal patch and central band are darker green, and the latter is outwardly edged with whitish below the front margin, and towards the inner margin. The female has rather more ample wings, and is generally of a darker hue, but in both sexes the basal patch and central band are blackish ; the hind wings are dark greyish brown, inclining to blackish in some females, and there is a blackish central dot and two or three curved lines. In ab. *fasciata* Cockayne, the basal area and the median band are blackish green except for a light green area round the discoidal spot. The rest of the fore wing is much paler than usual and almost devoid of markings.

The long caterpillar is yellowish green, with an interrupted red line along the middle of the back ; two green points on last ring are usually pink-tipped. It feeds on oak, birch, ash, sloe, apple, etc., in July and August.

The moth occurs in woodlands, but is not easily disturbed in the daytime from its lurking-place in bush or tree. In the autumn it may be found at ivy-bloom, and in the spring, after hibernation, has been taken at sallow.

The species appears to be widely distributed over England and Wales, Scotland up to Moray, the Hebrides, and Ireland.

Abroad, the range extends throughout the greater part of Europe, to Asia Minor and Transcaucasia.

The Autumn Green Carpet (*Chloroclysta miata* Linn.)

Somewhat similar to the last, but the general colour of the fore wings is paler, inclining to whitish, and the basal patch and central band are pale green tinged with greyish ; there is no rosy suffusion, but the wavy submarginal line is distinctly white. The hind wings are greyish white, with black discal dot, and dark-grey curved lines (Pl. **70,** 4, 5).

The caterpillar is pale green, inclining to yellowish, especially between the rings, and with a more or less distinct dark green line along the middle of the back ; the points on the last ring are pinkish brown, and there is a line of the same colour along the centre of the under surface of the body.

It feeds on alder, birch, oak, sallow, etc., and may be beaten out from June to August.

The moth is out in September and October, when it may be obtained at ivy-bloom, and in the following spring, after hibernation, it visits sallow catkins.

The range in the British Isles agrees pretty closely with that of the last species, but in Scotland it extends to the Orkneys and Shetlands.

Abroad, its range includes the greater part of Europe and extends to central Asia.

The Common Marbled Carpet (*Dysstroma truncata* Hufn.)

Four examples of this very variable species are shown on Pl. **69,** 1–4. There are a number of modifications of each of the forms, and several of these have been named. In the typical form the median band is clouded with grey dusting (Fig. 1) ; Fig. 2 is ab. *rufescens* Ström (Yellow Marbled Carpet) ; Fig. 3 is ab. *perfuscata* Haw. (The Brown Marbled Carpet) ; Fig. 4 shows a specimen from Stornoway, Isle of Lewis, which appears to be a modification of the typical form of *truncata*, but it has some of the character of *concinnata*.

The caterpillar is long, slender, and wrinkled, especially on the sides ; the ground colour is green, inclining to yellowish ; three lines along the back, the central one dark green, and the others yellowish ; sometimes a rosy stripe, or a series of dashes along the sides ; the points on the last ring are green, or rosy.   It feeds, in the autumn and again in the spring after hibernation, on sallow, birch, hawthorn, bilberry, wild strawberry, etc.   It will also eat rose, but as the specimens resulting from caterpillars reared on rose are frequently small, such food is probably unsuitable ; garden strawberry, on the other hand, is an excellent pabulum.   A photograph of the caterpillar by the late H. Main is shown on Pl. **76,** 1.   There is a second brood in late June and in July.   The first generation of the moth is out in May and June, and the second emerges in the autumn ; specimens, possibly of a third generation, have been seen in December in favourable localities.

The species, which frequents woods and hedgerows, and is pretty generally common, is to be found almost everywhere throughout the British Isles.   It has been recorded from the Orkneys but not, however, been noted from Shetland.

The distribution abroad extends to Amurland and western China.

The Arran Carpet (*Dysstroma concinnata* Steph.)

Most closely related to *D. truncata* Hufn., of which it may well be a race.   The majority of specimens are distinguishable by the fuscous and white dappled median band of the fore wing and the dark hind wing with the conspicuous row of pale subterminal spots and the well-marked postmedial fascia, which is rather thicker than in *truncata*.

Known principally from the Isle of Arran, where it occurs on open moorland from about 400 feet upwards.   It is single brooded, appearing in July and August, though occasional specimens have been taken in late June.   Normal *truncata* occurring on the island are double brooded, appearing in May and June and again in August and September, favouring

1. Red-green
Carpet.

2. Red-green
Carpet.

3. Red-green
Carpet.

4. Autumn
Green
Carpet.

5. Autumn
Green
Carpet.

6. Spruce
Carpet.

7. Pine
Carpet.

8. Pine
Carpet.

9. Spruce
Carpet.

10. Grey
Pine
Carpet.

11. Grey
Pine
Carpet.

12. Grey
Pine Carpet
(ab. *obliterata*).

13. Chestnut-coloured
Carpet.

14. Spruce
Carpet.

15. Chestnut-coloured
Carpet.

16. Juniper
Carpet.

17. Juniper
Carpet
(ssp. *scotica*).

18. Juniper
Carpet.

19. Juniper
Carpet
(ssp. *scotica*).

1. **Grass Rivulet:** *caterpillar.*
2. **Waved Carpet:** *caterpillar.*
3, 3a. **Yellow Shell:** *eggs, natural size and enlarged, and caterpillar.*

the lower elevations and resting rather on tree-trunks and boughs than on the granite rocks favoured by *concinnata*.

Ab. *centumnotata* Heydem. has the central band of the median area pure white and ab. *perfuscata* Heydem. has the median area blackish brown (Pl. **69**, 9-12).

Specimens reputed to be *concinnata* have been recorded from the mainland of Scotland and also from Achil Island off the coast of Co. Mayo.

Sheldon found no difference between the larvae of *concinnata* and the variable *truncata* ; those of the Achil Island *Dysstroma* he found to be quite different in colour from those of Arran, all being entirely green, both before and after hibernation.

Rayward, who has studied carefully the genitalia of both sexes of *truncata* from various parts of the British Isles and compared them with those of *concinnata*, has concluded that there are no differences that can be depended upon as good characters for separating the two species.

The Dark Marbled Carpet (*Dysstroma citrata* Linn.)

This is another exceedingly variable species (Pl. **69**, 5-8), and here again four examples have been chosen to illustrate something of the range of aberration. In some specimens the general colour of the fore wings is tawny or rust-colour, or they are strongly suffused with that tint (ab. *ferruginea* Prout). South had such examples from Lewis and the Shetlands. Ab. *thingvallata* Staud. has the fore wings white, with black basal patch and central band, and he had seen at least one example from Yorkshire that closely approached this variety.

The caterpillar is not very unlike that of the last species, but it is rounder in appearance, the general green colour is paler, and the points on the last ring are blunt. It feeds from April to June on sallow, birch, bilberry, and wild strawberry (Pl. **76**, 2, after Hofmann). The moths are out in July and August, and may be found resting on tree-trunks, rocks, or stone walls ; at night, when it is active on the wing, it is said to be seen often in numbers on the flowers of the rush, and this habit has been noted more particularly in Scotland.

The species affects woods and moors, and appears to be found more or less commonly throughout the British Isles.

Abroad, the range extends from North America, through Europe to western China.

The Juniper Carpet (*Thera juniperata* Linn.)

On Pl. **70**, Figs. 16 and 18 represent the sexes of the typical form of this species. Figs. 17 and 19 represent the small and rather more strongly marked Scottish form, subsp. *scotica* B. White. In these small forms a noticeable character is the brownish band on the fore wings, between the central band and the outer margin ; this band is only indicated by a dusky greyish shade in the larger form. Most of the examples of the small form from the Isle of Hoy have also a dark central line on the hind wings. In ab. *divisa* Strand, the central band of the fore wings is often broken below the middle, in both forms.

The caterpillar is yellowish green, inclining to a black tinge on the back, along which are three lines, the central one dark green, and the others yellow and rather broad ; a whitish stripe low down along the sides is sometimes marked with yellow and red, and there is a red thread above it ; head, pink tinged ; two points on last ring of the body. It feeds in July and August, on juniper. The moth is out in October and November, and may be found plentifully flying at night about the juniper bushes.

Berkshire, Kent, Surrey, and Sussex appear to be the only English counties in which it is established, and it is probably most plentiful in the last named. It has, however, been recorded from Suffolk, Lancashire, Yorkshire, and Durham ; also from Caernarvonshire in North Wales. It is more widely spread throughout Scotland, including the Hebrides and the Orkneys, where the moths fly in July. Reported from Counties Mayo, Sligo, Galway, and Antrim in Ireland—also from Achill Island.

Abroad, the range extends to northern and central Europe and to parts of Italy.

The Chestnut-coloured Carpet (*Thera cognata* Thunb.)

This is a generally smaller species than the last referred to, and it is more glossy in appearance. The fore wings are brown, sometimes grey brown, more or less tinged with reddish, and the basal patch and central band are darker ; these markings are usually white-edged, and there is a wavy whitish sub-marginal line. Hind wings whitish, tinged with smoky grey. Specimens from the Hebrides are strongly purplish ; and Kane states that some he reared from Sligo caterpillars are more richly coloured than any that he has seen from Scotland (Pl. **70**, 13 ♂, 15 ♀).

The bright green caterpillar is stouter than that of the last species. It is of a bluish hue along the back, and marked with three lines, the central one greenish and the others whitish and broad ; there are sometimes reddish markings low down on the sides, just edging the broad white spiracular line. It feeds in May and June, earlier or later in some seasons, on juniper ; it turns to a dark green chrysalis in a frail cocoon spun up among the litter under the juniper bushes.

The moth is to be found in July and August among juniper growing in the hilly and maritime haunts of the species in North England, Wales, Scotland, and Ireland.

Abroad, it occurs in central Europe and North America.

The Grey Pine Carpet (*Thera obeliscata* Hübn.)

In its typical form (Pl. **70**, 10, 11), the fore wings of this species are a warm cinnamon brown, varying to smoky brown, with an evenly and strongly marked median band. The postmedian line is smoothly lunulate, rarely jagged in appearance. The subterminal line, usually weakly marked, is lunulate. Ab. *obliterata* B. White, almost unicolorous blackish with faintly marked median lines, is represented by Pl. **70,** 12. The moth flies in May and June.

The larva is bright green with three whitish dorsal lines, the central one broad, and the spiracular lines are yellowish. The roundish head is green, lined with white ; the legs are pink. It normally feeds on Scots pine but will also eat silver fir and any of the spruces ; it is found in the autumn and again in April and early May (Pl. **79,** 1).

The moth is generally common in pinewoods throughout the greater part of the British Isles. Abroad, the range extends to northern and central Europe and Transcaucasia.

The Spruce Carpet (*Thera variata* subsp. *britannica* H. J. Turner)

The British race of this species (Pl. **70,** 6, 9, 14) is grey to greyish brown. On the fore wing, the areas preceding and following the median band are mixed with white and the ante-median line is usually preceded by and the dentate post-median followed by a white line. The dentate, white sub-terminal is usually strongly marked. The moth appears a little earlier than the preceding species and is double brooded, flying in May and early June and again in August and September.

The larva, which is similar in other respects to *obeliscata*, can be readily distinguished by its green legs. It feeds in the autumn and again in April on spruces and firs but never on Scots pine. The second brood larvae are to be found in June and July.

The moth is widely distributed throughout the British Isles and probably occurs wherever its food plant is to be found. The range abroad is similar to that of the preceding species.

1, 2, 3, 4, 5, 6. **July Highflyer.**
7, 8, 9, 10. **May Highflyer.**
11, 12. **Ruddy Highflyer.**

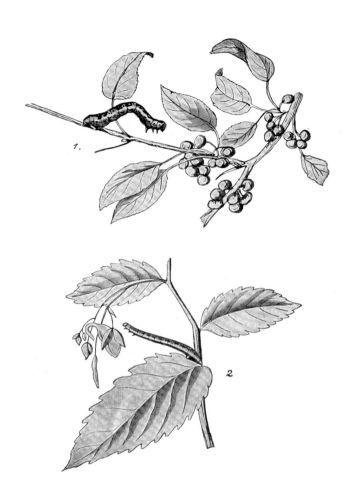

1. **Dark Umber:** *caterpillar*.
2. **Netted Carpet:** *caterpillar*.

The Pine Carpet (*Thera firmata* Hübn.)

The pale reddish grey fore wings have a rather darker central band and round-edged basal patch, but the latter is often indistinct, and the band, which is always deeply indented about the middle of its inner edge, is sometimes not well defined. The hind wings are whitish, tinged more or less with greyish or pale brownish, but always paler than in any form of *T. obeliscata*, with which it is often confused (Pl. **70**, 7, 8).

The caterpillar is bluish green above, and green beneath; three lines along the back, the central one a darker tone of the ground colour, the others whitish; head reddish, marked with brown on each cheek. It feeds in April and May (June in Scotland) on Scots pine; Barrett states that there is a second brood in August (Pl. **79**, 2).

The moth is out in September and October, and may be disturbed from the pine boughs, or occasionally seen resting on the trunks, but it is more frequently met with at night when it flies naturally, and has been known to visit the sugar patch. Barrett, who considered this species to be double brooded, gives June and July for the first flight of moths. Certain it is that moths have been reared even as late as October from spring caterpillars. The protracted season in which both larvae and moths can be found is probably due to the fact that the larvae feed up at very varying rates rather than to there being two broods. As adverted to, the pale reddish forms of *T. obeliscata* are sometimes confused with *T. firmata*, but in addition to other differences indicated above, it may be noted that in the male of the latter the antennae are bipectinated except towards the tips. Most of the pine-woods throughout England seem to produce this delicate insect more or less frequently; the same remark applies to Wales. In Scotland it is found up to Aberdeen, and also in the Hebrides. Local in Ireland, being recorded from the counties of Tyrone, Down, Fermanagh, Westmeath, Dublin, Kildare, Wicklow, and Kerry.

Abroad, the range extends to northern and central Europe.

The July Highflyer (*Hydriomena furcata* Thunb.)

Some idea of the variable character of this species (*elutata* Hübn.) may be formed from the selection of half a dozen examples shown on Pl. **72**, 1–6. The typical form has the fore wings greyish, with dark bands and a modification without the dark bands seems to be ab. *cinereata* Prout. In the form *sordidata* Fab., the general colour of the fore wings is greenish, and the bands are dark; ab. *obliterata* Prout is of the same colour, but the bands are absent. Ab. *fusco-undata* Staud. has the general colour reddish, with dark bands; without dark bands it becomes *testaceata* Prout. Blackish or sooty forms are referable to *obscura* Peyer (Fig. 4). Frequently in the green forms, and less often in the reddish, there is a broad whitish central stripe, and a narrow one on the basal area; in the green form again the basal and central areas are occasionally crossed by red bands, and this is one of the prettiest forms of the species and, so far as is known, occurs only in the large sallow-feeding specimens.

The egg (Pl. **80**, 1*b*) when figured, February 8, 1908, was whitish as regards the shell, but the interior was dark greenish. In April the caterpillar appeared to be formed, but it did not leave the shell until early in May.

The full-grown caterpillar (Pl. **80**, 1, 1*a*) is brownish, inclining to blackish; whitish between the rings, white lines along the back and sides, and tinged with red along the spiracular region. It feeds, in May and June, on sallow, willow, poplar, hazel, bilberry, and heather. The moth is out in July and August, but South had seen the small bilberry-feeding form (Pl. **72**, 5, 6) on a corner of Exmoor, North Devon, in great profusion in late June, whilst in the same district the sallow-feeding, larger form appeared about a fortnight later, at which time specimens among bilberry were not numerous, and rather shabby in appearance.

Except perhaps in the Shetlands, this species is to be found in all parts of the British Isles. It is very common in hedge-rows, and around the margins of woods ; the smaller race frequents woods where bilberry is established, and also occurs on mountains and moors.

Abroad, the range extends to Amurland, China, Japan and also to Iceland and North America.

The May Highflyer (*Hydriomena coerulata* Fab.)

The typical and commoner form of this species is shown on Pl. **72**, 7 and 8. The ground colour, usually pale green, is sometimes almost white but more frequently it is tinged with greyish brown, thus leading up to the blackish ab. *obsoletaria* Schille (Pl. **72**, **9**, 10).

The caterpillar is brownish grey, or purplish grey, dotted with black and dappled with dark brown : of the three lines along the back, the central one is black and swells out on the middle of each ring, the others are pale ; a clear stripe of the ground colour below the black spiracles, and a slender line above them. The general colour is sometimes pale pinky brown or ochreous. It feeds on alder throughout the summer and autumn, and may be found in its domicile of spun-together dry leaves even in November, and sometimes later. Occasionally, a few caterpillars will feed up quickly, and attain the moth state in July or August, but the bulk do not become chrysalids until later in the year, and the moths emerge therefrom in May and early June (Pl. **80,** 2).

The species seems to occur, more or less freely, wherever there are alders throughout the greater part of the British Isles.

Abroad, the range extends to eastern Siberia and Amurland.

The Ruddy Highflyer (*Hydriomena ruberata* Freyer)

This species is most readily distinguished from the last by the short oblique black streak on the tips of the rather narrower fore wings ; there are also black streaks between the veins and below the tips of the wings, as in the last species, but they are generally shorter and often hardly traceable.

The ground colour ranges from pale grey (sometimes with a green tinge) through brownish grey to reddish brown ; usually central and outer marginal bands of a darker shade are present, but these characters may be very indistinct or entirely lost in the general coloration (Pl. 72, 11, 12).

The caterpillar is pale brown, dappled with grey ; three dark greyish lines along the back ; spiracles and the usual dots black, the latter with fine hairs ; head, reddish brown, plates on first and last rings of the body light brown. It feeds at night, during the summer and autumn on sallow, especially *Salix aurita*, and willow, spinning together the leaves at the top of a twig to form a retreat during the day.

The moth is found in hedges, woods, and on heaths, in May and June ; it may be occasionally beaten out of sallow bushes, but flies in the early evening, and is then more readily obtained.   The species is widely distributed, but not generally common, in England and Wales, in Scotland to Sutherland, in the Hebrides and is found in Orkney, where specimens are numerous but rather small in size, and the caterpillars, according to McArthur, feed on heather as well as on sallow. Decidedly uncommon in Ireland, and chiefly in the north (Donovan).

Abroad, the range is similar to that of *H. furcata* except that this species does not occur in Iceland.

The Brown Scallop (*Philereme vetulata* Schiff.)

The male is always smaller than the female, and is noticeable for its long body with tuft of hairs at the extremity. The wings in both sexes are dingy brown, or greyish brown, and the usual lines on fore wings are blackish, the space between first and second often dusky (Pl. 75, 5).

The caterpillar is short and stout, and in form very like

that of the winter moth; the back and a central dorsal stripe are black, the latter bordered with white, the sides are yellow ; the spiracular line is black, broken, and unconnected ; the spiracles are black; the head is black, and the edge of the first ring of the body is yellow. (Crewe.) It feeds, in May and June, on purging buckthorn (*Rhamnus catharticus*), and is to be found between two or more leaves, which it spins together as a hiding place.

In June and July the moth may sometimes be obtained by beating bushes of buckthorn, or the herbage below and around ; this plan works best when operated just before dusk. As a British insect it is found almost exclusively in England, and is most frequent in the southern and eastern counties, but widely distributed in the west to Worcester, and has been found in Lancashire, Westmorland, and Yorkshire. In the last-named county, caterpillars were obtained freely at Askham Bogs in 1900. Three specimens were taken in North Kerry in 1939.

When Stephens wrote of this insect in 1831 he noted its occurrence " in a lane near Fulham." In 1906 South obtained specimens on the Putney side of Wimbledon Common.

The range abroad extends to eastern Siberia.

The Dark Umber (*Philereme transversata* Hufn.)

The blackish oblique band on the fore wings of this ochreous brown species (Pl. 75, 3 ♂, 4 ♀) is sometimes indicated only by the blackish lines, the space between them being hardly darker than the general colour. Sometimes all the wings are suffused with blackish brown, and in such specimens the only distinct marking is the whitish submarginal line (ab. *haste-donensis* Lambill.).

The caterpillar is green, with three lines along the back, the central one dark green, and the others yellow ; the hind legs are marked with purple, and a stripe of the same colour runs along under the spiracles. In another form the general colour is greyish with a reddish brown stripe along the back and series of spots of the same colour along the sides. It may be found in May and June, concealed between buckthorn leaves fastened together to form a retreat (Pl. **73,** 1).

The moth flies in late June and in July, and may be disturbed in the daytime from buckthorn bushes. It is widely distributed, and often common in the south of England, but is rare in the north ; and has also been recorded from South Wales.

Note.—This species has also been known as *rhamnata* Schiff., but as *transversata* is an earlier name it will have to be adopted. Following Prout, both this and the preceding species are now placed in the genus *Philereme* Hübn.

The Tissue (*Triphosa dubitata* Linn.)

The fore wings of this glossy species (Pl. **75,** 1) are pale brown, tinged more or less strongly with rosy or purplish ; there are numerous darker and paler cross lines, the most distinct and constant being the blackish basal, and the two forming the edges of the central band ; the latter are marked with black ; the submarginal line is whitish, wavy, and sometimes broken up into dots. The species varies considerably in tint, some specimens inclining to pale greyish brown, others to smoky brown. Hind wings, whitish grey, with several darker grey cross lines ; in dark specimens these wings are smoky grey. Ab. *cinereata* Stephens, is a small pale greyish form, almost without rosy tinge and with fewer cross lines.

The caterpillar (Pl. **83,** 1) is yellowish green with darker green stripes and lines. In another form there are four pale yellowish lines along the back and a yellow stripe low down along the sides. It feeds on buckthorn (*Rhamnus*), the leaves of which it fastens together with silk, and so forms a retreat. It will also eat sloe and bird-cherry (*Prunus padus*).

The moth is out in August and through the autumn, when it sometimes visits the flowers of ivy, ragwort, etc. ; after hibernation it is again seen, perhaps even more frequently, in April and May, and is then occasionally found at sallow catkins. The species seems to have been noted from nearly all the English counties, but becomes rare from Yorkshire northwards. In Wales, and in Ireland, it is apparently widely distributed, but in Scotland it seems confined to southern localities, and is only rarely met with.

Abroad, the distribution spreads to Amurland, China, and Japan.

The Scarce Tissue (*Rheumaptera cervinalis* Scop.)

This species is very similar to the last, but the wings are not glossy, only reddish on the outer margin, and the black marked lines edging the central band of the fore wings are less irregular, the inner ones usually being much straighter. On the under side of the hind wings of the male is a fold enclosing hairs ; this is on the inner margin, just above the anal angle (Pl. **75**, 2).

The thickset caterpillar (Pl. **83**, 3, after Hofmann) is greyish inclining to greenish ; four white lines along the back, the central pair enclosing a dark line, the others are bordered below with dark greyish ; the black spiracles are set in yellowish blotches, and the plates on first and last rings are brown ; head, reddish brown, glossy (adapted from Fenn). It feeds on the barberry (*Berberis vulgaris*), *Berberis stenophylla*, and the holly-leaved barberry (*B. aquifolium*) grown in gardens, in June and July. The moth is out in May and June, but in favourable seasons has appeared in late April. When on the wing at night it is freely attracted by light, but otherwise not often noticed. The species has occurred in many of the English counties from Devon to Durham, but it seems to be only common in the eastern counties, and most frequent perhaps in Suffolk. It has been recorded from South Wales, but is seemingly absent from Ireland.

The range abroad extends to Amurland and Japan.

The Scallop Shell (*Rheumaptera undulata* Linn.)

Wings pale greyish, sometimes ochreous tinted, and crossed by numerous dark grey wavy lines inclining to blackish on the front margin of the fore wings ; the waves of the central pair of lines on the fore wings often meet and so form a series of rings ; sometimes the space between the eighth and twelfth lines is of a dusky hue, and occasionally it is distinctly darker and band-like ; the outer margin of all the wings is brownish and traversed by a wavy white line. The male has tufts of blackish hair in a fold on the inner margin of the hind wing, this is noticeable on the upper side, but is best seen from the under side (Pl. **75, 7**).

The somewhat dumpy caterpillar is reddish brown with four yellowish lines along the back ; a greyish stripe along the sides, and a creamy stripe along the black spiracles ; head, pale brown and glossy. It feeds on sallow, aspen, and bilberry, and may be found from August throughout the autumn in spun-together leaves at the tips of the shoots (Pl. **83,** 2).

The moth is out in June and July, and occurs in woods where there is a good growth of bilberry, or in marshy spots where sallow bushes abound.

In England the species is widely distributed over the southern and eastern counties ; its range extends through the Midlands to Cheshire, Lancashire, Cumberland, and Westmorland, rarely in Lincoln and Yorkshire, and once recorded in Durham ; it occurs in Wales and in Scotland, but only in the more southern part of each country. It is not plentiful in Ireland, but widely distributed. The range abroad includes northern and central Europe, Amurland, and also North America.

The Argent and Sable (*Rheumaptera hastata* Linn.)

About 1741 Wilkes figured this species as " The Mottled Beauty," but Harris in 1778 gave it its present English name. On Pl. **77** are shown two examples of the typical form

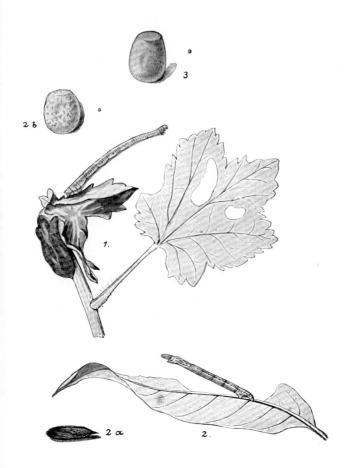

1. **The Spinach**: *caterpillar.*
2, 2a, 2b. **Chevron**: *eggs, natural size and enlarged, caterpillar and chrysalis.*
3. **The Phoenix**: *eggs, natural size and enlarged.*

1. The Tissue.

3, 4. Dark Umber.

2. Scarce Tissue.

5. Brown Scallop.
8. The Streak.
11. Broom-tip.

6. Chimney Sweeper.
9. Chimney Sweeper.
12. Grey Carpet.

7. Scallop Shell.
10. The Streak.
13. Broom-tip.

(Figs. 13, 15). As regards variation there is a considerable reduction of the black marking—so much so occasionally that of the central black band only a few dots remain around the discal spot, and perhaps a speck or two below it, and a dot or two on the inner margin (ab. *demolita* Prout). A smaller form with the white areas of the wings much reduced forms a race in some Scottish localities and is referable to *nigrescens* Cockerell (Pl. **77**, 16, 18) ; such specimens have frequently been mistaken for *R. subhastata* Nolcken, a species which does not seem to occur in the British Isles. The type of *nigrescens* is figured in Newman, " British Moths," p. 157, as a variety of *Melanippe hastata*.

The rather stumpy caterpillar is dark olive green, inclining to blackish, and somewhat shiny ; the skin along the sides puckered and marked with ochreous ; a black line along the middle of the back ; head, black and glossy. It feeds in July and August, later in the north, on *Vaccinium myrtillum* (bilberry), *V. uliginosum* (bog bilberry), *Myrica gale* (bog myrtle), birch, and sallow. It spins together the leaves at the tips of the twigs, and so forms a cocoon-like habitation. The moth is out in May and June, and even July in the north. It flies in the afternoon sunshine around and over birch trees, and occasionally alights on the leaves. It has been taken in Kent, and more frequently in Essex and Suffolk, but it is more plentiful in Oxfordshire and Berkshire, and from Surrey to Dorset and Wiltshire ; also in Herefordshire and Worcestershire, and on high ground in North Wales, Staffordshire, and Derbyshire ; its range extending through Cheshire and Lancashire to Cumberland and Northumberland, but only odd specimens have been reported from the last-named county and from Durham. The egg and the caterpillar are shown on Pl. **85**, 1, 1a.

It is widely distributed, and often common in places, throughout Scotland, including the Hebrides and the Shetlands. In Ireland it is local, but has occurred plentifully in some of its haunts in that country.

The range abroad spreads to Amurland, China, Iceland, Labrador, and North America.

The Grey Carpet (*Lithostege griseata* Schiff.)

The more or less greyish moth, shown on Pl. **75, 12,** varies in tint, some specimens being decidedly more grey than others. At the apex of the fore wings is a short blackish dash, and from this a curved dusky line may be traced to the inner margin. The female has the wings rather shorter than those of the male.

The slender, dark-lined, greenish caterpillar feeds on the seed pods of flixweed (*Sisymbrium*), and treacle mustard (*Erysimum*), in July and August. When reared in captivity it will thrive on other kinds of Cruciferae.

The moth is out in June, sometimes in late May ; it is exceedingly local in Britain, and only occurs in the Breck district, where it was first met with about 1860. Tuddenham, in Suffolk, is a noted locality, as also is Thetford, in Norfolk.

Abroad, the range extends through Europe to northern Persia and central Asia.

The Streak (*Chesias legatella* Schiff.)

The most striking features of this shining brownish coloured species are the oval-shaped marks on the cell area of the fore wings, and the long whitish streak running to the tips of the wings (Pl. **75,** 8 ♂, 10 ♀).

The long caterpillar (Pl. **68,** 2) is deep green, with a darker line along the middle of the back, and whitish lines along the sides and the under surface ; the spiracles are reddish, encircled with black, and the head is flecked with brown. It feeds in the spring on broom (*Cytisus scoparius*).

The moth is out in September and October, has been recorded flying by day, and may be found at night flying about the broom bushes for a short time, and later on it sits upon the twigs. It occurs in almost every part of the British Isles where the food plant of the caterpillar is well established.

Abroad, the range extends to central and south-western Europe.

The Broom-tip (*Chesias rufata* Fab.)

A noticeable character in this glossy, greyish moth (Pl. **75,** 11 ♂, 13 ♀) is the black mark on the upper part of the second cross line of the fore wings (which probably suggested the English name " Chevron " given to the species by Donovan) ; following the mark is a reddish or ochreous flush, extending to the tips of the wings.

The long, green caterpillar inclines to bluish above, and to paler green beneath ; a darker line along the middle of the back, then a slender whitish line edged with darker green, and between this and the white spiracular line there is another slender whitish line. It feeds, in August and September, on broom ; when full grown it enters the earth, and there turns to a reddish brown chrysalis, the wing cases of which are greenish. South was indebted to the late A. J. Scollick for the caterpillar and chrysalis figured on Pl. **68,** 1, 1*a*.

The moth emerges the following year, from May to July, but its time of appearance is uncertain, and it may come up in early spring or not until early autumn. Sometimes it will remain in the chrysalis for two winters.

In England the species occurs in the counties of Kent, Surrey, Sussex, Berkshire, Hampshire, Devon, Somerset, Hereford, Worcester, Stafford, Leicester, Cheshire (rare in the last five), Cumberland and Yorkshire (recorded once from each county), Norfolk, Suffolk ; also Glamorgan, and other parts of South Wales. In Scotland it is found in the south, but is more frequent from Perthshire to Moray. Probably occurs in other British localities where there is plenty of broom. In the Scottish race the ground colour is of a deeper bluish-grey ; it has been named subsp. *scotica* Richardson.

Abroad, the range extends through central and southern Europe to north-western Asia Minor. It also extends to North Africa.

The Chimney-sweeper (*Odezia atrata* Linn.)

This white-tipped but otherwise plain black moth (Pl. **75**, 6 ♂, 9 ♀) is very constant, and except that specimens after having been on the wing for a day or two become sooty brown, there is nothing much to note. It is the fringe at the tip of the fore wings rather than the tip itself that is white, and this sometimes extends for a short distance along the fringe of the outer margin. Haworth's English name for this insect (his *chaerophyllata*) was " The Looping Chimney Sweeper " in reference to its caterpillar, and to distinguish it from his " Chimney Sweeper," " Chimney Sweeper's Boy," and other oddities in the vernacular among the Psychids.

The caterpillar, which feeds in the spring on flowers of the earth-nut (*Conopodium denudatum*, or *Bunium flexuosum*), is green, and paler on the sides than on the back ; there are three darker green lines along the back, the central one merging into reddish on the last ring, and the others narrowly edged on each side with white ; a whitish stripe runs below the red spiracles.

The moth is a sun lover, and flits about flowers growing among or near its food plant, in June and July.

The species is widely distributed over England, Wales, Ireland, and Scotland, but it does not appear to have been noted north of Moray in the last-named country. It is always very local, frequents moist fields, borders of woods, and even waysides.

The range abroad extends to Amurland.

The Lesser Treble-bar (*Anaitis efformata* Guenée)

Dr. K. Jordan (1923, *Nov. Zool.*, 30 : 243) was the first to

1. **Common Marbled Carpet:** *caterpillar.*
2. **Dark Marbled Carpet:** *caterpillar.*
3. **Barred Yellow:** *caterpillar.*

1. The
Treble-bar.

2. The
Treble-bar.

3. Lesser
Treble-bar.

4. Manchester
Treble-bar.

5. Lesser
Treble-bar.

6. Common
Carpet.

7. Common
Carpet
(ssp. *obscurata*).

8. Common
Carpet.

9. Galium
Carpet.

10. Wood
Carpet.

11. Galium
Carpet.

12. Small Argent
and Sable.

13. Argent
and Sable.

15. Argent
and Sable.

14. Small Argent
and Sable.

16. Argent
and Sable
(ssp. *nigrescens*).

17. Small Argent
and Sable.

18. Argent
and Sable
(ssp. *nigrescens*).

confirm *A. efformata* as a good species, distinct from *A. plagiata* with which it had long been confused. *A. efformata* can usually be distinguished superficially by its smaller size, on the average paler coloration, generally slightly straighter ante-median band on the fore wing and perhaps more obtuse angulation of the postmedian line. The males may be distinguished readily by the claspers which, in *efformata*, are short, blunt, and elbowed in the middle, but in *plagiata* are long (six times as long as broad), narrow, and pointed. In the females the last abdominal segment is shorter and rounder than in *plagiata* in which it extends well beyond the level of the hind wings and is generally bent downwards (Pl. **77**, 3, 5).

The larva, which is indistinguishable from *plagiata*, except for its smaller size and perhaps lighter coloration, feeds on *Hypericum*.

In England, it occurs westward as far as Dorset and north-wards as far as Selby in Yorkshire. It is double brooded and flies at the same time and often with *plagiata*.

Abroad, the range extends through central and southern Europe, North Africa, and Asia Minor.

The Treble-bar (*Anaitis plagiata* Linn.)

This is a greyish white species, of which specimens of both sexes are shown on Pl. **77**, 1 ♂, 2 ♀. The chief variation is in the cross central bars of the fore wings which are sometimes much widened, and occasionally joined from the middle to the inner margin (ab. *fasciata* Garbsk.); or the space between these two bars is more or less filled up with dark grey.

The long caterpillar is brown, inclining to reddish or to greenish, with several darker and paler lines on the back and a yellowish line low down along the sides. It feeds on St. John's wort (*Hypericum*) in June and July; the caterpillars, hatching in the autumn, are not mature until the following April.

Usually there are two generations of the moth, the first appearing in May and June, and the second in August and September. The species is pretty generally distributed over the British Isles, extending to the Hebrides and the Orkneys ; and will probably be found in all localities where its food plant occurs freely. It affects cliffs and sandhills by the sea, rough places on chalk slopes, and sometimes the moths fly up in numbers as we walk over the herbage in such spots. The Scottish race differs in its blue-grey colouring and has been named subsp. *scotica* Richardson.

The range abroad extends to Western India and Japan.

The Manchester Treble-bar (*Carsia sororiata* subsp. *anglica* Prout)

In general character this species somewhat resembles that last considered. It is, however, much smaller, and there are reddish clouds on the outer marginal area.

This reddish shading is more or less absent in the type, which is otherwise less variegated than *anglica*, the subspecies to which our British specimens are referable (Pl. **77,** 4).

The caterpillar is of somewhat stoutish build, and reddish brown in colour ; three darker lines along the back, and yellow stripe low down along the sides, the latter edged above with black on the front three rings, and blotched with pinkish on the middle rings ; the head is rather paler than the body, and the dots on the latter are yellow. It feeds on cowberry (*Vaccinium vitis-idaea*), bilberry (*V. myrtillus*), and cranberry (*V. oxycoccos*), and seems to have a preference for the flowers of these plants : April to June.

The moth is out in July and August among the *Vaccinium* in its swampy haunts on the heaths and moors of the north of England, and Scotland, including the Hebrides, even to the Shetlands. It is known from the Isle of Man and also occurs in North Ireland. In England it does not seem to have been noted south of Staffordshire.

The range abroad extends to eastern Siberia, Amurland, and North America.

The Common Carpet (*Epirrhoë alternata* Müll.)

The white ground colour of this species is nearly always obscured, to a greater or lesser extent, by greyish markings and suffusions on the basal area ; the outer margin is broadly bordered with dark grey, and the white band between this and the dark grey central band is intersected throughout its length by a grey line (Pl. **77,** 6, 8). The central band varies in width ; it is often contracted below the middle (ab. *tenuifasciata* Schima), sometimes completely severed at this point (ab. *divisa* Osthelder), and in ab. *degenerata* Haw., both portions are much reduced in width. Pl. **77,** 7 represents a specimen from the Isle of Lewis ; this brownish grey example is of the Hebridean subsp. *obscurata* South. There are intermediate modifications leading up to a form in which the whole of the central third of the fore wings is whitish, with the usual cross lines dingy grey, and some tiny clouds of the same colour around the black discal spot.

The caterpillar is very like that of the last species referred to, but it is rather smaller in size and rougher in appearance. There is variation in the general colour, from pale fawn through greenish brown, to dull or bright green, and sometimes the markings are tinged with reddish (Hellins).

It feeds on bedstraw in June and July, and a second brood occurs in September. The figure of the brownish, inclining to reddish, chrysalis (Pl. **85,** 4), is from a photo by the late H. Main, and is twice the natural size.

The moth is out in May and June, and, in the south especially, again in August and September. It is generally distributed over the British Islands, but so far has not been noted from the Shetlands.

The range abroad extends to eastern Siberia, Amurland, North America, and Iceland.

The Wood Carpet (*Epirrhoë rivata* Hübn.)

The broad, clear white borders of both edges of the dark central band of the fore wings, coupled with the clearer white of the hind wings, and the generally larger size of the moth, should distinguish this species from its very close ally, *alternata* ; but it must be added that some forms of the latter species approach the present one exceedingly close (Pl. **77,** 10).

The caterpillar is brown or olive brown, dotted and freckled with white ; three lines on the back, the central one black, the others whitish, not seen on rings 5–8, which have dark V-shaped marks enclosing white ones ; sometimes there is a V-mark instead of lines on ring 4 ; head, large, pale brown sprinkled with blackish, and marked with a blackish V, the apex of which appears to meet the central line of the body. It feeds, at night, in August, on bedstraw (*Galium mollugo*, and *G. verum*), but will thrive very well on cleavers or goose-grass (*G. aparine*). The chrysalis, which is enclosed in a cocoon of silk coated with earth, is reddish brown, thorax and wing-cases paler, shining. A coloured drawing of the caterpillar, kindly lent, with others, for this volume, by the late A. Sich, has been used for the figures on Pl. **85,** 2, 2*a* ; but the description of the caterpillar, and also of the chrysalis (Pl. **85,** 2*b*), are from material that Mr. Pope, of Exeter, was good enough to furnish. In captivity a second brood may be reared in August.

The moth is out in July and early August, and although local, is not uncommon in bushy places on downs, etc., also in lanes, in chalk districts, in most of the southern and eastern counties. In the north of England it is far more local and uncommon, but is known to occur in Cheshire, Yorkshire, and Cumberland, and has been recorded from Durham. It is found in Wales, and in Scotland has been noted as very local in Roxburghshire and rare in Clydesdale and Arran. Donovan states that in Ireland it is " very rare " ; Galway, King's Co., and Cork.

1. Cloaked
Pug.

2. Cloaked
Pug.

3. Shaded
Pug.

4. Yarrow
Pug.

5. Thyme
Pug.

6. Plain
Pug.

7. Slender
Pug.

8. Maple
Pug.

9. Haworth's
Pug.

10. Lead-
Coloured
Pug.

11. Foxglove
Pug.

12. Foxglove
Pug.

13. Foxglove
Pug
(ssp. *hebudium*).

14. Toadflax
Pug.

15. Marbled
Pug.

16. Pinion-
spotted
Pug.

17. Mottled
Pug.

18. Valerian
Pug.

19. Netted
Pug.

20. Netted
Pug
(ssp. *ochracae*).

21. Marsh
Pug.

22. Triple-
spotted
Pug.

23. Netted
Pug
(ssp. *fumosae*).

24. Netted
Pug
(ssp. *fumosae*).

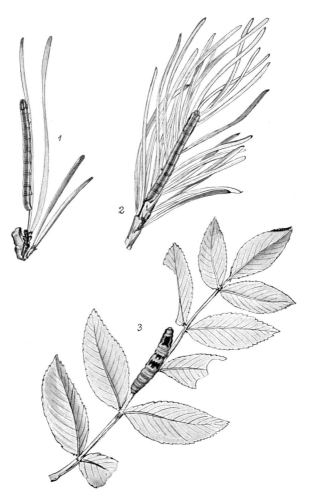

1. **Grey Pine Carpet:** *caterpillar.*
2. **Pine Carpet:** *caterpillar.*
3. **Welsh Wave:** *caterpillar.*

Abroad, the range extends through central and southern Europe to central Asia.

The Galium Carpet (*Epirrhoë galiata* Schiff.)

The more usual forms of this species are represented on Pl. **77**, 9, 11. Fig. 9 is the portrait of a form occurring in Yorkshire, Sussex, Devon, and probably elsewhere, in which the central band is blackish and solid-looking ; this seems to be referable to ab. *chalybeata* Hübn. Besides varying in tint of ground colour, and in the amount of freckling or mottling, there is modification in the width of the central band.

The caterpillar is brown, dotted with black, and striped with blackish brown on the back, and with pale brown on the sides ; the head is light brown, sprinkled with black, and marked with a dark V. It feeds on bedstraw in late June and July, and there is a second brood in August and September. The figure of the caterpillar on Pl. **85,** 3, is from a coloured drawing by the late A. Sich.

The moth is out in June, sometimes later in the north and earlier in the south, where it occurs as a second generation in August. It is chiefly found in chalk and limestone districts, and may be easily put up from the herbage among which it secretes itself during the day. In the seaboard counties of England, from Kent to Cornwall, it is especially common on the coast, but is also to be met with in suitable inland localities in these counties, and also in Surrey, Middlesex, Hertfordshire, Buckinghamshire, and Oxfordshire. It is always rare on the eastern side, but on the west, including Wales, it is more or less frequent from Somerset and Wiltshire to Westmorland. Not uncommon in Yorkshire, principally in the West Riding, and an odd specimen has been recorded from Durham. Somewhat rare in Scotland, but it has been noted in Berwick, Wigtown, Arran, Clydesdale, the Isle of Canna, and Perthshire to Moray. In Ireland it is local, although often plentiful on the coast.

Abroad, the range extends to eastern Siberia.   Southwards it extends to North Africa.

The Small Argent and Sable (*Epirrhoë tristata* Linn.)

On Pl. **77** are shown three examples of this variable species. Figs. 12, 14 represent the typical form.   Fig. 17 is a black-marked specimen from Yorkshire.   All these have the central band more or less entire, but this character may be broader or narrower, and is sometimes divided into two parts (ab. *interrupta* Heinrich), and these reduced to very small proportions ; the white projections into the outer marginal border of all the wings is not infrequently enlarged, in some cases so much so that the borders are separated into two parts, and also reduced in width.

The caterpillar is grey brown, ochreous brown between the rings and on the underside ; a dark line along the back, and a dark-edged, pale line on each side ; a black dot on each ring at the junction of the dark upper and pale lower areas ; head, grey brown, with blackish freckles. It feeds, in July and August, on bedstraw, preferring the heath kind (*Galium saxatile*), but will eat the large hedge kind (*G. mollugo*).

The moth is out in June, or from late May, and in some parts specimens are seen in August. Its haunts are moors and upland heaths, and its British distribution extends from Dartmoor and Exmoor, in Devon, through western England and Wales to Westmorland.   It appears to be very local in Somerset, Gloucestershire, Herefordshire, Montgomery, Shropshire, and Cheshire ; from Staffordshire and Derbyshire northwards, and through Scotland, it becomes more plentiful ; and has been recorded from the Shetlands.   In Ireland it is local, but common where it occurs.

Abroad, the range extends through northern and central Europe to Armenia, central Asia, and Mongolia. It extends also to North America.

The Slender-striped Rufous (*Coenocalpe lapidata* Hübn.)

The rather pointed fore wings are pale brownish, and are crossed by several fine wavy and rather darker lines, and three more distinct, slightly curved lines, one of which is at the base and two are on the central area. The outer margin of the hind wings, which are pale brown, more or less shaded with dusky, is irregular (Pl. **87**, 1).

Caterpillar, whitish yellow above, inclining to pale buff below ; lines of grey freckles along the back and sides, the lower one broader and darker ; head, grey, freckled with darker. According to Hellins, who reared it from the egg, it feeds in May and June, on traveller's joy (*Clematis vitalba*). The natural food is doubtful, but is said to be grass. In France the caterpillar is said to feed on *Thalictrum* sp.

The moth is out in September and early October, and is found in Scotland on the hills, in rough grassy and rush-covered spots, at elevations ranging from 300 to 800 feet. In Ireland, it is not uncommon in Antrim, Donegal, Fermanagh, Sligo, Mayo, and Galway. Barrett states that a specimen has been taken at Shap Fell in Westmorland.

Abroad, the range extends to eastern Siberia.

The Dentated Pug (*Anticollix sparsata* Tr.)

At one time this greyish brown species (Pl. **87**, 12, 15) was known by the English name of " Broom Scallop," but it is now usually referred to, in the vulgar tongue, as the Dentated Pug. The hind wings have their outer margins toothed rather than scalloped, and the insect has nothing to do with broom.

The rather long caterpillar is pale green, with four white lines along the back, and one on each side ; a whitish stripe along the black spiracles. Head, pale brown, rather flat above. (Adapted from Porritt.) It feeds on the yellow loosestrife (*Lysimachia vulgaris*), in July and August, or even later. Fens and marshy woodlands are the haunts of the moth, which is out in June and early July. It hides among the coarser vegetation, and is not always easily disturbed therefrom ; neither is it often noticed when on the wing at night, although it is sometimes found at the flowers of buckthorn.

Localities for the species are the fens of Cambridgeshire, Huntingdonshire, and Norfolk, the boggy parts of the New Forest, Hampshire ; Dorset (Bloxworth and Hyde, etc.) ; Cheshire (Delamere Forest) ; Yorkshire (bogs near York, and Thorne Waste).

The range abroad extends to Japan.

The Small Waved Umber (*Horisme vitalbata* Schiff.)

At first sight this moth (Pl. **87,** 2) might be mistaken for a small specimen of the Waved Umber (*Menophra abruptaria*), but it will be noted that the dark stripe on the fore wings starts from the middle of the inner margin, and runs to just below the tips of the wings ; the outer margin of the hind wings is not wavy, and the antennae of the male are not pectinated.

The caterpillar, which feeds on traveller's joy (*Clematis vitalba*), in June–July, and in September–October, is greyish brown, with three blackish lines along the back, the central one broader than the other two, especially on the middle of each ring, where it swells out into a black spot.

In May and June, and again in August, the moth may be disturbed from the food plant growing in masses in hedgerows, etc. It occurs in most of the southern counties of England, westward to Herefordshire and South Wales, and eastward to Suffolk. Forsythe states that it is local in the Lancaster district.

The range abroad extends to Amurland and Japan.

The Cumbrian Umber (*Horisme aquata* Hübn.)

In 1882 J. W. Tutt was sent five specimens of this species, which had been standing in a collection in Cumberland as pale aberrations of *vitalbata* (*Ent. Rec.*, 1900, xii. 35, 82, 85). They bore no data labels and their place of capture is uncertain, though it was believed to have been the Lake District, possibly in Cumberland. Since that date four other specimens have been found in old British collections. Three are without data labels and the fourth is labelled " Sherwood Forest," though this locality was considered by Dr. Cockayne to be a most unlikely one (*Ent. Rec.*, 1952, lxiv. 73–5 (Pl. **87, 4**).

The moth, compared with *H. vitalbata*, is smaller and paler with a straighter postmedian line and with the abdomen pale grey instead of dark brown.

The larva feeds on *Anemone pulsatilla* and *A. ranunculoides* and will also eat *Clematis vitalba*.

Abroad the range extends through Europe to central Asia and northern China.

The Fern (*Horisme tersata* Schiff.)

The general colour of this species (Pl. **87, 3**) is pale brown, with a tendency to reddish in some specimens, and to greyish in others.

Caterpillar, pale brownish inclining to ochreous ; on each side of an irregular blackish line along the centre of the back is a pale yellowish line, and there are white spots on the back of the middle rings. It feeds on *Ranunculus* and *Clematis* in August and September. The moth is out in June and July, and will be found in similar localities to those mentioned for *H. vitalbata* and, except that it has not been recorded from Lancaster, its range in England is much about the same.

The distribution abroad extends to Japan.

The Cloaked Pug (*Eupithecia pini* Retzius)

In mid-June, 1845, this fine pug (Pl. **78, 1, 2**) was detected in England. It was first noted in a plantation of spruce fir at Black Park, Buckinghamshire, and for many years this was the only known British locality. At the present time it is obtained more or less regularly in the New Forest, and has been recorded, chiefly in single specimens, from Wilt-shire, Essex, Cambridgeshire, Suffolk, Yorkshire, and Durham. It is not uncommon in Scotland up to Inverness, but is most plentiful in Perthshire.

Kane (*Catalogue of the Lepidoptera of Ireland*) states that it is spreading over an extensive area in Ireland, as a result of the planting of spruce fir.

The caterpillar, which feeds in the spruce cones, and eats the immature seeds, is dingy white with a pinkish tinge, and suffused with blackish above ; the lines along the back and sides, when present, are whitish but not distinct ; head, and raised dots on the body, black ; a brown plate on the first ring : July and August. Cones containing caterpillars may be secured by visiting a known locality for the species towards the end of August, especially immediately after a gale.

The moth may be dislodged from its resting place among the branches of the spruce in June, sometimes earlier or later.

Abroad, the range includes North America, central and northern Europe, and Amurland.

The Shaded Pug (*Eupithecia subumbrata* Schiff.)

The grey, or greyish brown lined, whitish species shown on Pl. **78,** 3, has been known by three names in Britain. It was named and described by Stephens, in 1831, as *piperata* (The Speckled Pug), from a specimen, or specimens, taken at Riddlesdown, near Croydon, Surrey ; later, it was considered to be the *subumbrata*, of the *Vienna Catalogue* (1775) ; in any case it is certainly that of Guenée. It is also the *scabiosata* of Borkhausen.

Crewe describes the caterpillar as yellowish green, with three dark lines on the back, the outer one not clearly defined ; a yellow line on each side of the head, and of the last ring of the body.

It feeds on flowers of one of the hawkbits (*Leontodon hispidus*), and hawk's-beard (*Crepis taraxacifolia*), etc., from

July to September. In June, and early July, the moth may be started up from the herbage, as the collector walks over rough ground inland, or more frequently on the coast. It also occurs in fens, marshy places in woods, etc.

The species occurs in Wiltshire, Buckinghamshire, Berkshire, Hertfordshire, Surrey, and in the seaboard counties from Norfolk in the east to Gloucestershire in the west, also in South Wales ; in the north it is found in Lancashire, Yorkshire, Durham, and Northumberland. It is not common in Scotland, but has been reported from various parts, extending from Wigtown to Argyll and Aberdeen. In Ireland it is also a coast insect, from Donegal to Cork.

Abroad, the range extends throughout Europe to central Asia.

The Yarrow Pug (*Eupithecia millefoliata* Rössler)

The first example of this new addition to the British *Eupi thecias* was taken at Ham Street in Kent by Dr. C. de Worms and another was taken at Sandwich in Kent on July 15, 1939, but their identity was not established until the late nineteen-forties. In the autumn of 1947, seed heads of *Achillea mille-folium* were gathered at Ramsgate for the purpose of rearing specimens of *Phalonia dipoltella* Hübn., and the following year, in addition to the micros, there emerged also from these seed heads three further specimens of *E. millefoliata*.

In build and wing-shape it is similar to *subnotata* and as in that species, the areole is divided. The wings are rough-scaled, grey mottled with white, brownish grey and blackish grey ; the transverse lines are fine and numerous (Pl. **78**, 4).

The larva is rugose and deeply segmented. The head is elongate, somewhat flattened and small. The spiracles are strongly developed, white ringed with dark brown. The ground colour is sandy brown suffused with yellowish white and brownish grey, with a V-shaped dark brown medio-dorsal marking, pointed anteriorly, on segments two to ten. Sub-dorsal stripe broadened in the middle of each segment, wavy, grey brown. Completely unmarked examples are rare. It feeds on the flowers and seeds of milfoil (*Achillea millefolium*) in August and September but by day it usually hides amongst or beneath the flower and seed clusters. The larva has been figured by Mr. G. Haggett in *Proc. S. Lond. ent. & nat. Hist. Soc.*, 1955: 159, pl. 8: 2a–2f (1957).

The moth flies in June and July. In England it occurs along the south coast from Kent to Hampshire and has been recorded from the inland localities of Canterbury, Ham Street, and Lewes ; it has also been recorded from Essex ; its range abroad extends through central and southern Europe, Armenia, Asia Minor, and eastwards to the Urals.

The Plain Pug (*Eupithecia subnotata* Hübn.)

The fore wings of this species are pale ochreous brown, inclining to pale reddish on the outer marginal area ; the most distinct markings are a pale cross band beyond the black discal dot, and a pale winding submarginal line. The hind wings are smoky grey, with whitish wavy cross lines, the most distinct being the outer (Pl. **78,** 6). The stoutish and somewhat stumpy caterpillar is green, or pale yellowish brown, with three darker lines and marks on the back ; a yellowish line low down on the sides. It feeds on flowers and seeds of orache (*Atriplex*), and goosefoot (*Chenopodium*) : August and September, figured on Pl. **86,** 1, 1a, from coloured drawings by the late A. Sich. In July, the moth may be disturbed from its food plant or adjacent herbage, or it may be seen resting on palings or fences. It flies at night, and will come to light.

Not uncommon in many places in the southern half of England, and found in the rest of the country, chiefly on the coast, to Hartlepool in Durham, also in Wales. Once recorded from south Scotland, and noted from the coast near Dublin ; from Wicklow, also at Lurgan, Armagh, in Ireland.

Abroad the range extends through Europe to Asia Minor.

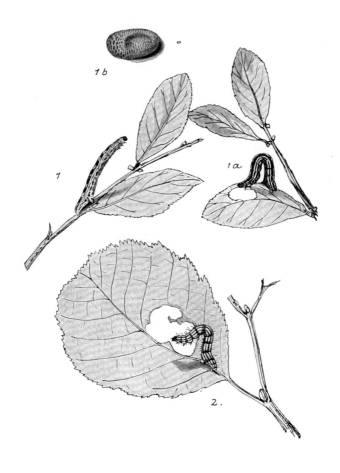

1, 1a, 1b. **July Highflyer:** *eggs, natural size and enlarged, and caterpillars.*
2. **May Highflyer:** *caterpillar.*

1. Lime-
speck
Pug.

2. Lime-
speck
Pug.

3. Edinburgh
Pug
(ssp. *arceuthata*).

4. Edinburgh
Pug
(ssp. *millieraria*).

5. Edinburgh
Pug
(ssp. *arceuthata*).

6. Satyr
Pug.

7. Satyr
Pug
(ssp. *curzoni*).

8. Satyr
Pug
(ssp. *callunaria*).

9. White-
spotted
Pug.

10. Wormwood
Pug.

11. Wormwood
Pug.

12. Ochreous
Pug.

13. Currant
Pug.

14. Bleached
Pug.

15. Ling
Pug.

16. Wormwood
Pug.

17. Wormwood
Pug.

18. Common
Pug.

19. Common
Pug.

20. Common
Pug.

The Thyme Pug (*Eupithecia distinctaria* subsp. *constrictata* Guenée)

This delicately marked species (Pl. **78**, 5), has the fore wings whitish grey, with three slender blackish curved cross lines, and some less distinct greyish ones ; the outer margin is slightly darker, and traversed by a wavy whitish line ; discal spot black and conspicuous.

South had not seen specimens from the Hebrides, but, according to Barrett, these have a more decided grey tint.

The rather long, wrinkled caterpillar is dark green, inclining to yellowish between the rings, with a broad purplish red line along the back. It feeds on the flowers of wild thyme (*Thymus serpyllum*), in August and September.

The moth is out in June and July, and inhabits dry places where there is an abundant growth of wild thyme. It is easily alarmed, and quickly rises on the wing from its hiding-place among the herbage.

The species is, or has been, found in most of the southern counties of England, from Sussex to Cornwall, on the western side from Somerset to Westmorland, including North Wales and the Isle of Man ; also recorded from Buckinghamshire, Yorkshire (Richmond), and Northumberland. In Scotland it occurs chiefly on the west to Sutherland, and in the Hebrides ; in Ireland it is widely spread, but most frequently met with on the coast.

Abroad, the range extends through Europe and Asia Minor to Transcaspia, and southwards to North Africa.

The Slender Pug (*Eupithecia tenuiata* Hübn.)

The fore wings are rather rounded ; grey, more or less tinged with brownish, and with ochreous or reddish brown along the front edge ; the latter with dusky clouds upon it ; the cross lines are dark grey brown and fairly distinct, and the discal spot is black (Pl. **78**, 7). A melanic form, bred from a larva taken in north-east England, has been named ab. *johnsoni* Harrison.

Caterpillar, rather stumpy, and dingy yellowish green in colour, the sides and middle of the back rosy ; a series of dusky spots, edged by black lines or short streaks, along the back; and a row of pinkish oblique stripes on the sides. It feeds, in the spring, in sallow catkins, and the moths may often be bred in numbers, in June and July, from those catkins which fall most readily from the bushes when we go " a-sallowing." Moths frequently rest on the stems, and where there is a clump of well-grown sallows, a good series may be obtained.

The species is partial to fens and marshy places, and is found in such situations over the greater part of the British Isles, including the Isle of Man and the Hebrides.

Abroad, this species is distributed in central and northern Europe, and also noted from Transcaucasia.

The Maple Pug (*Eupithecia inturbata* Hübn.)

The fore wings are greyish brown, with many darker cross lines ; the outer margin is darker and traversed by a pale line ; discal dot, dark grey and not very distinct (Pl. **78**, 8). This species was long known as *subciliata* Dbldy., but is now referred to *inturbata* Hübn.

In May and June the caterpillars may be beaten from maple, which is apparently the only food plant, and of which they have a decided preference for the flowers. When full grown, and just prior to pupation, the larva is yellowish green with a purplish stripe along the back, and whitish lines along the sides.

The moth may be jarred from the branches of the maple in July and August ; it is occasionally seen resting on fences, etc. It seems to be found in England and Wales, in most places where there is a mature growth of maple.

Abroad, the range extends through central Europe.

Haworth's Pug (*Eupithecia haworthiata* Dbldy.)

The fore wings of this species (Pl. **78**, 9) are pale greyish, with dark cross lines, and still darker narrow bands ; hind wings, similar, but markings less distinct. Resembles *sub-umbrata* in size, but the wings are somewhat rounder, darker, and not so silky in appearance ; the body, near the thorax, is ochreous brown. Also known as *isogrammaria* H.Sch., but *haworthiata* Dbldy., is stated by Prout to be the older name.

In July and August the caterpillar (Pl. **92,** 3) may be found in the flower-buds of the traveller's joy or old man's beard (*Clematis vitalba*). It is green, with a bluish or pinkish tinge, and there are generally three darker stripes along the back, but these are sometimes absent ; occasionally the ground colour is yellowish.

The moth is out in June and July, and may be seen flying about *Clematis* in the sunshine, but such specimens are not often worth taking. It is easily reared from caterpillars, which will thrive on flowers of garden *Clematis*, and may be obtained by the score, either by beating, or by searching for discoloured or black-specked flower buds of the traveller's joy.

The species is most frequent in the south of England, but it occurs in all the eastern, some of the midland, and also in the northern counties to Lancashire and Yorkshire ; in the last-named county, Porritt states that the caterpillars were found in profusion on *Clematis* near Wadworth, Doncaster, in 1901. It inhabits South Wales and Ireland.

Abroad, the species ranges to Amurland and China.

The Lead-coloured Pug (*Eupithecia plumbeolata* Haw.)

The small, obscurely marked species, represented on Pl. **78,** 10, has the fore wings whitish grey, sometimes assuming a yellowish tinge ; a number of rather wavy, darker cross lines, and a more or less clearly defined pale band beyond the middle ; discal spots always tiny and rarely distinct.

The stumpy caterpillar is yellowish green, with three pur-plish red lines along the back, the central one swollen on each ring, and the others irregular ; sometimes the back is suffused with purplish red. It feeds on the flowers of cow-wheat (*Melampyrum*) and yellow rattle in July and August.

The moth is out in May and June, and is readily induced to fly out from among cow-wheat, or the other herbage around. It may be found in most of the English counties, wherever its food plant abounds ; in South Wales and in Merionethshire in N. Wales ; in Scotland to Sutherland, and in Ireland from Cork to Donegal.

The range abroad extends to Amurland.

The Toadflax Pug (*Eupithecia linariata* Schiff.)

Very similar to the next species, but generally smaller, neater and more glossy looking. The central band of the fore wing is blacker, without ochreous clouding below the middle, and the edges are not wavy. The hind wings are darker, and the only distinct band is a whitish one beyond the middle (Pl. **78**, 14). Ab. *nigrofasciata* Dietze is darkened with an almost solidly black median band.

The caterpillar is yellowish green, with a series of dull olive or rust coloured spots or bars along the back, bordered on each side by a dusky olive line ; in some examples the markings are absent (Crewe). It feeds in the flowers of yellow toadflax (*Linaria vulgaris*), and may be reared on flowers of the snap-dragon (*Antirrhinum*). It is hardly necessary to examine each blossom separately to find the caterpillar, except, per-haps, to make sure when doubtful about the quarry being there. Probably, a handful of the flower sprays gathered in August or September in any locality in the southern half of England where the food plant abounds would furnish moths in the following May or June. The *Linaria* should be secured on a dry day for choice, but when brought home it need not be put in water ; just throw it into an airy breeding cage, and hopefully await emergence of the perfect insects in due course. Sometimes caterpillars attain the moth state the same year.

The range of the species in England extends to Durham,

1. Pimpinel
Pug.

2. Grey
Pug.

3. Grey
Pug.

4. Campanula
Pug.

5. Campanula
Pug
(ssp. *jasioneata*).

6. Campanula
Pug
(ssp. *jasioneata*).

7. Tawny-Speckled
Pug
(ssp. *oxydata*).

8. Tawny Speckled
Pug
(ssp. *subfulvata*).

9. Tawny Speckled
Pug
(ssp. *cognata*).

10. Bordered
Pug.

11. Scarce
Pug.

12. Larch
Pug.

13. Angle-
barred Pug.

14. Ash
Pug.

15. Angle-
barred Pug.

1. **The Tissue:** *caterpillar*.
2. **Scallop Shell:** *caterpillar*.
3. **Scarce Tissue:** *caterpillar*.

but it seems to be rather uncommon from the Midlands north-wards. It is found in Wales, and has been recorded once from Scotland (Inverurie), and once from Ireland (Dublin) and from Tyrone.

Abroad, the range extends through Europe and Asia Minor to Transcaucasia.

The Foxglove Pug (*Eupithecia pulchellata* Steph.)

The fore wings are pale ochreous brown with a dusky basal patch limited by a black line ; a greyish central band inclining to blackish near the costa, and clouded with ochreous below the middle ; the black-and-white edges are wavy ; a reddish stripe across the wing before the central band, and a similar, but more irregular, one beyond the band. The hind wings are whitish grey, with several dark grey bands (Pl. **78**, 11 ♂, 12 ♀).

In subsp. *hebudium* Sheldon, from the Hebrides, the usual reddish stripes are replaced by narrower dark brown ones ; the space left by the reduction in width is white, giving the insect a decidedly grey appearance. Specimens of this form have also been recorded from Co. Cork (Pl. **78**, 13).

The caterpillar lives in the flowers of the foxglove (*Digitalis purpurea*) and feeds therein upon the stamens and the imma-ture seeds. It enters by boring through the side walls, and then secures the longer lobe of the blossom to the shorter upper one with a few silken threads. Tenanted flowers have a rather faded look and are easily detected. July is the best month, but the caterpillar may be found earlier as well as later.

The moth is out in May and June, and is found in almost every part of the British Isles where the foxglove is common.

Abroad, the range extends through central Europe east-wards to the Urals and southwards to North Africa.

The Marbled Pug (*Eupithecia irriguata* Hübn.)

The fore wings are whitish and rather shining, the discal spot is black and very distinct, but the dark grey-brown

o—VOL. 2

markings, which are only well defined on the front and outer marginal areas, vary in intensity (Pl. **78,** 15).

The long, slender and roughened caterpillar is dull yellowish green ; three lines along the back, the central one reddish and expanded on the middle rings, the others yellowish ; head, reddish. It feeds on oak, in late May and in June. The moth is out in April and May, and is sometimes found on fences or palings in the neighbourhood of oak woods, but may be jarred from the oak boughs, on the undersides of which it usually sits.

The New Forest in Hampshire is, perhaps, the best British locality for the species, but it has been found in Dorset (Glanville's Wootton), Devon (Exeter district, Tiverton, etc.), Sussex (Abbots Wood, St. Leonard's Forest, etc.), Wiltshire (Savernake Forest) ; also oak woods in Surrey, Berkshire, Gloucestershire, Herefordshire, and Glamorgan. On the eastern side it occurs in Suffolk (Bury and Needham), and Norfolk. In 1958 it was recorded from Fifeshire.

Abroad, it occurs locally in central and southern Europe, North Africa, and Kurdistan.

The Mottled Pug (*Eupithecia exiguata* Hübn.)

In some respects this species (Pl. **78,** 17) is not unlike *E. abbreviata*, but in the typical race the general colour of the fore wings is pale grey inclining to brownish ; a good character is the blackish band before the submarginal line, which is interrupted by patches of the ground colour, one above, and the other below, the middle ; the submarginal line is whitish towards the inner margin.

Some specimens bred by Dr. Cockayne from larvae obtained in East Aberdeenshire on *Pyrus aucuparia* appear to be a well-differentiated local race and were described as such by Prout under the name *muricolor*. The specimens are distinct in colour, of a very cold grey, tinged scarcely, if at all, with brownish ; the markings are rather strong, especially the dark spots at the bases of the abdomen, the fore and the hind wings. The fuscous subterminal patches are also prominently marked.

Caterpillar, long and thin ; dark green ; a series of yellow dotted reddish marks on the back, and a yellow-edged reddish line low down along the sides. It feeds, in the autumn, on hawthorn, sloe, currant, sallow, ash, etc.

The moth is out in May and June, and is sometimes seen at rest on the stems and branches of trees, fences, etc., and may be beaten out of hedgerows.

Widely distributed throughout England, Wales, Scotland to Perthshire, and Ireland.

Abroad, the range extends to central and northern Europe.

The Pinion-spotted Pug (*Eupithecia insigniata* Hübn.)

The greyish white fore wings have a blackish basal line, and three slender double lines between this and the outer margin ; three blotches on the front margin of the wings, the middle one blackish, the others brown with dashes of the same colour below ; discal spot, black and streak-like (Pl. **78**, 16).

The long, slightly roughened caterpillar is green, inclining to yellowish, especially between the rings ; reddish marks on the back connected by a slender line of the same colour ; head, green, flecked with reddish. It feeds, on apple, eating flowers and leaves, in May and June. Also said to eat hawthorn and sloe. The moth is out in April and May, but it is rarely met with in the open. If, however, one is lucky enough to capture a female, and fertile eggs are obtained, moths should hardly fail to result. From these the stock might go on increasing year by year for quite a long period. Ten specimens presented to the National Collection of British Lepidoptera in 1904, by the late Mrs. Hutchinson, were bred in April of the previous year, and were the direct descendants of a female captured in 1874, at Grantsfield, Herefordshire.

Other counties in England from which the species has

been recorded are—Worcester (Birchwood), Gloucester, Somerset, Wiltshire, Hampshire (Hayling Island), Sussex, Surrey, Kent, Berkshire, Buckingham, Huntingdon, Cambridge (once bred from mixed larvae beaten from hawthorn on the " Gogs "), Suffolk (beaten from hawthorn at Brandon, Tuddenham, etc.), and Norfolk. It has also been recorded from Wales (Montgomeryshire).

Abroad, the range extends through central Europe to Asia Minor and Kashgar.

As *insigniata* Hübn. is claimed to be at least two years older than *consignata* Borkh. the former name has been adopted for this species.

The Valerian Pug (*Eupithecia valerianata* Hübn.)

The fore wings of this species (Pl. **78**, 18) are brownish grey, with indistinct darker cross lines, and a wavy whitish submarginal line ; the latter is sometimes not clear, except towards the inner angle.

Caterpillar, rather short, bright green, with three darker green lines along the back ; a whitish line low down along the sides, and the ring-divisions are yellow. It feeds, in July and August, on flowers and seeds of all-heal, or cat's valerian (*Valeriana officinalis*).

The moth is out in May and June ; its haunts are in fens, marshes, and damp spots affected by its food plant, but, as a rule, it is more usually taken in the caterpillar state. A local, but widely distributed species in England ; occurs also in Wales and in Ireland.

Abroad, the range is similar to that of the preceding species.

The Marsh Pug (*Eupithecia pygmaeata* Hübner)

This species (Pl. **78**, 21) may be distinguished from *haworthiata*, which it approaches in size and general appearance, by its more pointed fore wings and the white dot at the inner angle of these wings.

1. Golden-rod
Pug.

2. Brindled
Pug.

3. Oak-tree
Pug.

4. Juniper
Pug
(ssp. *anglicata*).

5. Juniper
Pug
(ssp. *anglicata*).

6. Juniper
Pug
(ssp. *anglicata*).

7. Narrow-winged
Pug.

8. Narrow-winged
Pug.

9. Dwarf
Pug.

10. V-Pug.

11. Bilbury
Pug.

12. Bilbury
Pug.

13. Green
Pug.

14. Green
Pug.

15. Green
Pug.

16. Double-striped
Pug.

17. Double-striped
Pug.

18. Double-striped
Pug.

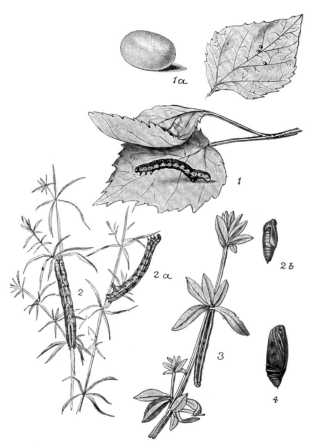

1, 1a. **Argent and Sable**: *eggs, natural size and enlarged, and caterpillar.*
2, 2a, 2b. **Wood Carpet**: *caterpillars and chrysalis.*
3. **Galium Carpet**: *caterpillar.*
4. **Common Carpet**: *chrysalis.*

The long, thin caterpillar is yellowish green ; a pale olive line along the middle of the back, connecting a series of urn-shaped blotches of the same colour ; two pale olive, irregular lines on each side. It feeds, in June and July, on flowers of stitchwort (*Stellaria holostea*) and mouse-ear chickweed (*Cerastium vulgatum*).

The moth is out in May and June, sometimes later ; examples of a second brood have been obtained in August and September. It flies in the afternoon, but only when the sun shines, and where the food plant grows freely.

The species occurs in all the eastern counties of England, in Hertfordshire and Buckinghamshire, and in the northern counties to Cumberland and Northumberland. It has been recorded from the Isle of Man. In Wales it has been recorded from Colwyn, Denbighshire ; in Scotland it is widely spread to Inverness-shire ; it is widely distributed in Ireland.

Abroad, the range extends through central and northern Europe to Amurland.

The Netted Pug (*Eupithecia venosata* Fab.)

This moth has also been named by the old authors " the Pretty Widow Moth." On Pl. 78 are shown four examples ; the typical form (Fig. 19), in which the fore wings are pale greyish, with black cross lines, two of which are edged with whitish ; *fumosae* Gregson (*nubilata* Bohatsch =) (Figs. 23, 24) —the Shetland race—is brownish grey, with the markings obscure ; ab. *bandanae* Gregson is a variegated modification of the last race ; Fig. 20 depicts the Orkney race *ochracae* Gregson (*orcadensis* Prout =), which has the ground colour darkened, but ochreous or clay yellow, not smoky.

Specimens from North Devon have a rather darker tone of the typical coloration, and those from North Wales and from Ireland incline to brownish.

The rather stumpy caterpillar is greyish brown above, and pale greenish or yellowish below ; three darker brown lines

along the back ; head, blackish. It is found from late June
to early August, in the seed capsules of the campions (*Silene
inflata, S. maritima*, etc.). Pl. **88,** 4, from a coloured drawing
by the late Mr. A. Sich.

The moth is out in May and June, and is widely distributed
over the British Isles.

Abroad, the range extends through Europe, eastwards to
central Asia and southwards to Morocco.

The Lime-speck Pug (*Eupithecia centaureata* Schiff.)

The characteristic features of this white, or greyish white,
species (Pl. **81,** 1 and 2) is the bluish grey blotch on the front
margin, in the lower end of which is the black discal spot.
Occasionally, the blotch is much reduced in size (ab. *albidior*
Heinrich) but it is usually large, and sometimes there are
indications of a dusky stripe from it to the inner margin.

Fig. 6.—Lime-speck Pug at rest (×2).

When freshly laid, the egg is whitish, but changes to pale
orange. The caterpillar (Pl. **88,** 2, 2*a*) is greenish, with more
or less connected reddish marks on the back, or green inclining
to yellowish, or bluish, without markings. It feeds through
the summer on flowers of ragwort, knapweed, scabious, yarrow,
golden rod, and the late R. Adkin found it on gladiolus.

The moth, which is often common in gardens, is out from May to August, and specimens of a second brood occur in September and October.

It is widely distributed over the British Islands, occurs in the Hebrides, but on the mainland of Scotland it does not, apparently, extend north of Perthshire.

Abroad, the range extends through Europe, Asia Minor eastwards to central Asia and southwards to North Africa.

The Triple-spotted Pug (*Eupithecia trisignaria* H.Sch.)

The most noticeable markings on the rather shiny, pale brown fore wings of this species (Pl. **78, 22**) are the black discal spot and two blackish clouds above it on the front margin. A completely black form has been named ab. *angelicata* Prout.

The stoutish caterpillar is green, with three darker green lines along the back, and a wavy yellowish line low down along the sides ; head, black. It feeds, in the autumn, on flowers and seeds of angelica and cow-parsnip, but the former is its chief food.

June and July are the months for the moth, but it is rarely met with in the open. The only English counties in which the species has been noted are Surrey, Sussex, Dorset, and Devon in the south ; from Herefordshire in the west its range extends through Worcestershire, Warwickshire, Leicestershire, and Derbyshire to Lancashire and Yorkshire. In Scotland, Renton records it as common at Hawick, in Roxburghshire ; and it was recorded from Argyllshire in 1902. Rare in Ireland, recorded from Fermanagh, Dublin, and Cork.

Abroad, the range extends through central Europe.

The Edinburgh Pug (*Eupithecia intricata* Zett.)

The typical light grey *intricata* is an inhabitant of northern Scandinavia and does not occur in these islands. In southern England the species is represented by subsp. *arceuthata* Freyer

(Freyer's Pug) (Pl. **81**, 3, 5) ; in Scotland it is represented by subsp. *millieraria* Wnuk. (Edinburgh Pug) (Pl. **81**, 4).

Subspecies *arceuthata*, whilst retaining the pale grey ground colour of the typical form, is suffused with cinnamon brown and often with violet grey, especially noticeable in fresh specimens in the marginal band ; the white-edged transverse lines, especially the basal, first and second, are usually distinct and the veins are often marked with black and white. It has a wide distribution in southern England from Dorset and Wiltshire eastwards to Kent.

Subspecies *millieraria* Wnuk. is smaller and of a darker, reddish brown. It occurs from Roxburghshire to Sutherland,

The stout, shiny-skinned larva is green with three slender lines along the back ; the central one is dark green, the other two pale yellow. Spiracular line broad, pale yellow or white. Spiracles reddish yellow. Head and legs green. The larva has been more fully described and figured by Mr. G. Haggett in *Proc. S. Lond. ent. & nat. Hist. Soc.*, 1955 : 162, pl. 7 : 2a, 2b 1957). It feeds on various species of Juniper, *Cupressus* especially *C. macrocarpa*, *Chamecyparus lawsonia* and related forms, *Thuya* and Tamarisk from mid-summer until late September and October and pupates in a loose cocoon on the food plant. The moth flies in May and June.

Abroad, the range includes N. America, northern and central Europe.

The Satyr Pug (*Eupithecia satyrata* Hübn.)

Three specimens are depicted on Pl. **81**. Fig. 6 represents the typical pale brownish grey form, in which the cross lines are indistinct, and the veins are marked with white and dusky. Fig. 8 shows the rather browner, moorland race, subsp. *callunaria* Dbldy., and Fig. 7 depicts the Shetland race subsp. *curzoni* Gregson ; a brown form, prevalent in S. England, is referable to subsp. *fagicolaria* Robson and Gardner. *E. satyrata* has at times been confused with *E. pernotata* Gn., and with *E. cauchiata* Dup. These are both separate species and do not occur in Britain.

The caterpillar is greenish with a series of purplish brown-edged, dusky green, Y-shaped marks along the back, above the yellow spiracular line is a row of slanting purplish blotches ; sometimes the general colour is paler, and the markings on the back and sides rosy ; occasionally, the whole of the back is rosy (adapted from Crewe). It feeds on the flowers of knap-weed (*Centaurea nigra*), scabious, hawkweed (*Hieracium*), heath, sallow, etc., etc. : August and September.

The moth is out in May and June, and is found in woodlands, and on heaths and moors. It is widely distributed over the British Isles.

Abroad, the range includes North America, northern and central Europe, and central Asia.

The White-spotted Pug (*Eupithecia tripunctaria* H.Sch.)

This greyish brown species (Pl. **81**, 9) will be recognised by the white spot at the lower end of the whitish submarginal line on the fore wings ; not infrequently there is a second white spot placed on the line about the middle, and sometimes a third near the front margin ; the hind wings have a white dot at the anal angle, and, occasionally, a second is placed a little beyond. Ab. *angelicata* Barrett is blackish with the discal spot and the veins showing blacker, but without white spots (Pl. **88**, 5). The caterpillar is pale lemon yellow, or yellowish green ; three brown lines along the back, the central one with brown marks upon it ; some brownish marks on the sides. Variable in general colour, and the markings sometimes absent. It feeds on the flowers of angelica (*Angelica sylvestris*), hogweed (*Heracleum sphondylium*), and other Umbelliferae. It has also been reared on a diet of elder leaves : August, September, or even later. Our figure (Pl. **88**, 5) is from a coloured drawing by the late A. Sich. The moth emerges in May and

June, sometimes earlier in confinement, and then a second generation has resulted in July.

Widely distributed in England, in many localities the caterpillars are not uncommon, although the moth may never be seen at large. Also occurs in South Wales, in Scotland to Aberdeenshire ; and in Ireland it has been found in Sligo, Tyrone, Kerry, and Cork.

Abroad, the range extends to northern and central Europe, central and eastern Asia, and Japan.

The Wormwood Pug (*Eupithecia absinthiata* Cl.)

The fore wings are reddish or purplish brown ; cross lines indistinct, but represented on the front edge by black marks, discal dot black, submarginal line whitish interrupted, often indistinct, except above the inner margin (Pl. **81,** 10, 11, 16, 17). The short, stout, and roughened caterpillar varies in colour, and may be yellowish green, deep rose colour, or dirty reddish brown ; a series of lozenge-shaped reddish spots on the back, faint towards each end (often absent in green forms) ; oblique yellow stripes on the sides form borders to the marks on the back (adapted from Crewe). It feeds, in the autumn, on the flowers of ragwort, golden rod, aster, yarrow, hemp-agrimony, etc. The moth is out in June and July.

The species is generally common in the south of England, and is widely distributed over the rest of that country, Wales, and Ireland. In Scotland its range extends to Moray.

Abroad, the distribution spreads to Amurland.

The Ling Pug (*Eupithecia goossensiata* Mabille)

The fore wings are rather narrower and more pointed at the tips than those of the last species ; the ground colour of the fore wings is of a paler reddish brown, and frequently tinged with greyish ; the hind wings are usually greyish brown (Pl. **81,** 15). The caterpillar, which feeds in August and September on the flowers of heath (*Erica*), and ling (*Calluna*), is pinkish with dusky marks on the back, most distinct on the middle rings ; a yellowish line low down along the side has dusky marks upon it ; head, dusky olive, marked with white (adapted from Crewe).

It may be mentioned here, that *knautiata* Gregson, which was described as a distinct species, is by some authorities considered to be a form of this species, whilst others refer it to *absinthiata*. The caterpillar is stouter than that of *goossensiata*, varies in colour from whitish to green, and even purplish brown, but not to pinkish ; it feeds on the flowers and seeds of *Knautia arvensis*. The moth is out in June and July, and occurs on heaths and moors throughout England, Wales, and Ireland. In Scotland, it is obtained freely in some parts of the south, and its range extends to the Hebrides and the Orkneys.

Abroad, the range extends to northern Europe and the western parts of central Europe.

Eupithecia goossensiata was wrongly called *E. minutata* Schiff. by Doubleday and other authors.

The Bleached Pug (*Eupithecia expallidata* Dbldy.)

The ample wings light brown in colour, with large black discal spot, and smaller black marks on the front edge of the fore wings, distinguish this species (Pl. **81**, 14) from its closest British allies.

The caterpillar feeds, in September and October, on flowers of golden-rod (*Solidago virgaurea*) and ragwort (*Senecio jacobaea*), but it will thrive on those of michaelmas daisy, and probably the asters of the garden. It varies in ground colour, but this is usually some shade of green, and there are brownish spots and lines on the back.

The moth is out from late June until August, and may be put up from among golden-rod during the day, or netted as it flies about the plant in the gloaming.

It is rather local, but occurs in most of the southern counties of England, from Kent to Devon, and westward from Somerset to Hereford and South Wales ; also recorded from North Lancashire. Rare in Scotland, and only noted from Perthshire and Aberdeenshire. Reported from Derry, Westmeath, Down, Louth, Dublin, Wicklow, and Cork in Ireland.

Abroad, the range extends to central Europe.

The Currant Pug (*Eupithecia assimilata* Dbldy.)

This species (Pl. **81,** 13) is similar in marking to *absinthiata*, but the wings are shorter and rounder ; the fore wings are a trifle redder in tint, and the white mark at the termination of the submarginal line is usually more conspicuous.

The rather slender caterpillar, figured on Pl. **88,** 6, from a coloured drawing by the late A. Sich, is yellowish green, inclining to yellow between the rings ; three darker green lines on the back, the central one most distinct, the others rather broad and not well defined ; sometimes the central line is tinged with brown, as also is the front edge of each ring. It feeds on currant and hop, and is said to eat the leaves of gooseberry also. The first brood is in June and July, and the second in the autumn. The moth is out in May and June and in August. It frequents gardens, and hides among the foliage, or occasionally sits on walls or palings ; from hedges where the wild hop grows freely it may be beaten out in the daytime, but it flies in the twilight, sometimes in numbers, around the hop bines.

Widely distributed over England, Wales, Scotland up to Ross, and the Hebrides ; in Ireland it has been noted from Tyrone, Dublin, Cork, Galway, Down, and Sligo.

Abroad, the range extends through central Europe to central and eastern Asia.

The Common Pug (*Eupithecia vulgata* Haw.)

This pug varies in colour from pale grey brown through reddish brown to blackish. In some of the lighter coloured

1, 1*a*. **Plain Pug:** *caterpillars.*
2, 2*a*. **Dark Spinach:** *caterpillars.*

1. Slender-striped
   Rufous.

2. Small Waved
   Umber.

3. The Fern.

4. Cumbrian
   Umber.

5. Small
   Seraphim.

6. The Seraphim.

7. Yellow-barred
   Brindle.

8. Small
   Seraphim.

9. The Seraphim.

10. Yellow-barred
    Brindle.

11. Early
    Tooth-striped.

12. Dentated
    Pug.

13. Early
    Tooth-striped.

14. Barred
    Tooth-striped.

15. Dentated
    Pug.

16. Barred
    Tooth-striped.

specimens the darker cross lines and the whitish submarginal lines are all well defined ; more frequently, perhaps, most of the markings are indistinct or absent, but the small black discal dot and a white spot above the outer angle of the fore wing remain fairly clear. Pl. **81,** 18, 20, depict the typical form, Pl. **81,** 19, the strongly darkened, sometimes almost black, ab. *atropicta* Dietze, which is common in the London area. The caterpillar (Pl. **88,** 3) is brownish, inclining to reddish, dotted with white ; a series of dirty green marks along the back, and a pale yellow wavy line low down along the sides. It feeds on the leaves of sallow, hawthorn, bramble, bilberry, ragwort, golden-rod and various other plants. There are at least two broods in the year, one in June and July, and the other in the autumn. The moth flies in May and June, and again in August, and is often common, almost everywhere, over the greater part of the British Isles.

The range abroad extends to eastern Siberia and Amurland.

The Campanula Pug (*Eupithecia denotata* Hübn.)

The faint reddish-tinged pale-brown fore wings distinguish this species (Pl. **82,** 4). The blackish marks on the front edge are minute, the cross lines are usually indistinct and often absent ; the discal spot, however, is black and conspicuous, and the whitish submarginal line is very wavy. In general colour, the caterpillar is pale brownish ; lines and marks on the back, dark brown or blackish. It feeds on the seeds of the nettle-leaved bell-flower (*Campanula trachelium*), and may be reared on the flowers of the various kinds of *Campanula* grown in gardens : August and early September. The moth is out in July, but is rarely seen in a state of nature. Caterpillars, however, are not uncommon, where the food plant is plentiful, in several of the English counties from Worcestershire southwards to Kent and Cornwall : also in Norfolk.

Except that the ground colour inclines to dark greyish brown and the cross markings are rather more in evidence, subsp. *jasioneata* Crewe (Jasione Pug) is somewhat similar to pale specimens of the typical race (Pl. **82,** 5, 6). The caterpillar feeds on the seeds of sheep's bit (*Jasione montana*), is very like that of typical *denotata* and occurs in the same months. Mr. Prout has pointed out that the paler forms of this race are not easily separable from *denotata atraria* H.Sch., a mountain race of this species. The Jasione Pug was first added to the British list in 1878.

The moth is out in May and June, but it is very rarely seen at large, though caterpillars are found locally in Devon and Somerset, England ; at Barmouth, in Merionethshire, North Wales, and the Isle of Man ; and frequently along the sea-coast of southern and south-western Ireland (Donovan). Possibly, it awaits discovery in several other parts of the British Isles, and almost certainly in the west of England. In ascertaining new localities for the species, the best method of investigation would be to search for the caterpillars.

The Grey Pug (*Eupithecia castigata* Hübn.)

Although, as the English name suggests, this insect is greyish, there is always a tinge of ochreous in the composition of its general colour (Pl. **82,** 2, 3). Not infrequently the ground colour is decidedly brownish in tint. The markings vary in clearness, but are most distinct in the paler forms. A blackish form (ab. *obscurissima* Prout) occurs in the north of England and other British localities, and in the Clydesdale district of Scotland, and was formerly known as the " Paisley Pug."

The longish caterpillar (Pl. **88,** 1) is pale or dusky olive, varying to reddish brown, with a series of darker marks on the back. It feeds, from August to October, on the foliage of almost any plant.

The moth is out in May and June, and occasionally a few specimens emerge in the autumn. Generally distributed over the British Isles, but apparently not noted in the Orkneys and Shetlands.

Abroad, the range extends to Amurland and North America.

The Tawny Speckled Pug (*Eupithecia icterata* de Villers)

Three forms of this species are shown on Pl. **82.** Fig. 8 represents the reddish form subsp. *subfulvata* Haw., and Fig. 7 (from Lancashire coast) the dark subsp. *oxydata* Treitschke. Between these two extremes, there are various intermediate forms, showing more or less distinct cross lines. Subsp. *cognata* Steph. (Fig. 9), described from Edinburgh specimens, is not uncommon in Scotland. The wings are marbled with whitish and grey, without any clear area of fulvous, except perhaps in the median nervures, in extreme cases all fulvous shading is absent.

The caterpillar is reddish brown, with a chain of oval, olive brown spots along the back ; there are also two brownish interrupted lines ; the spiracular line is white. Sometimes the general colour is ochreous brown, or grey brown. It feeds, in September and October, on yarrow, and will thrive on tansy, and the flowers of garden chrysanthemum.

The chrysalis of this species is said to differ from that of *E. succenturiata* in being of a rich red colour, inclining to buff on the wing cases.

In July and August, the moth may sometimes be seen resting on fences, but it is more frequently hidden away among herbage. At night it will visit flowers, especially those of the ragwort.

The species is widely distributed over England and Wales, and in Scotland up to Moray. In Ireland, it is common wherever its food plant occurs.

Abroad, the range extends to northern and central Europe and the Atlas Mountains in North Africa.

The Bordered Pug (*Eupithecia succenturiata* Linn.)

The fore wings are white, clouded and suffused with dark grey on all the margins. The greyish clouding sometimes covers the whole area of the wings, except a very limited space under the black discal spot (ab. *disparata* Hübn.) (Pl. **82,** 10).

The caterpillar is reddish brown, paler in some specimens than in others ; a series of blackish spear-head marks along the back, connected by a blackish line, and a dusky line on each side ; a whitish line along the spiracles. It feeds, in September and October, on mugwort (*Artemisia vulgaris*), tansy (*Tanacetum vulgare*), and yarrow (*Achillea*). It may be reared on garden chrysanthemum. Chrysalis, dark buff inclining to brown ; wing cases olive green ; Fig. 7 on Pl. **88** is from a photo by the late H. Main, and is enlarged to twice the natural size.

The moth is out in July and early August ; it is not readily put up from its hiding-place among herbage, but at night, when on the wing, it will come to light.

The species is most frequent, perhaps, on the coast, but it is widely distributed over England and Wales. "Local and scarce" in Ireland, but is recorded from counties Tyrone, Down, Armagh, Louth, Dublin, and Kerry ; Kane states that he met with it in some numbers on Lambay Island. Once reported from Ayrshire, Scotland.

Abroad, the range extends to northern and central Europe and central Asia.

The Ochreous Pug (*Eupithecia indigata* Hübn.)

Captured specimens of this pale greyish ochreous brown species nearly always have a washed-out appearance, and even freshly emerged examples are unattractive. In some specimens, cross lines are more or less traceable on the fore wings ; in others four or five tiny dusky dots will be noted on the front edge ; as a rule, the only clearly defined character is the black discal spot (Pl. **81,** 12).

1, 1a. **Grey Pug**: *egg, enlarged, and caterpillar.*
2, 2a. **Lime-speck Pug**: *caterpillars.*
3. **Common Pug**: *caterpillar.*
4. **Netted Pug**: *caterpillar.*
5. **White-spotted Pug**: *caterpillar.*
6. **Current Pug**: *caterpillar.*
7. **Bordered Pug**: *chrysalis.*

1. November
Moth.

2. November
Moth.

3. Small
Autumnal
Moth.

4. November
Moth.

5. Small
Autumnal
Moth.

6. Autumnal
Moth.

7. Autumnal
Moth.

8. Pale
November
Moth.

9. Pale
November
Moth.

10. Northern
Winter
Moth,
male.

11. Northern
Winter
Moth,
female.

12. Northern
Winter
Moth,
male.

13. Winter
Moth,
male.

14. Winter
Moth.
female.

15. Winter
Moth,
male.

The long caterpillar is greenish yellow or yellowish red ; three lines on the back, the central one brownish, but often only distinct on the front rings ; the others, and also one low down along the sides, yellowish ; head, reddish (adapted from Crewe). It feeds, in June and July, on the inflorescence and on the brown scales at the base of the needles of pine and larch, or may be reared on juniper. It never eats the needles themselves (Cockayne).

The moth is out in May and June, and sometimes there seems to be another emergence in the latter part of the summer. It frequents pine woods, where it rests upon the trunks and branches of the trees.

Generally distributed over the whole of England ; has been found in South Wales, and occurs in the Hebrides, Perthshire, Aberdeenshire, and Inverness-shire, in Scotland. In Ireland, it has been noted from Tyrone, Derry, Fermanagh, Cork, and Galway.

Abroad, it is distributed throughout northern and central Europe.

The Pimpinel Pug (*Eupithecia pimpinellata* Hübn.)

A portrait of this species, which, as a British insect, was first noted in Suffolk nearly ninety years ago, will be found on Pl. **82**, 1. The fore wings are pale brownish, except on the front edge, which is greyish ; the black discal spot is distinct and rather long ; the median vein and its branches are dotted with black, and most of the cross lines are only distinct on the front margin, where they are blackish ; the rather wavy whitish submarginal line is sometimes marked with blackish. In some specimens the costal half of the fore wings is greyish, and the other portion only tinged with pale brownish.

The long caterpillar is green, with three purplish lines along the back, the central one wider and more distinct than the others ; the head is purple. Sometimes purple, with two lines of a deeper shade on each side of the back (Crewe). It feeds, in the autumn, on flowers of burnet-saxifrage (*Pimpinella*) and is fully fed in October. The moth is out in June and July, and in the late afternoon is occasionally put up from among its food plant or the herbage around, but such specimens are rarely worth keeping, unless of the female sex, when eggs may be obtained.

The species has a wide distribution in England, especially in the southern half ; it occurs in Wales, and also in Ireland, but not in Scotland.

Abroad, it occurs throughout Europe to central Asia and has been recorded from the Atlas Mountains in North Africa.

The Scarce Pug (*Eupithecia extensaria* subsp. *occidua* Prout)

The conspicuously marked insect represented on Pl. **82,** 11, is, so far, only known to occur, in Britain, on the coasts of Norfolk and Yorkshire. It was first discovered in the latter county about 1874 ; in 1887 it was found on the Norfolk coast, and caterpillars were also obtained from the sea wormwood (*Artemisia maritima*) in the autumn.

The long caterpillar, which feeds on the flowers and foliage of its food plant, is green, with three lines along the back, the central one dusky and the others whitish ; a white stripe low down along the sides is edged below with rosy brown. It will thrive on the cultivated southernwood or " lad's love " (*Artemisia abrotanum*). The larva has been figured by Mr. G. Haggett in *Proc. S. Lond. ent. & nat. Hist. Soc.*, 1955 : 161, pl. 8 : 1a–1d (1957).

The moth is out in June and July, and may be found in its haunts among the sea wormwood, not only on the coast of Norfolk, but quite possibly, here and there, in suitable places on the east coast from Essex to the Humber. Caterpillars may be obtained in August and September.

Abroad, the range extends eastwards to Amurland.

The Narrow-winged Pug (*Eupithecia nanata* subsp. *angusta* Prout)

The rather variable species represented on Pl. **84**, 7 and 8, will easily be recognised by its long pointed fore wings, which in colour are whitish grey, darkened by brownish cross stripes, a whitish spot before the small, black discal dot. Ab. *oliveri* Prout is a melanic ; the fore wing is black, tinged with brown ; the white postmedian band and subterminal line are scarcely traceable. The hind wing is much darkened posteriorly. It is known from Wolverhampton and Sutton Coldfield.

The long, thin, caterpillar, which feeds on ling or heather in the autumn, is whitish with a greenish tinge : the sides are marked with red, and there are some reddish spots on the back.

On almost all heather-clad ground throughout the British Isles, this pretty little moth will be found, more or less commonly, during the months of May and early June, and sometimes there is a second flight in July and August.

Abroad, the range extends through northern and central Europe to eastern Asia.

The Angle-barred Pug (*Eupithecia innotata* Hufn.)

The greyish-brown fore wings of this species (Pl. **82**, 13–15) are crossed by darker oblique lines, which are angled on the front margin ; the submarginal line is white and irregular, especially at each end.

The caterpillar is variable, but generally some shade of green, occasionally purplish red ; lines on the sides yellowish, and sometimes there are dusky purplish marks on the back. It feeds, in August and September, on ash, and is said to eat *Artemisia*, *Laurustinus*, and the flowers of scabious. The moth is out in late June and July, and sometimes a second generation appears in the autumn.

This species is widely distributed over England, Scotland as far north as Sutherland and the Hebrides, and Ireland.

Subsp. *fraxinata* Crewe, the Ash Pug, is very similar to the typical form, but smaller, and the markings are less distinct (Pl. **82,** 14). *Tamarisciata* Freyer is also considered by some authorities to be a form of *E. innotata*. Some moths reared from larvae obtained in 1905, on tamarisk in Cornwall, have been referred to *tamarisciata*.

The Golden-rod Pug (*Eupithecia virgaureata* Dbldy.)

The fore wings of this obscurely marked species (Pl. **84,** 1) are pale greyish brown inclining to ochreous; the discal spot is black, the veins are marked with dark brown and white, and the whitish submarginal line terminates in a white spot above the inner angle.

The caterpillar varies in colour from grey brown or purplish grey to reddish brown; a series of blackish triangular spots on the back, and yellowish oblique stripes on the sides. It feeds on the flowers of the golden-rod (*Solidago virgaurea*), in the autumn; also on ragwort (*Senecio*). The moth is out in May and early June, but in captivity there is apparently a second emergence in July and early August. The caterpillars from which these smaller and rather darker specimens result, hatch from the egg in May and feed on the flowers of beaked parsley (*Anthriscus sylvestris*).

Widely distributed in England, Wales, and Ireland.

The range abroad extends to north-east Siberia; and the species has been recorded from Japan.

The Brindled Pug (*Eupithecia abbreviata* Steph.)

The ochreous grey fore wings of this species (Pl. **84,** 2) are crossed by dark, bent lines, and marked with black on the veins; the central area is sometimes whitish, and generally paler than the ground colour. A melanic form, ab. *hirschkei* Bast., is found in many parts of Britain.

Caterpillar, slender, ochreous brown in colour, with browner lines and redder V-shaped marks on the back. It feeds on

1. Small White Wave.
4. Small White Wave.

2. Dingy Shell.
5. Dingy Wave.
7, 8. Welsh Wave.

3. Small Yellow Wave.
6. Small Yellow Wave.

9. Waved Carpet.
12. Waved Carpet.

10. Drab Looper.
13. Drab Looper.

11. Bloomer's Rivulet.
14. Bloomer's Rivulet.

1, 1a. **November Moth**: *eggs, natural size and enlarged, and caterpillar.*
2, 2a. **Beautiful Carpet**: *caterpillars and chrysalis.*

oak, in June and July. The moth is not uncommon in oak woods, in April and May, and may be beaten from the boughs in the daytime, and not infrequently found resting on the trunks. Generally distributed, but in Scotland not noted north of Perthshire. Very common throughout Ireland.

Abroad, the range extends to central and southern Europe and Transcaucasia.

The Oak-tree Pug (*Eupithecia dodoneata* Guenée)

This species (Pl. **84,** 3) differs from the last in being smaller, paler in colour, more distinctly marked, and with a rather larger and more conspicuous discal spot.

The caterpillar feeds, in June and July, on young leaves of oak, the flowers of the evergreen oak (*Quercus ilex*), and haw-thorn. It is orange, or ochreous red, with blackish marks connected by a line of the same colour along the back, and yellowish stripes and lines on the sides.

The moth is out in May and early June, and occurs in some of the woods in most of the southern counties of England, and on the west to Worcestershire. It has been recorded from Yorkshire and Cumberland; from Glamorgan, South Wales; and Ireland, but is scarce though distributed north and south.

Abroad, it occurs throughout Europe and has been recorded from North Africa.

The Juniper Pug (*Eupithecia sobrinata* Hübn.)

Two specimens are shown on Pl. **84**: Fig. 4 represents a more or less typical example from the Surrey downs, and Fig. 5 a pale form from Forres in Scotland. The species varies in tint of ground colour, and in the strength of marking, in all its localities; but in Scotland there is a greater tendency to pale forms than in England. Mr. H. McArthur obtained an exten-sive and most variable series from heather, at Aviemore, in Inverness. A pale-brownish tinged white pug found in Kent and the Isle of Wight (Pl. **84,** 6), at one time referred to *E.*

ultimaria Boisd. and afterwards known as *stevensata* Webb, is really, according to Prout, subsp. *anglicata* H.Sch.

The dark green, sometimes reddish-marked, caterpillars may be beaten from juniper bushes, from April to early June. The moth is out from late July to early October, and may be found in nearly all parts of the British Isles where the food plant occurs, and occasionally in localities from which juniper appears to be absent.

Abroad, the range extends through northern and central Europe and locally in southern Europe.

The Larch Pug (*Eupithecia lariciata* Freyer)

This species (Pl. **82,** 12) is very like *castigata* Hübn., but the fore wings are rather longer, the ground colour is whiter, and the dark grey or blackish cross lines are rather more angled and slanting ; the hind wings are paler, and especially so on the front margins. Ab. *nigra* Prout is uniformly sooty black, with deeper black cell marks and veins.

The long caterpillar is bright green, with a darker green line along the back, merging into reddish on the last ring ; sometimes reddish ochreous with the line along the back brownish. It feeds, in June and July, on larch, and will also eat spruce.

The moth is out in May and early June, and may be jarred from larch trees, or sometimes be found at rest on their stems.

As a British species, it was first met with in Surrey, in 1862, then it was noted in Sussex, and shortly afterwards in Yorkshire. At the present time, it will probably be found in any locality where larch is plentiful. Sporadically distributed in Ireland.

Abroad, the range extends through Europe to central Asia. It also occurs in Kashmir.

The Dwarf Pug (*Eupithecia tantillaria* Boisd.)

The fore wings of this species (Pl. **84,** 9) are pale greyish white, discal spot black, cross lines irregular dark grey inclining to brownish, usually most distinct on the front margin.

The long, slender caterpillar is orange red or dull ochreous green ; three dusky olive lines along the back, the central one often only distinct on the front rings ; a yellow line low down along the sides. It feeds, in June and early July, on spruce (*Picea excelsa*). The moth is out in May and June, and rests by day among the branches of the spruce.

The species is local, but has a wide distribution in England and Wales wherever the foodplant occurs. It has also been recorded from Inverness-shire in Scotland.

Abroad, the range extends to northern and central Europe and the Caucasus.

Eupithecia phœniceata Rambur

A specimen of this species was taken in the Penzance district of Cornwall on September 11, 1959, by Dr. C. de Worms. In 1960 two further specimens were taken in a garden containing much *Cupressus macrocarpus* near Penzance by Mr. A. Richardson, one on September 6 and one on September 16, and Mr. F. Lees took a specimen near Torquay on September 24.

E. phoeniceata is a native of the western Mediterranean, occurring in S. Spain, S. France, Italy, Sicily, and Algeria. There the moth flies in September and October (Pl. **140**).

The larva feeds on the foliage of various species of cypress and on *Juniperus phoenicea*.

The Green Pug (*Chloroclystis rectangulata* Linn.)

Of this variable species three examples are shown on Pl. **84**, 13–15.

The stumpy caterpillar is of a pale yellow green colour, with a more or less distinct reddish or dark green line along the back, and reddish ring-divisions. It feeds in flowers of hawthorn, wild apple or crab, and of apples and pears grown in orchards and gardens. It is found in April and May, and the moth is out in June and July.

The species is common throughout the greater part of England and Wales, and its range extends to Ross in Scotland. It has a wide distribution in Ireland.

Abroad, it occurs throughout Europe and western Asia. It has also been recorded from Egypt and Ussuri.

The Bilberry Pug (*Chloroclystis debiliata* Hübn.)

As a British insect, this species (Pl. **84**, 11, 12) was first found in Devon, and was then known by the English name of " The Devon Pug." As the yellowish green caterpillar, marked with a darker line along the back and a yellowish one low down on the sides, feeds on bilberry, in April and May, and is by no means confined to Devon, the popular name here adopted is more suitable.

When quite fresh the moth, which is out in June and July, has a very delicate tinge of green, but this quickly fades out, leaving a pale greyish white insect. In the typical form (Fig. 12) the black central lines are fairly well defined, but in ab. *nigropunctata* Chant. (Fig. 11), the lines are represented by a series of dots.

The species is common in some of the sheltered hollows among the hills in Devon and Somerset, and South used to find it in abundance in the Martinhoe district, in the former county. The moths were rarely disturbed from the food plant during the day, but towards dusk they flew in numbers around small trees of mountain ash.   Other counties in which it is known to occur are—England : Cornwall, Hampshire (New Forest), Sussex (Blackdown), Surrey (Netley Heath and Leith Hill) Kent, Worcestershire, Staffordshire, Leicestershire, and Lancashire (formerly on Chat Moss). Wales : Monmouthshire, Glamorgan and Pembroke. Scotland : Aberdeen. Ireland : Wicklow, Waterford, Cork, Kerry, Galway, and Sligo.

Abroad, the range extends through central Europe to the Urals.

The V-Pug (*Chloroclystis coronata* Hübn.)

This is " *Phalaena* " *v-ata* Haw., and also the V-Pug of that author. A later English name for the species is " The Coronet Pug," an Anglicism for the Latin specific name, and has reference to the black upper part of the outer cross line which is twice angled and bears a fanciful resemblance to a coronet; the lower angle is, however, most distinct, therefore Haworth's English name seems most suitable as it indicates the V-mark, which is a noticeable character of this delicate green species (Pl. **84,** 10).

The caterpillar is yellowish green, with three reddish lines along the back, the central one most distinct and sometimes forming triangular marks, or lozenges. The ground colour varies, and may be greener, yellower, or occasionally greyish; and the markings are not always present.

There are two generations, the first in June and July, and the second in the autumn, and in confinement a third brood is sometimes obtained. The blossoms of various plants are eaten, but those of sweet chestnut, hemp-agrimony (*Eupatorium cannabinum*), golden-rod (*Solidago*), clematis, and purple loosestrife (*Lythrum salicaria*), are perhaps favourites. Hawthorn and bramble have also been mentioned as food plants.

The moth is out in most of the months from May to August, but seems to be most frequent in the first named.

Generally distributed in the southern half of England, extending into South Wales including Cardiganshire, rare in Yorkshire and in Roxburghshire, Scotland. Widely distributed in Ireland. The range abroad extends to Japan.

The Double-striped Pug (*Gymnoscelis pumilata* Hübn.)

This species varies a good deal in the tint of the ground colour and the cross markings. Three forms are depicted on Pl. **84,** 16–18.

The caterpillar ranges in colour from yellowish green to

reddish ; on the back there is a dark green or blackish line, and often a series of marks of the same colour ; the lines on the sides are yellowish. It feeds chiefly in or on the flowers of furze, broom, holly, clematis, hawthorn, etc., from May to September. There are certainly two broods, possibly more. The specimens of the first, or spring, generation are usually larger in size and more strongly marked than those of the summer brood.

The moth is most frequent, perhaps, in April, May, July, and August, but it may be met with in either of the months from January to November. Pretty generally distributed over the British Isles, including the Hebrides and the Orkneys.

Abroad, the range of this species is extensive, including central and southern Europe, the Mediterranean islands, Asia Minor, North Africa, Madeira, and the Canary Islands.

The Seraphim (*Lobophora halterata* Hufn.)

Fore wings whitish, with two greyish bands on the basal area ; first and second lines greyish, variable in width, and sometimes only represented by marks on the front or inner margins ; there is a black central dot, and the outer area beyond the submarginal line is clouded with dark grey, especially on the upper half. Sometimes the wings are so thickly stippled with the darker colour that they appear to be greyish, with interrupted and indistinct whitish cross lines. A rather frequent form has the fore wings tinged with ochreous, and of this tint is ab. *zonata* Thunb., which has the basal bands and outer marginal border blackish, the central area being without cross lines (Pl. **87,** 6 ♂, and 9 ♀).

The caterpillar is green, darker below and between the rings ; the most distinct markings are two yellow lines along the back ; head, notched ; body wrinkled, and with two points on the last ring. It feeds on aspen and other kinds of poplar and also sallow, in June and July.

The moth appears in May, and continues out well into June,

especially in its northern localities. It rests on the trunks of poplar trees, or on the stems of bushes around, and is sometimes easily alarmed, and flies off on the collector's approach, whilst at other times it sits quietly, and may be easily boxed. At dusk it may be seen flying around the poplars.

Widely distributed in the southern half of England, and only found where poplars, chiefly aspens, are well established. From Worcestershire its range extends northwards to Staffordshire, Leicestershire, Derbyshire, and Cheshire ; and it has been recorded from Yorkshire and Cumberland ; also from Glamorganshire, South Wales. In Scotland it seems not to have been noted in the south, but is found more or less frequently from Perthshire to Sutherlandshire. Scarce in Ireland, but locally distributed, north and south (Donovan).

Abroad, its range extends to Amurland, Japan, and North America.

The Small Seraphim (*Mysticoptera sexalata* Retz.)

This is a much smaller species than the last. The fore wings are whitish, with brownish grey, or blackish grey, cross lines and bands ; the central most distinct towards the front margin, where it encloses a black dot ; hind wings greyish, with black central dot (Pl. **87**, 5, 8).

The green, much wrinkled caterpillar has three whitish lines or stripes along the back, and in some examples there is a white line low down along the sides ; the head, which inclines to yellowish, is notched, and there are two pinkish points on the last ring of the body. It feeds on sallow and white willow (*Salix alba*) in August and September.

The moth is to be found in May and June, and, in some years, again in July and August. It inhabits woods and hedgerows where sallow is plentiful, but, perhaps, is obtained more freely in fens. Occasionally it may be beaten from the hedges, but it is active on the wing just before the close of day, and then disports itself over and about the sallow bushes. It occurs in suitable localities in most of the eastern and southern counties of England, and has been reported from some of the northern ones, also from Glamorgan, in South Wales, and from Perthshire in Scotland. Kane states that it has been found throughout Ireland, but is always local and scarce.

Abroad, the range includes central and northern Europe and south-eastern Russia.

The Yellow-barred Brindle (*Acasis viretata* Hübn.)

The general colour of the fore wings is olive green, varying from pale to dark, the wavy cross lines are blackish, dotted with black, and sometimes there are whitish lines between them ; those on the central area are often united by a blackish cloud, and so form a band, and not infrequently the basal area is also blackish marked (Pl. 87, 7, 10). The ground colour is very apt to fade if the insect is exposed to moisture of any kind, as, for instance, when pinned in a damp collecting box, but South had one bred specimen of a reddish ochreous colour, and he was assured that it was of this tint when it emerged from the chrysalis. An old English name was " The Brindle-barred Yellow."

The thick-set caterpillar is green, more or less tinged with pinkish ; three interrupted pink lines on the back, the central one sometimes inclining to purple, and broken up into spots ; the head is brown, sometimes marked with purplish, and there are two tiny points on the last ring of the body. It varies in the green tint and also in marking. It feeds on flowers and leaves of holly, ivy, dogwood, privet, etc., in June and July, and in some sheltered southern localities again in September and October.

The moth is out in May and early June, and where a second generation is developed, in August and early September. It sits in the daytime on tree-trunks, but more especially those with smooth bark ; the stems of holly are a favourite resting place, but at Box Hill South had occasionally seen a specimen

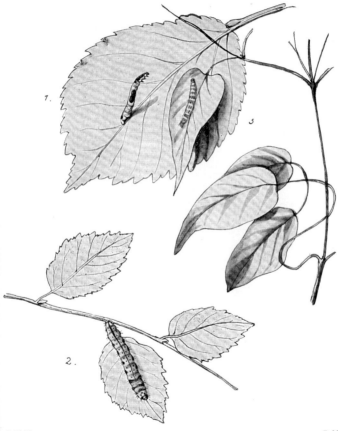

1. **Blomer's Rivulet:** *caterpillar.*
2. **Small White Wave:** *caterpillar.*
3. **Haworth's Pug:** *caterpillar.*

1. **Northern Winter Moth:** *eggs, natural size and enlarged.*
2, 2a. **Barred Tooth-striped:** *caterpillar and chrysalis.*
3, 3a, 3b. **Early Tooth-striped:** *eggs, natural size and enlarged, and caterpillar.*

on the trunk of a beech tree. Barrett states that it also rests on the trunks of fir trees, and that it is then very easily seen. Night is its time of activity, and it is then attracted by light.

The species seems to be widely distributed, but locally and not generally common, throughout England, Wales, and Ireland ; it has been recorded from the Isle of Man ; it has only been recorded from Rosemount, Ayr, and one or two other localities in the south of Scotland.

The range abroad extends to western India, Amurland, and Japan.

The Barred Tooth-striped (*Trichopteryx polycommata* Schiff.)

The general colour of the species represented on Pl. **87,** 14♂, 16♀, is greyish, inclining to ochreous or to whitish ; but occasionally it is clouded with dark greyish on the basal area, and there is a broad band of the same colour on the outer marginal area ; in such specimens the central band becomes less conspicuous. In ab. *caliginosa* Cockayne, the ground colour of both wings is uniformly brown and all the markings are very indistinct.

The eggs are yellow when laid and turn pink after about three days. The caterpillar (Pl. **93,** 2) feeds in May and June, on privet, at first on the leaf buds, and afterwards on the expanded leaves. It will also eat ash and honeysuckle. In colour it is rather deep green, with three fine lines along the back, the central one darker than the ground colour, and the others whitish and irregular ; a whitish stripe low down along the sides ; two points on the last ring of the body. The chrysalis (Pl. **93,** 2*a*), which is enclosed in an oval earthen cocoon, is dark yellowish brown, inclining to blackish on the wing cases.

The moth may be found at night, in March and April, sitting on the privet hedge, and may then be easily boxed, as it seems very disinclined to fly at that time, but earlier in the evening it flits along the hedgerows, and is equally easy to net. The finest specimens, however, are obtained from among those at rest.

The species appears to be very local in Britain, but it occurs in the Brighton, Lewes, and Emsworth districts of Sussex ; Hampshire, Wiltshire (Salisbury), Somerset, Devon (Sidmouth), Gloucestershire, Herefordshire, Worcestershire (Malvern), North Lancashire, Cumberland, Northampton, Berkshire, Essex, and Kent. In Scotland it has been reported from Clydesdale and Arran, but has not been noted from Ireland.

Abroad, the range extends to central Europe and Russia.

The Early Tooth-striped (*Trichopteryx carpinata* Borkh.)

The whitish fore wings of this species are tinged with grey or greenish grey, the cross lines and bands vary in intensity, and, as a rule, are more distinct and complete in the female than in the male (Pl. **87,** 11♂, 13♀). A form of not infrequent occurrence in Scotland (ab. *fasciata* Prout) has blackish bands, which show up in strong contrast with the general whitish colour of the wings.

The caterpillar is green, with rather darker lines along the back, and a yellow stripe low down along the sides ; the two points on the last ring are also yellow. It feeds, in June and July, on honeysuckle, sallow, birch, and alder. The moth is out in April and May, and seems to be more or less common in woodlands throughout the greater part of the British Isles. In Scotland it appears to be most plentiful from Perthshire northwards to Sutherlandshire. Larvae have been found on the Isle of Rhum (Inner Hebrides), but it has not been reported from the Orkneys, Shetlands, or Outer Hebrides. (Early stages are shown on Pl. **93,** 3–3*b*).

The boles of trees are favourite resting places, and upon them, and also upon gate-posts, etc., the moth is often met with in the daytime.

Abroad, the range extends to eastern Siberia.

The Autumnal Moth (*Oporinia autumnata* Borkh.)

The two examples of this species shown on Pl. **89,** Figs. 6 ♂ and 7♀ represent the typical form. In ab. *sandbergi* Lampa, the median area is defined by two fuscous bands.

The caterpillar is somewhat similar to that of *O. dilutata*, but there is a yellowish tint in the general green coloration, and it is rarely marked with reddish. It is found chiefly on birch, alder, fir, and larch, but will eat hawthorn, and probably the foliage of other shrubs and trees. May and June.

The moth is out in September and October, sometimes later. It may be dislodged from trees in the daytime, but it seems to be rarely noticed at rest on the trunks.

The species is so often confused with *O. dilutata* that its distribution in our islands has not, so far, been clearly ascertained. However, it certainly occurs in the following counties —Hampshire ; Surrey ; Sussex ; Kent ; Lancashire (Liverpool district) ; Cheshire (Delamere Forest) ; Yorkshire (Cleveland district) ; North Durham (birch woods) ; Cumberland (Carlisle). In Scotland it is found on the Isle of Rhum, in Clydesdale, Perthshire, where it was first noted by Weaver in 1851, Kincardineshire, Aberdeen, and probably further north ; in Ireland it is recorded from the counties of Donegal, Tyrone, Fermanagh, and Down in the north, and Wicklow in the south. Prout notes that he has seen a specimen from Swansea in South Wales.

The Small Autumnal Moth (*Oporinia filigrammaria* H.-Sch.)

This is a close relative of *O. autumnata*, but it rarely assumes the silvery white typical coloration of that species. A male specimen and an example of the female are depicted on Pl. **89,** 3 ♂, 5 ♀.

The caterpillar, which feeds in the spring on bilberry and heather, is green, with yellow lines, a line of darker green between the two central yellow lines along the back ; head, green, inclining to brown above.

The moth appears in August and early September, and may be found on the moors, resting on rocks, stones, and even on the ground, as well as on the stems of its food plants.

As a British species it was first recorded by Weaver, who obtained it in the Isle of Arran in 1841 ; but Edleston, writing in 1842, states that he had taken specimens off stone walls near Staley Bridge, in the Manchester district, " every year for the last three years." It appears to be peculiar to the British Isles and is found in suitable localities from North Staffordshire, through Cheshire, Lancashire, Yorkshire, and northwards over England and Scotland to the Hebrides and the Orkneys. In Ireland it is known to occur in Antrim, Derry, Donegal, Fermanagh, Galway, Limerick, Dublin, and Wicklow.

The Pale November Moth (*Oporinia christyi* Prout)

O. christyi was described from specimens taken by the late W. M. Christy, in whose honour the species was named. It is very similar in appearance to *dilutata* but the wings are usually glossier and often have a yellow tinge. Usually the postmedial fascia on the fore wing in *dilutata* is wavy and passes through the cell spot ; in *christyi* it is angled at the subcostal vein and then runs straight to the inner margin without passing through the cell spot which, in this species, is weak and often wanting (Pl. **89**, 8, 9). The wing markings are, however, very variable ; in ab. *oblita* Allen the ground colour of the wings is smoky brown ; in ab. *latifasciata* Prout the basal and median areas are fuscous whilst the ground colour is whiter than in typical specimens ; ab. *nigra* Harr. is a wholly black form found locally in the north of England. The males of these two closely related species can be readily distinguished by the position of the two projections or octavals which are to be found on the ventral surface of the eighth abdominal segment at the posterior edge. A rub or two with a camel-hair brush will remove the covering scales and expose them ;

1, 2, 3, 4, 5. **The Magpie** *varieties*.
6, 7, 8. **Clouded Magpie** *varieties*.

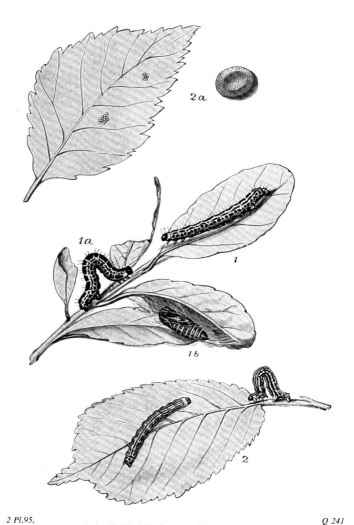

1, 1a, 1b. **The Magpie:** *caterpillars and chrysalis.*
2, 2a. **Clouded Magpie:** *eggs, natural size and enlarged, and caterpillars.*

in *dilutata* they are on the average 0·43 mm. apart, in *christyi* they are 0·23 mm. Once a male of each species has been examined, the differences are sufficiently great to recognise either species at a glance.

The larva is very variable; the ground colour may be green, red brown or purple brown, more or less spotted with ill-defined purple brown or chocolate brown markings. These markings are, apparently, never black or clay coloured. It feeds on beech, wych elm, and sallow, from April until June.

This woodland moth flies in October and November, is ocally common in many parts of England and Wales and is widely distributed in Scotland and Ireland. Abroad, the range is known to include Scandinavia, Germany and Czecho-slovakia, but will probably be found eventually to be much greater.

The November Moth (*Oporinia dilutata* Schiff.)

The more usual forms of this common autumnal species are those represented by Figs. 1, 2 and 4, Pl. **89**. In ab. *obscurata* Staud. the ground colour is suffused with fuscous but with the parts which are usually palest remaining somewhat paler and the bands still traceable in dark fuscous; ab. *melana* Prout is uniformly blackish.

The eggs (Pl. **91**, 1*a*) were yellowish when laid, but soon changed to crimson red.

The caterpillar is green, inclining to whitish below, often marked, more or less distinctly, with purplish red, as a central line, or series of spots, along the back, and sometimes as bands on the ring division. It feeds on the foliage of trees, such as elm, oak, birch, etc., also on sallow, hawthorn, sloe, apple, plum, and other fruit trees. April to June (Pl. **91**, 1).

The moth is out in October and November in the south, but earlier in the north. It is an inhabitant of woodlands, and may be disturbed from bushes, trees, and sometimes may be seen on the trunks of the latter, and on fences. At night it flies lazily and will occasionally visit ivy then, and even sugar, but is more frequently attracted by light.

FIG. 7.—NOVEMBER MOTH AT REST.

The species is pretty generally common throughout England and Wales, Scotland up to Moray, and Ireland.

The Northern Winter Moth (*Operophtera fagata* Scharf.)

This species is generally larger than the last-mentioned. The fore wings are marked somewhat as in that species, but they are paler in colour and more glossy ; hind wings whitish and glossy. In the female, the wings are useless for flying, but still they are larger than those of *brumata*. The front pair have a blackish band (Pl. **89**, 10 and 12 ♂, 11 ♀; ova Pl. **93**, 1).

The caterpillar is greenish, with a greyish stripe along the back, another edged above with yellow along the black spiracles, and a greyish line between the stripes ; the head is black.

It feeds, in May and June, on birch, and the moth does not appear until October or November.

At one time considered to be a purely northern species : the earliest known British specimens, four in number, having been captured at Petty Pool, Delamere, Cheshire, on October 31, 1848. It is now known, however, to have a wide distribution in the south of England. Northwards, its range extends throughout England and Scotland up to Moray and it also occurs in the Hebrides. It is found in South Wales ; also in a few localities in the north of Ireland.

Abroad, the range extends through northern and central Europe to south-eastern Russia.

The Winter Moth (*Operophtera brumata* Linn.)

In orchards and gardens wherein are fruit trees one may have noticed that the trunks of the trees have broad bands around them. If these bands are examined, they will be seen to be covered with a sticky compound, which has been put there for the purpose of trapping the almost wingless females of the Winter Moth, as they crawl up the tree after emergence from the chrysalis. In spite of such devices, and other precautionary measures taken to safeguard the trees from attack, the foliage of apple, pear, etc., will not be quite free from the caterpillars of this species in their season.

The male has greyish brown fore wings, which are crossed by numerous rather darker wavy lines ; in some examples there is a dark, more or less distinct, central band (ab. *huenei* Prout). The ground colour is very much darker in some specimens than in others, and examples of a unicolorous sooty brown colour are not infrequent (ab. *unicolor* Lambill) ; Barrett mentions an almost buff-coloured specimen. In the female, the small structures representing wings are brownish, with indications of a darker band towards the outer margin of the front pair.

A small, purplish brown form, reared in January, 1882, from

caterpillars found in Cumberland, feeding on sweet gale (*Myrica gale*), was described as a new species under the name *myricaria* Cooke (*Entom.*, xv. 57). This has been referred by Staudinger to *O. fagata*, as a form of that species, but it is now considered to be a race of *brumata*.

(a)   (b)

FIG. 8.—WINTER MOTH AT REST : (a) MALE (×2), (b) FEMALE (×3).

The caterpillar is green, with a stripe of darker green along the back ; on each side of this are two white lines, and along the black spiracles is a pale yellowish line ; head, green, sometimes marked with blackish. It feeds on the foliage of trees and bushes and has been found feeding on heather ; it sometimes abounds in April and May.

The moth appears during the winter months, and has been noted as early as October and as late as February (Pl. **89**, 13, 15 ♂, 14 ♀).

Generally distributed throughout the British Isles.

Abroad, the range extends through northern and central Europe to north-eastern Amur.

1. The
Magpie.

2. The
Magpie.

3. Clouded
Magpie.

4. Clouded
Magpie.

5. Clouded
Border.

6. Scorched
Carpet.

7. Sloe
Carpet.

8. Clouded
Border.

9. Clouded
Silver.

10. Clouded
Silver.

11. Clouded
Border.

12. Common
White Wave.

13. Common
Wave.

14. White-pinion
Spotted.

15. Common
White Wave.

16. Common
Wave.

1. **Scorched Carpet:** *caterpillars.*
2. **Clouded Border:** *caterpillar.*
3. **Common White Wave:** *caterpillar.*

The Small White Wave (*Asthena albulata* Hufn.)

The delicately lined white moth shown on Pl. **90,** 1 ♂ and 4 ♀, is chiefly a woodland species. It is generally common in the south of England, occurs more or less frequently throughout the northern half, and is widely distributed in Wales. In Scotland, it is said to be locally common in Clydesdale, and to be found in Arran and in Perthshire. It is plentiful at Dromoland, Co. Clare, Ireland, not uncommon in parts of Galway, and is also recorded from other counties.

The caterpillar is found, in July and August, on birch, hazel, and wild rose. In general colour it is green, inclining to bluish at each end, and tinged with yellowish along the ridge on the sides ; the back is marked with crimson (Pl. **92,** 2, after Hofmann).

The moth is out in May and June, and sometimes July, and individuals of a second generation occasionally appear in August or September.

Abroad, the range extends throughout Europe and Western Asia.

The Drab Looper (*Minoa murinata* Scop.)

The grey brown or ochreous brown wings of this delicate, but unattractive little moth (Pl. **90,** 10, 13), are silky in texture. After it has flown for a time, the wings become paler, and lose most of their sheen.

The thick-set, roughish caterpillar is reddish brown, dotted with pale ochreous ; there is a slender white line along the middle of the back, and black oblique streaks on the sides ; a blackish wavy line along the area of the spiracles is bordered below with yellowish. It feeds on wood spurge (*Euphorbia amygdaloides*) and also, South had reason to believe, on petty spurge (*E. peplus*), a rather common weed in some gardens, from July to September. In forward seasons the moth, which flies in the sunshine, has been noted in late April, but May and June are the best months for it. In the New Forest, and elsewhere, it has occurred in August. On one occasion South stated that, in a garden at Brockenhurst, several specimens were taken in the autumn, and it was supposed that they resulted from eggs laid by a damaged female that had been captured in the woods and turned out into this garden. It has been taken at lamps, at Dorking among other places.

The species has been recorded from Pembrokeshire, Glamorgan, and Monmouth, in South Wales ; and it appears to be found in most of the counties of England southwards from Worcester, Hereford, Gloucester, Oxford, and Buckinghamshire. Except that it has been doubtfully recorded from Stowmarket, Suffolk, it does not seem to be found in the eastern counties ; and I cannot find that it has been noted from Devon or Cornwall.

The range abroad extends to Amurland.

The Waved Carpet (*Hydrelia testaceata* Don.)

The typical, greyish-dusted, white form is depicted on Pl. **90**, 9 ♂ and 12 ♀. According to Bankes (*Entom.*, xl. 33), in one restricted area in mid-Kent this species varies in the direction of melanism, and he described two forms as under : ab. *intermedia* Bankes has the usual coloration, but the wings are thickly dusted with dusky brown, chiefly along the front edge of the fore wings, and the cross lines are more distinct than in the type. In ab. *goodwini* Bankes all the wings have the whitish ground colour largely obscured by dusky brown powdering.

The rather spindle-shaped caterpillar is purplish brown, inclining to greenish on the sides and below at each end ; on the back of the middle rings are whitish V-marks, and the last three rings incline to purplish red above (adapted from Fenn). It feeds on the young leaves of alder, birch, and sallow, in July and August (Pl. **71**, 2). The moth is out in June, and hides by day among the bushes, but may be seen occasionally on tree-trunks. Its haunts are in damp woods and plantations, and it occurs in most of the English and Welsh counties, although it is rarely common, except in the south of England. In Ireland it has been noted as scarce in counties Wicklow, Kerry, Galway, and Sligo.

The range abroad extends to Amurland and Japan.

The Small Yellow Wave (*Hydrelia flammeolaria* Hufn.)

This pretty little species (Pl. **90**, 3, 6) has the pale yellowish wings marked with ochreous brown lines, which vary in thickness, and a dash of the same colour on the fore wings, from the central pair of lines to the middle of the outer margin.

The caterpillar, which feeds in August and September, on maple, and in the northern counties on alder, is green, inclining to whitish between the rings.

The moth is out in June and early July, sometimes from mid-May in warm localities. It is widely distributed over England and Wales, and in the southern counties of England it occurs in hedges wherever the maple grows, but in the midlands and northwards it is chiefly found among alder. In Scotland it is known from Kirkcudbrightshire, is local and rare in Clydesdale, and is known to occur in Perthshire.

Abroad, the range extends to Amurland and Japan.

The Dingy Shell (*Euchoeca nebulata* Scop.)

This pale ochreous brown species (Pl. **90**) is in the male (Fig. 2) more or less sprinkled and shaded with darker brown, and the three brown cross lines are consequently often obscure, and rarely as distinct as in the female (Fig. 5).

The green caterpillar has a yellow line running down the middle of a dark stripe along the back, and this stripe is bordered on each side with yellow, and broken up by the yellow ring divisions ; head, with a black spot on each side. It feeds, in July and August, on alder.

The moth is out in June and early July, and will be found in almost every locality in England where the alder flourishes, most plentifully, perhaps, on the eastern and western sides. It has been recorded from North and South Wales, but it does not seem to have been noted from Ireland or Scotland.

The range abroad extends to Amurland and Japan.

The Welsh Wave (*Venusia cambrica* Curtis)

This moth, of which two portraits are given on Pl. **90,** 7 ♂, 8 ♀, is known also by the English name of " Cambric Wave." It was not ascertained to be an inhabitant of Britain until 1839, when it was figured and described by Curtis from specimens obtained in Cardiganshire in Wales.

In its typical form the fore wings are white, inclining to greyish, with a number of brownish or dark grey cross lines ; two pairs on the central area are marked with black. Sometimes the wings are greatly suffused with smoky grey, and this tint in examples from the Sheffield and Rotherham districts of Yorkshire assumes a much darker hue, so that all the markings are obscured, but the veins are blacker (ab. *bradyi* Prout). In ab. *lofthousei* Prout the fore wing is suffused with fuscous but remaining longitudinally rayed with white in the distal area ; hind wing not infuscated.

The caterpillar (Pl. **79,** 3) is green, marked with some irregular reddish blotches ; a yellowish line along the back. It feeds in August, earlier or later in some seasons, on mountain ash (*Pyrus aucuparia*), and the moth, which rests by day on tree-trunks, is out in July and early August. The haunts of the species are chiefly in hilly localities of the northern counties of England, but it has also been reported from Gloucestershire (Cotswolds), Somerset (Weston-super-Mare), and Devon (Dulverton). In Wales it occurs in Merionethshire, as well as in Cardiganshire ; it occurs on the Isle of Man, and in Scotland it spreads from Roxburghshire, where it is locally common among mountain ash, through Clydesdale to Inverness, and is recorded from the Isle of Rhum in the Hebrides. It is widely distributed in Ireland. The range abroad extends to Japan and North America.

Blomer's Rivulet (*Discoloxia blomeri* Curtis)

The earliest British specimens of this species (Pl. **90,** 11 ♂ and 14 ♀) were taken in Castle Eden Dean, Durham, and among the first to detect these was Captain Blomer, after whom Curtis named the species in 1832. It is still found in that locality, but is also known to occur in Cumberland, Lancashire, Yorkshire, Lincolnshire, Derbyshire, Staffordshire, Merionethshire, Worcestershire, Herefordshire, Glamorgan, Gloucestershire, Somerset, Devon, Wiltshire, Oxfordshire, and Buckinghamshire.

The slender caterpillar is yellowish green, generally marked with pinkish brown on the back, but most or all such markings may be absent. It feeds, on wych elm (*Ulmus montana*) (Pl. **92,** 1), in August and September. The moth is out in June and July, earlier or later in some seasons. As a rule, it sits on the trunks of beech trees, but South had seen it on the stems of cherry and fir, though hardly ever on wych elm. Occasionally, newly emerged specimens have been noted on the leaves of dog's mercury (*Mercurialis perennis*).

The range abroad extends to Amurland and Japan.

ENNOMINAE

The Clouded Magpie (*Abraxas sylvata* Scop.)

A more or less typical example of each sex of this variable species will be found on Pl. **96.** Fig. 3 represents a male, and Fig. 4 a female; the slightly marked ab. *pantarioides* Spitz somewhat approaches the Continental species *A. pantaria* Linn. in appearance, and it is probable that such individuals have done duty for the species just named in some of the older collections of British lepidoptera. On Pl. **94** are shown the leaden tinted form (*suffusa* Tutt) (Fig. 6), sometimes not infrequent in certain Yorkshire localities ; a specimen with smoky fore wings (Fig. 7), taken with a few other examples of the same form in a wood in Buckinghamshire, in 1907, when also the strongly banded form (Fig. 8) was secured by Mr. A. J. Scollick. Between the extremes and the more typical forms all kinds of intergrades occur, but it is not possible here to discuss these in detail.

The pale greenish yellow eggs and two caterpillars are figured on Pl. **95**, 2, 2a. The latter are whitish, inclining to yellowish on the back, and lined with black ; stripe below the black spiracles, yellow ; head, black and glossy. The food is wych elm (*Ulmus montana*), but beech and hazel are said to be eaten at times : August to October. The moth is found in May and June, sitting about on the leaves of dog's mercury, and other vegetation in its woodland haunts. Although it sometimes occurs sparingly in the southern seaboard counties, it is far more frequent in the west, ranging from North Devon to Cumberland, and including Wales. It occurs in Sussex, is common in Buckinghamshire, and northwards to Northumberland, and extends into Dumfriesshire. In Ireland, not uncommon at Killarney, and reported from a few other localities. Abroad it ranges eastwards to Japan.

The Magpie (*Abraxas grossulariata* Linn.)

The specimen represented by Fig. 1 on Pl. **96** shows this highly variable species in its typical and most frequent form. Fig. 2 on the same plate depicts an example of the ordinary darker forms leading up to ab. *hazeleighensis* Raynor, in which the whole of the fore wing area between the orange bands is blackish, except two tiny white specks near the front margin. Not infrequently the black spots on the outer margin of the fore wings exhibit a tendency to spread inwards, and very occasionally they unite with the series of spots outside the orange band, as in Pl. **94**, 1, which represents a specimen kindly lent by the late R. Adkin with blackish-tinged hind wings. Sometimes the ground colour of all the wings is yellowish (ab. *lutea* Cockerell), but the markings are of the usual pattern. The example of this form Pl. **94,** 3) was reared from a large number of caterpillars collected at Purley, in Surrey, and was the only example among the moths resulting therefrom that was worth retaining. The very fine variety shown on Pl. **94,** 5, is ab. *varleyata* Porritt, which occurs in Yorkshire, but is mostly reared in captivity

FIG. 9.—MAGPIE MOTH AT REST (ENLARGED).

from eggs obtained from a wild female in the first place, and subsequent pairings ; the specimen figured is an especially fine example of the female sex, raised among others of the same form by Mr. G. T. Porritt of Huddersfield, who was good enough to lend it for the purpose. Many other varieties of this species have been named and described by the Rev. Gilbert H. Raynor, but reference can only be made here to two of these ; one is ab. *melanozona*, a Scottish form, in which there is a black blotch with traces of yellow in it at the base of the fore wings ; a large black discal spot in the white central area ; a black band, widening towards the front margin, before the faint yellow band, the latter followed by four black spots ; hind wings with central black spot, and two series of black spots beyond, seven in each series, separated by a well-defined white area. Fig. 2 on Pl. **94** represents a specimen of this variety. The handsome cream-coloured specimen (Pl. **94**, 4) is ab. *dohrnii* Koenig. These insects were also kindly lent by the late R. Adkin.

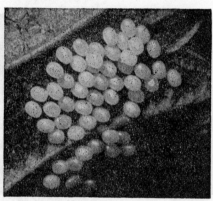

FIG. 10.—EGGS OF MAGPIE MOTH ON CURRANT LEAF (ENLARGED ×5)

The caterpillar and chrysalis are figured on Pl. **95**, 1–1*b*; the former is creamy white, marked on the back with black blotches and dots, and lines of black dots on the sides ; between the lower two rows is a broad reddish line ; head, black ; sometimes the whole body is black. It occurs in gardens, and sometimes is a serious pest where currants and goose-berries are cultivated ; it frequently abounds on *Euonymus japonicus*. In the open country it feeds on sloe and hawthorn ; sometimes it is found on elm (low growth in hedges), apple, navelwort (*Cotyledon umbilicus*), orpine (*Sedum telephium*), and in the Hebrides, on ling (*Calluna*). August to May, or

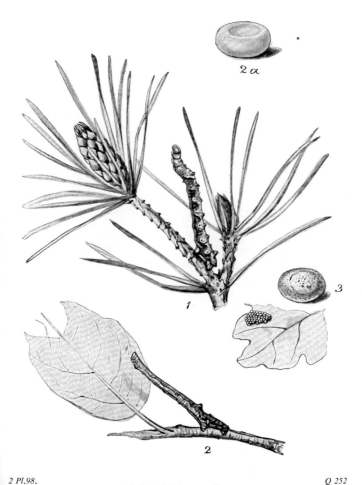

1. **Barred Red:** *caterpillar.*
2, 2a. **Barred Umber:** *egg, natural size and enlarged, and caterpillar.*
3. **Light Emerald:** *eggs, natural size and enlarged.*

1. Barred
Umber.

2. Barred
Red
(ab. *prasinaria*).

3. Barred
Red,
male.

4. Barred
Red,
female.

5. Light
Emerald.

6. Large
Thorn,
male.

7. Large
Thorn,
female.

8. August
Thorn,
male.

9. August
Thorn,
female.

early June, are the months in which it is found as a rule; occasionally it does not hibernate, but feeds up and attains the moth state in the autumn of the year that it hatches from the egg. The moth is out, normally, in July and August, and is distributed over the greater part of the British Isles.

The range abroad extends to eastern Siberia, China, and Japan.

The Clouded Border (*Lomaspilis marginata* Linn.)

Figs. 8 and 11 on Pl. **96** represent the more usual forms, in both sexes, of this rather common, but pretty, little moth. Occasionally, specimens are obtained in which, with the exception of a dark patch or two on the front margin, the wings are entirely white or slightly tinged with pale yellowish (ab. *pollutaria* Hübn.); a modification of this form is shown in Fig. 5.

Ab. *nigrofasciaria* Schöyen, has a rather broad blackish band across the central area of each wing, and indications of such bands, in the shape of spots or dots, are seen in many examples of the species; occasionally, the irregular dark border of the outer margin of the wings is traversed by an interrupted whitish line.

The caterpillar is yellowish green, with three dark green double lines on the back, the central one blotched with purplish brown on the last ring; head, green, marked with purplish brown. The figure (Pl. **97**, 2) is from a drawing in colour by the late Mr. Sich. It feeds on sallow, willow, and aspen, and may be found almost throughout the summer from June. The moth is also met with during the summer months, but seems to be most frequent in May and June. The species prefers moist localities where sallows abound, and in such places seems to occur pretty generally over the British Isles. In Scotland, however, it has not, apparently, been noted north of Moray.

The range abroad extends to Amurland and Japan.

The Scorched Carpet (*Ligdia adustata* Schiff.)

The bluish grey band on the outer third of the fore wings
varies in width, and the velvety black marking thereon varies
in amount ; this area of the wings is also more or less clouded
with reddish brown, and the underside of all the wings is
much suffused with reddish brown, which gives the insect
the burnt or scorched appearance to which both Latin and
English names refer (Pl. **96**, 6).   In June and early July, and
again in late August and September, the red-spotted, bright
green caterpillar may be beaten from the spindle bushes
(*Euonymus europaeus*) in hedgerows (Pl. **97**, 1, is from a
coloured drawing by the late Mr. Sich).

The moth is out in late April sometimes, but it is more
frequent in May and June, and as a second generation in
August, earlier or later in some seasons.   It may be beaten
out of hedges in which spindle is growing.   The species is
not uncommon in most of the southern English counties, but
in the northern ones its occurrence is more casual.   It has
been recorded from North Wales ; in Ireland it is fairly
common in some western and southern counties, and rare in
the east and north ; in Scotland, only noted from the south-
east, and doubtfully from Arran, and the Hebrides.

Abroad, its range extends to Asia Minor.

The Sloe Carpet (*Bapta distinctata* Herr.-Schäff.)

This blackish grey species (Pl. **96**, 7) has been confused in
the past with *pictaria* Thunb., which is referable to *Cleora
lichenaria*, and it was then known by the popular name of
" The Grey Carpet."   As the caterpillar feeds on the foliage
of the sloe, and the moth is fond of resting on the stems and
twigs, and appears at the time the bushes are wreathed in
their snowy blossoms, the Sloe Carpet seems to be rather
more suitable than are most of the names by which our moths
are popularly known.

The caterpillar is dusky brown, with blackish V-shaped

marks upon the back, white marks on rings 7 and 8, and a
black line on the last ring. It feeds at night, in June and
early July, and as it remains on the bushes during the day,
it may be obtained by beating. At night the moths fly about
the bushes for a short time, and then sit on the twigs, when
they may be secured. Of course, a lantern will be a necessity.

Barrett states that stunted bushes on open heaths and hillsides are preferred to hedgerows.

The species is very local, but generally not uncommon
where it occurs, as, for example, in the New Forest, Hampshire ; the Loughton and Colchester districts, Essex ; and in
some parts of Kent. It has been noted from Tilgate Forest,
and other localities in Sussex ; and also from Surrey, Berkshire,
and Suffolk. Abroad, the range extends to Asia Minor.

The White-pinion Spotted (*Bapta bimaculata* Fabr.)

The two cross lines on the fore wings of this silky white
species (Pl. **96,** 14) commence in blackish spots on the front
margin ; often they are only indicated by series of dots, and
are rarely really distinct. Occasionally, a greyish submarginal
line or band is present.

The darkish green caterpillar has a series of purplish marks
on the back ; head, inclining to yellowish, and powdered with
purplish. It feeds, in June and July, on hawthorn and will
eat the leaves of wild cherry and plum ; it may be beaten
from its food plant in the daytime. The moth is out in May
and June, and shelters in bushes, etc., in woods and hedgerows. During the day it is frequently put up from its hiding-
places, but its usual time of flight is the evening, when it is
readily seen and not difficult to capture. It is local, and
perhaps most frequently met with in those parts of South
England where the wild cherry flourishes. Occurs more or
less commonly in most of the southern counties, but north
of Gloucester, Oxford, and Norfolk it has only been noted
from North Lancashire, Westmorland, and Cumberland. In

Wales the late Mr. C. G. Barrett found the moth rare in Pembrokeshire, and there is also a record from Anglesey. In Ireland from Kerry only.

The range abroad extends to China, Korea, and Japan.

The Clouded Silver (*Bapta temerata* Schiff.)

In its silky, white wings this species (Pl. **96**, 9 ♂, 10 ♀) is similar to the last mentioned. It is, however, rather larger, and there are greyish clouds on each side of the outer cross line, but there are no blackish spots on the front edge of the fore wings. The clouding referred to is heavier and darker in some specimens than in others, but occasionally, chiefly in the female, is almost absent.

The green caterpillar, when full grown, is ornamented with brown-bordered reddish spots on the back, but these markings are absent in its earlier stages. The head is paler than the body, and has a reddish spot on each side. It feeds, in July and August, on sloe, plum, and bird cherry in this country, but the Continental authors give birch, willow, rose, etc. The moth is out in May and June, and occurs throughout England and Wales, to Cumberland and occurs on the Isle of Man ; but it is far more frequent in the south than in the north. Barrett mentions a single specimen from Wigtownshire in Scotland. In Ireland, Kane stated that it is abundant at Clonbrock, Merlin Park, and in several other localities in Galway ; it is not uncommon at Killarney, Kerry ; and a few specimens have been taken at Powerscourt, Wicklow, and Sligo. Donovan says " From Tyrone to Cork."

The range abroad extends to Amurland and Japan.

The Common White Wave (*Deilinia pusaria* Linn.)

In its typical form (Pl. **96**, 12, 15) this white species has three dark grey almost parallel cross lines on the fore wings and two on the hind wings. The first or the second of these lines on the fore wings may be absent, occasionally both may

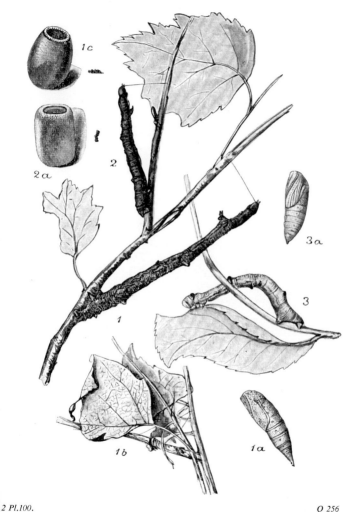

1 1*a*, 1*b*, 1*c*. **Large Thorn**: *eggs, natural size and enlarged, caterpillar, chrysalis and puparium.*
2, 2*a*. **Canary-shouldered Thorn**: *eggs, natural size and enlarged, and caterpillar.*
3, 3*a*. **Dusky Thorn**: *caterpillar and chrysalis.*

1, 2. **August Thorn,** *male and female.*
3, 4. **Canary-shouldered Thorn,** *male and female.*
5. **Dusky Thorn,** *male.*
6. **September Thorn,** *male.*
7, 8. **Early Thorn** (*1st brood*).
9. **Early Thorn** (*2nd brood*).
10. **Lunar Thorn.**

be missing and the third very faint. Not infrequently in undersized bred specimens the first line approaches the second line either throughout its length or near the inner margin, and more rarely the two are united ; in most of such aberrations the tips of the fore wings are rather more rounded than in typical specimens, and these are referable to ab. *rotundaria* Haw. (Round-winged Wave). South had over a dozen examples of this form, all of which were reared from caterpillars which had been kept on short rations when nearly mature ; in some, the outer margin of the fore wings is distinctly rounded, but in others it is much the same as in the larger typical form. The ground colour occasionally assumes a greyish tint, and sometimes this is tinged with pink ; more rarely the general colour is leaden grey (ab. *heveraria* Herr.-Schäff.).

The caterpillar, of which there are two broods, one in July and another in September, feeds on birch, alder, etc. It is purplish brown, spotted with white above, and greenish below on the first three rings. There is also a green form with purplish brown marks on the back (Pl. **97,** 3, from a coloured drawing by the late Mr. A. Sich). The moth is out in May, June, and August, and is generally common throughout the greater part of the British Isles.

Abroad, the range extends to eastern Siberia and Amurland.

The Common Wave (*Deilinia exanthemata* Scop.)

Somewhat similar to the last species, but sprinkled with ochreous grey ; the fore wings have three greyish cross lines, the first two less regular than those of *pusaria*, and the outer one distinctly curved ; variation in the lines is pretty much the same as in *pusaria* and its small form ab. *rotundaria*. Of the form showing the first and second lines more or less confluent, South had seven examples reared from collected caterpillars ; six are undersized, but the other is of quite ordinary size (ab. *approximaria* Haw.) ; another specimen, also bred, is thinly powdered with ochreous grey, and the lines are very indistinct (ab. *arenosaria* Haw.). The more usual forms are shown on Pl. **96**, 13, 16.

The caterpillar is green, inclining to yellowish or to brownish; some purplish red marks and white-edged black spots on the back; the ring divisions are yellow, and there are reddish brown or purplish red marks on the sides; the markings vary. It feeds on aspen and sallow, and may be beaten out at any time from July to September. The moth is out through the summer from May; its range in the British Isles is very similar to that of the last species, but it seems to have a preference for moist places.

The distribution abroad extends eastwards to Amurland.

The Barred Umber (*Anagoga pulveraria* Linn.)

Pale ochreous or reddish brown freckled with darker; the central dark reddish brown band is sometimes much narrowed below the middle; sometimes only the edges of the band are dark, the enclosed space being but little darker than the ground colour, or occasionally tinged with greenish; one example of the latter and two of the former were reared during 1908 from larvae received in July, 1907, from Mr. F. Pope of Exeter; a male specimen bred from the same batch of larvae, but which emerged in August of the year last mentioned, is distinctly tinged with rosy over all the wings; the narrow band on the hind wings, not usually extended to the front edge, is in this specimen entire, whilst the greenish banded specimen referred to above is without trace of a band on the hind wings. Two examples which are without locality, but which, South thought, came from the New Forest, have pale greyish brown fore wings banded with brown in which there is a tinge of olive. An example of the male is figured on Pl. **99**, 1. The eggs (Pl. **98**, 2a) were pale greenish yellow when laid, May 17 to 20; the larvae hatched out from May 31 to June 2.

1. Purple
Thorn
(*1st brood*).

2. Purple
Thorn
(*2nd brood*).

3. Lilac
Beauty.

4. Lilac
Beauty.

5. Scalloped
Hazel.

6. Scalloped
Hazel.
(ab. *nigra*).

7. Feathered
Thorn,
male.

8. Feathered
Thorn,
female.

9. Scalloped
Oak,
male.

10. Scalloped
Oak,
female.

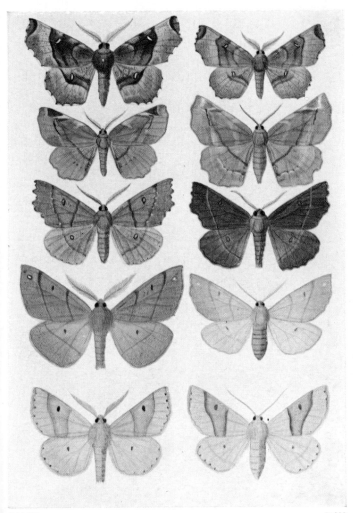

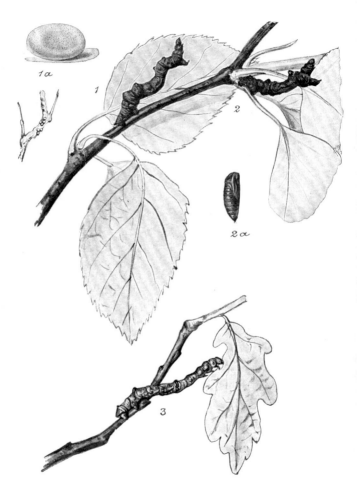

1, 1a. **Purple Thorn:** *eggs, natural size and enlarged, and caterpillar.*
2, 2a. **Lunar Thorn:** *caterpillar and chrysalis.*
3. **August Thorn:** *caterpillar.*

The caterpillar, which is also depicted on the plate, is reddish brown, mottled with yellowish brown. It feeds on birch, sallow, ash, etc., from June to August.

The moth, as a rule, does not emerge until the following spring, but sometimes specimens will come out the same year.

Although widely distributed over nearly the whole of the British Isles, the species seems to be rarely met with in large numbers. The range abroad extends to Amurland, Korea, and Japan.

The Barred Red (*Ellopia fasciaria* Linn.)

The typical form of this species is depicted on Pl. **99**, 3 ♂, 4 ♀, and Fig. 2 on the same plate represents ab. *prasinaria* Schiff., a form not uncommon in Germany, Switzerland, and other parts of the Continent, but which is very rare in Britain, and has been recorded from Kent and Suffolk. Sometimes, but chiefly in Scotland, the colour varies to a greyish or even yellowish tint ; the cross lines are often parallel or nearly so, and frequently approach each other about the middle ; the usual white edging to the cross lines is occasionally absent, and the enclosed space in such specimens is hardly darker than the general colour.

On Pl. **98**, 1, will be found a figure of the caterpillar, which is tawny brown with white-edged, connected reddish marks along the back. It has three pairs of prolegs. It feeds, from September to May, on Scots pine (*Pinus sylvestris*), and occasionally on larch. The moth is out in June and July, and sometimes in September. It may be jarred from the pine boughs, and is not infrequently seen resting on foliage of the undergrowth. Generally distributed in fir woods throughout Great Britain, and widely spread in Ireland. The larva also feeds on cedar and deodar.

The range abroad extends to eastern Siberia.

The Light Emerald (*Campaea margaritata* Linn.)

When quite fresh, this species (Pl. **99,** 5) is of a delicate whitish green colour, but the green tint is apt to fade or to change colour, so that the wings are sometimes almost ochreous white.

The eggs shown on Pl. **98,** 3, were kindly supplied by Mr. Norman Riley.

The caterpillar ranges in colour from greenish brown to purplish brown, and is frequently freckled with a darker shade of the general colour ; there is sometimes a pale patch on rings 6 and 7, and the sides are fringed with fine bristles along the spiracle area. It has three pairs of prolegs. It feeds, from September to May, on the leaves of oak, birch, beech, elm, etc., and during the winter will nibble the bark of the younger twigs, and also eat the buds.

The moth, which is partial to the woodlands, is out in June and July, and is pretty generally distributed over the British Isles except the Orkneys and Shetlands. Abroad the range extends eastwards to Transcaucasia.

The Large Thorn (*Ennomos autumnaria* Wernb.)

This fine species was first definitely ascertained to occur in Britain in 1855, but it had been reported as British at a much earlier date, and was figured by Wood in 1839. Up to 1859 it had only been recorded from the North Foreland and Margate in Kent, and from Brighton, Sussex. In 1862, a specimen was taken at Brighton and one at Deal, the latter a female. Two examples were secured at Gosport, Hampshire, in 1865, and one at Deal in 1867. Then, after an interval of ten years, three were captured in Hampshire (Alverstoke), and two years later a round dozen were obtained at Gosport. Specimens have also been recorded from Margate, Deal, Dover, Folkestone, Hythe, Ashford, Petts Wood, and Dartford in Kent, from Chichester, Sussex, and from Shoeburyness, Essex. It has been reared on several occasions from eggs obtained

1. Orange
Moth,
male.

2. Orange
Moth
(ab. *corylaria*).

3. Swallow-tailed
Moth.

4. Orange
Moth,
female.

5. Orange
Moth
(ab. *corylaria*).

6. Scorched
Wing.

7. The Brimstone.

8. Dark Bordered
Beauty,
female.

9. Dark Bordered
Beauty,
male.

10. Bordered
Beauty,
male.

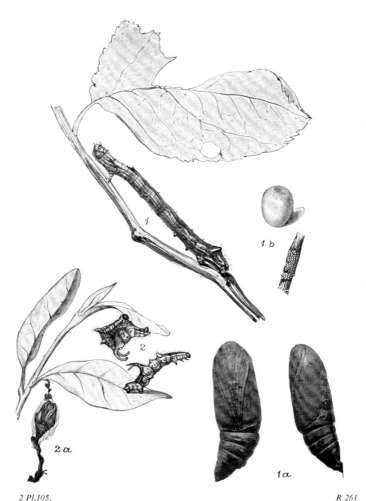

1, 1a, 1b. **Scalloped Hazel:** *eggs, natural size and enlarged, caterpillar and chrysalis, enlarged.*
2, 2a. **Lilac Beauty:** *caterpillars and chrysalis.*

from captured females, and is still more frequently bred from eggs deposited by the descendants of wild parents. In Ireland once only at Wexford.

The eggs are deep olive, with a white ring at one end ; and the caterpillar is brownish in colour, rather shining, and very twig-like. It feeds on birch, alder, hawthorn, sloe, plum, etc., and has been found on sycamore and cherry ; May to August. The early stages are figured on Pl. **100**, 1–1c. The moth (Pl. **99**, 6 ♂, 7 ♀), which varies in colour from pale to deep ochreous yellow, and also in the amount of purplish brown freckling, usually has the upper part of the outer marginal area some shade of tawny brown. Specimens of a greyish chocolate tint have been reared by Mr. Newman, of Bexley. Most of the specimens captured in England have been obtained at light in the autumn. The range abroad extends to Amurland and Japan.

The August Thorn (*Ennomos quercinaria* Hufn.)

The male (Pl. **101**, 1) is generally yellower than the female (Fig. 2), and it is in the former sex that brownish or red brown clouding on the outer area beyond the second cross line appears most frequently, but it occurs also in the female (Pl. **99**, 8 ♂, 9 ♀). Sometimes the wings are partly or entirely dull reddish brown. In ab. *carpinaria* Hübn., the wings are of a reddish ochreous colour.

The caterpillar (Pl. **103**, 3) is generally grey brown, mottled with reddish or olive ; but, according to Fenn, it is some-times greenish, without humps or projections. It feeds in the summer, on lime, birch, oak, hawthorn, etc. A chrysalis which South took out of its puparium (two leaves spun together with silk) on July 9, 1907, was green, with the upper surface tinged with yellowish ; a dark green central line, and a series of dark green irregular marks on each side ; the tail pointed and furnished with reddish hooks.

The moth is out in August and September, and may often be seen sitting on the boles of trees, generally low down. The species is widely distributed over England, and is much more frequent in the south than in the north. It has been recorded from Swansea in Wales; from Dumfries, Dunoon, and Monteith, in Scotland; and is frequent and generally distributed in Ireland (Donovan). The range abroad extends to Transcaucasia.

A hybrid resulting from a crossing of *E. autumnaria* ♂ and *E. quercinaria* ♀ has been named *dartfordi* Tutt (Tutt, "Brit. Lep.", vol. v., p. 31).

The Canary-shouldered Thorn (*Deuteronomos alniaria* Linn.)

This species (Pl. **101,** 3, 4) is generally easily recognised by the canary yellow coloured hairs of the thorax. The fore wings are yellowish, sprinkled with purplish grey, and crossed by two curved greyish brown lines, which not infrequently fall close together on the inner margin. In some female specimens that South reared from eggs, received from York, the wings are more or less tinged with dull tawny brown, especially on the outer area, and in two of them the thorax is also brownish tinged.

The at first green, and afterwards blackish slate-coloured, egg, with whitish ring, and the caterpillar are shown on Pl. **100,** 2, 2*a*. The latter is brownish, mottled with purplish above, and inclining to greenish below; head, rather paler brown. It feeds, from May to July, on birch, alder, etc. The moth is out in the autumn, and occurs in suitable wood-land and marshy places over England, Wales, and Scotland to Moray. It has been found in many parts of Ireland. Prout gives its range abroad as central Europe, southern France, northern Italy, Scandinavia and parts of Russia.

The Dusky Thorn (*Deuteronomos fuscantaria* Steph.)

Pl. **101**, 5 ♂, represent the usual form of this species; in some specimens the outer marginal pale purplish brown shading spreads inwards over the fore wings to the base; in other examples it is only seen on the upper part of the outer area.

The caterpillar is green, pretty much of the same tint as the underside of the ash leaf and the stalks, upon which it rests by day. In some examples the general colour inclines to pale brown, or reddish brown (Pl. **100**, 3). It has been noted that the green larvae are smooth and that the humps seem to develop with the intensity of the brownish colour. It may be found during the summer, and where the leaves are seen to have neat round holes in them, these should be examined, when this caterpillar will probably be found somewhere adjacent. Ash (*Fraxinus excelsior*) is the usual food, but possibly privet might answer as a substitute. The moth is out in August and September, and occurs in most parts of southern England where the ash flourishes; its range extends into South Wales, and northwards to Durham and Northumberland. Only doubtfully recorded from Ireland, and apparently unknown in Scotland.

Abroad the range extends to central Europe and the southern Baltic area.

The September Thorn (*Deuteronomos erosaria* Schiff.)

This species, shown on Pl. **101**, 6, varies in ground colour from pale ochreous to pale fulvous; the cross lines approach towards the inner margin, and sometimes the second line is bent inwards below the middle. Rarely the lines are entirely absent (ab. *unicoloria* Esp.). The central spot is generally absent, and when present is exceedingly faint. The twig-like caterpillar is brownish, with a greenish or purplish tinge. In its infancy it is a smooth-looking creature, but as it advances in growth knobs and humps appear, the most prominent of which are on rings 2, 5, 8, and 11 ; on the last ring there are two points. It feeds on oak chiefly, but will eat birch, lime, etc. : May to July. The moth is out in August and September, and occurs more or less frequently in most of the southern counties of England, but is rather scarce in the Midlands and northwards. It occurs in South Wales, and has been recorded from the south of Scotland. Very rare in Ireland. Abroad its range extends to Transcaucasia.

NOTE.—The species of *Ennomos* and *Deuteronomos* are fond of light, and in suitable spots, gas and electric lamps, in the streets, or even in the house when windows are open, will attract these moths. Most of the specimens of *autumnaria* that have been captured in Britain have occurred at light. *Quercinaria* is, perhaps, less often noted at light than its allies ; but, curiously, this species is more frequently seen at rest on tree-trunks, etc., than are either of the other kinds. Female moths taken at light may not always be in first-rate condition, but they will probably lay eggs, and should be kept for that purpose in a chip box. The caterpillars do not hatch out until the following spring. Put the eggs in a cool place.

The Early Thorn (*Selenia bilunaria* Esp.)

The sexes of the spring or typical form are depicted on Pl. **101**, 7 ♂, 8 ♀ and the paler summer form gen. aest. *illunaria* Esp. (July Thorn), is represented by Fig. 9.

The caterpillar is orange or reddish brown, sometimes inclining to purplish ; there are pairs of reddish raised points on the back of rings 7 and 8 ; the creature, when resting, is very like a twig. It feeds on birch, alder, sallow, hawthorn, sloe, etc., in May and June, and again in August and September. The moth is out in April and early May. In 1905, a male occurred at Carnforth, Lancashire, on June 8 ; the second generation appears in July and August. A third has been obtained in captivity, and the moths of this brood are similar to those of the second. It has happened that the emergence of some moths of the second, or summer, form has been delayed until the following February, but these remained true to their race and did not assume the spring form. A melanic form (*harrisonii* Wagn.) bred by Harrison occurs in Durham and Yorkshire.

Generally distributed throughout England and Wales, and often abundant, especially in the south. In Scotland, Renton states that it is common in Roxburghshire, but there is only one brood ; the range extends to Sutherlandshire. Widely spread in Ireland and plentiful in some parts. Abroad it ranges through Europe, Transcaucasia to eastern Siberia.

The Lunar Thorn (*Selenia lunaria* Schiff.)

A female of this species is shown on Pl. **101**, 10; the male is usually more clouded with reddish. A second generation is sometimes raised in captivity, and the males of this brood (ab. *delunaria* Hübn.) are somewhat paler, whilst the females incline to a yellowish tint. In some Scottish specimens the reddish markings are tinged with purple ; and ab. *sublunaria* Steph., from Derbyshire, and from Scotland also, has the coloration very similar to that of the spring form of *S. tetralunaria*.

The caterpillar is figured on Pl. **103**, 2. The ground colour is usually some shade of brown, ranging from greyish or greenish to reddish, variegated with darker or paler clouds, and with traces of pale lines on the back. It occurs in the open from July to September, but may be reared both earlier and later in confinement. It feeds on sloe, plum, oak, birch, etc. The moth, in May and June, is sometimes seen on hedges or on the plants growing below ; or it may be jarred from the branches of trees, when it is more apt to fall to the ground than to fly. Like others of this group it is fond of light, and is frequently attracted thereto at night. The species is rarely plentiful, and always more or less local, but it is widely distributed over the British Isles to the Orkneys.

Distributed throughout Europe with the exception of Spain, Portugal, and Greece, eastward to Asia Minor and Armenia.

The Purple Thorn (*Selenia tetralunaria* Hufn.)

On Pl. **102**, Fig. 1 represents a specimen of the spring brood, and Fig. 2 one of the summer brood (gen. aest. *aestiva* Staud.). The ground colour of the typical form is whitish, sometimes tinged with grey, and sometimes with pinkish; the patch at the tip, and the basal two-thirds of the fore wings, also the basal half of the hind wings, are purplish brown, varying almost to blackish; or they may be rich red brown. Gen. aest. *aestiva* is rarely whitish in ground colour, but this is frequently of a pinkish tinge, and the darker portions of the wings are brownish, inclining to olive; sometimes the general colour is ochreous brown with dark brown cross lines, and a rust-coloured lunule at the tips of the fore wings. The hybrid resulting from a female of this species that had paired with a male *bilunaria* has been named *parvilunaria* Bartel. At the time it is laid, the egg is pale olive green, but it changes to shining reddish, and just before hatching to purplish black (Pl. **103**, 1*a*).

The caterpillar is reddish brown, mottled with darker brown, and with pale greyish. It feeds on birch, alder, oak, sallow, cherry, etc.: June and July, and again in the autumn (Pl. **103**, 1).

The moth is out in April and May, and the second generation emerges in July and August. A few specimens of a third generation have been reared in October, but this is unusual.

The species is more or less local, and rarely common, at least in the moth state; it occurs in all the southern counties of England, and a few specimens have been recorded from some of the midland and northern counties, and from South Wales. In Scotland, noted from Inverness-shire, Rannoch, Perthshire, and a specimen was reared on April 25, 1901, from a caterpillar found at Dunkeld, in the same county, the previous autumn.

Abroad, the range extends to Amurland and Japan.

The Lilac Beauty (*Apeira syringaria* Linn.)

The sexes of this species are shown on Pl. **102,** and it will be noted that the male (Fig. 3) is rather smaller and decidedly more brightly coloured than the female (Fig. 4). An older English name is " Richmond Beauty," Wilkes. Figures of the curiously shaped caterpillar and chrysalis will be found on Pl. **105,** 2, 2*a*. The former is yellowish brown, variegated with reddish and violet ; it feeds on honeysuckle, lilac, and privet, and may be beaten or searched for in May and early June, after hibernation. South found it commonly on privet hedges in the Mill Hill district, Middlesex, but in woods, and especially in the New Forest, it is obtained from honeysuckle. In his experience, the privet-feeding caterpillars always produced larger moths than those reared from caterpillars fed on honeysuckle. The moth emerges in June and July, the former month chiefly in confinement, and from such early moths a second generation may be obtained in the autumn. The smaller, paler forms of this brood are known as *helvolaria* Robs. and Gardn.

Although most frequent in the southern half of England and Wales, the range of the species extends to the northern counties ; and single specimens have been recorded from Durham and Northumberland, but the species has not been noted in Scotland. In Ireland it occurs in Galway, Down, Waterford, Wexford, Kerry, and Cork.

The distribution abroad extends to Amurland and Japan.

The Scalloped Hazel (*Gonodontis bidentata* Clerck)

This species varies in ground colour, from pale whity brown through shades of grey brown, olive brown, ochreous, and dark brown to black ; the blackish cross lines of the fore

wings are generally edged with white, but the edging is sometimes absent, and occasionally it alone remains distinct ; the
central space enclosed by the cross lines is often darker than
the general colour, and not infrequently it is faintly reddish.
Pl. **102**, 5 ♂ represents the more usual form of the species.
Fig. 6 is the black ab. *nigra* Prout, which occurs on the mosses
of Lancashire, and in Yorkshire.

The caterpillar is sometimes pale blue green and black,
resembling lichen ; the yellowish and brown mottled, purplish
form is figured on Pl. **105**, 1 where also are shown the eggs
(turquoise blue, changing to reddish brown), and the reddish
brown chrysalis. The latter, which is twice the natural size,
is from a photograph by the late Mr. H. Main. The caterpillar
feeds on the foliage of oak, birch, sallow, hawthorn, sloe, plum,
larch, etc. ; it grows very slowly, and may be beaten out in
most of the months from July to October. The moth is out
in May and June, and sometimes earlier. Pretty generally
distributed over the British Isles, but not noted in the Orkneys
or Shetlands. The range abroad extends to Amurland and
Japan.

The Feathered Thorn (*Colotois pennaria* Linn.)

A more or less typical but rather small male specimen is
shown on Pl. **102**, 7, but the ground colour is frequently more
tawny in tint, and sometimes it is much paler inclining to
yellowish ; the cross lines may be either wider apart, or closer
together, and the inner one is often clouded with blackish ;
sometimes both lines become almost bandlike ; the submarginal line, usually interrupted, is occasionally well defined.
The female, often browner than the specimen depicted (Fig. 8),
is frequently tinged with purple, and occasionally with pink.

The batch of eggs, as deposited, was photographed by the
late Mr. Main. The egg is olive green with a ring of pale
specks around the micropylar end. The caterpillar is slaty
grey inclining to purplish, with a series of not clearly defined

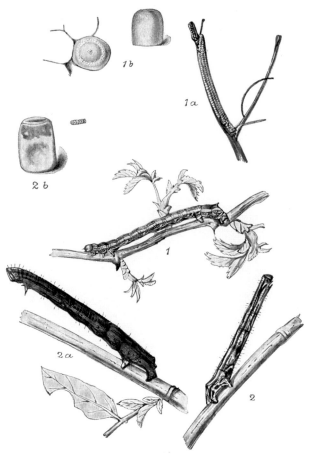

1, 1*a*, 1*b*. **Feathered Thorn:** *eggs, natural size and enlarged, and caterpillar.*
2, 2*a*, 2*b*. **Scalloped Oak:** *eggs, natural size and enlarged, and caterpillars.*

1. Little
Thorn.

2. Speckled
Yellow.

3. Sharp-angled
Peacock.

4. The Peacock
Moth.

5. Tawny-barred
Angle.

6. Spring
Usher,
male.

7. Early
Moth,
female.

8. Early
Moth,
male.

9. Spring
Usher,
male.

10. Spring
Usher,
female.

11. Spring
Usher,
male.

12. Scarce
Umber,
male.

13. Scarce
Umber,
female.

14. Dotted
Border,
male.

15. Dotted
Border,
male.

16. Dotted
Border,
female.

17. Dotted
Border,
male.

ochreous diamonds on the back and a row of ochreous dots on each side ; the raised points on the last ring are tipped with reddish (Pl. **106,** 1–1*b*). It feeds on oak, birch, poplar, sallow, apple, hawthorn, sloe, etc. April to June. The moth is out in October and November, but is seldom noticed in the day-time ; at night, the males are frequently seen at gas and electric light. The species is generally common in woodlands, especially as caterpillars, over the southern half of England and Wales, and occurs more or less frequently over the rest of the country, also in Scotland to Moray and Ross-shire, and in Ireland.

Abroad, it is found in central Europe, Asia Minor, and Trans-caucasia.

The Scalloped Oak (*Crocallis elinguaria* Linn.)

Fig. 9 on Pl. **102** shows the usual form of this species, in which there are blackish dots on the outer margins of all the wings. Fig. 10 depicts a form with the ground colour paler, and the outer marginal dots absent (ab. *trapezaria* Boisd.) The ground colour varies to almost whitish on the one hand and to reddish buff on the other ; the cross lines on the fore wings are distinct as a rule, but occasionally meet on inner margin (ab. *obviaria* Ljungdahl) ; the central space between the lines is most often brownish, sometimes tawny, but not infrequently this area is but little darker than the general colour. The blackish discal spot on the hind wings varies in size and somewhat in shape, but this and also the line beyond, are sometimes absent. Porritt (*List of Yorkshire Lepidoptera*) mentioned two gynandrous specimens. Eggs, pale grey, with darkish grey marking (Pl. **106,** 2*b*). The caterpillar, of which two figures from coloured drawings by the late Mr. A. Sich are given on Pl. **106,** 2, 2*a*, varies from ochreous grey to dark grey tinged with purple ; the front rings are often paler above, and the back has diamond-shaped marks upon it ; the elevation on the last ring is edged with black. It feeds on the leaves of most trees and bushes during the spring. The moth is out in July and August, sometimes earlier. A pretty generally distributed species throughout the British Isles, it has been taken in Skye, but so far it has not been noted from the Orkneys or Shetland.

Abroad, the range extends to eastern Siberia.

The Orange Moth (*Angerona prunaria* Linn.)

Typical males of this species are orange and the females pale ochreous, all the wings sprinkled or freckled with purplish grey (Pl. **104**, 1 ♂, 4 ♀). Ab. *corylaria* Thunb. (Pl. **104**, 2 ♂, 5 ♀), is brownish on the basal and outer marginal areas of the fore wings, and nearly the whole of the hind wings. The typical ground colour appears on the fore wings as a central band, but as a rule this does not quite reach the inner margin. Ab. *pickettaria* Prout, is a modification of the *corylaria* form, in which the typical ground appears on the front margin above the brownish basal patch, and also along the outer margin, thus narrowing the brownish border on that area ; in one male specimen the right pair of wings were *corylaria* and the left pair *pickettaria*. Another modification has the basal and outer marginal areas " a nondescript grey shade in the male and a golden brown in the female " (ab. *pallidaria* Prout). Ab. *spangbergi* Lampa, is of the typical form, but is without the dark freckles. Other aberrations have been named, and at least one gynandrous specimen is known. An extremely informative, illustrated paper on the variation of this insect was written by H. B. Williams (1947, *Proc. S. Lond. Ent. and Nat. Hist. Soc.*, 1946-7 : 123). The eggs, which are laid in June, hatch in about twelve days. The caterpillars feed slowly until September or October, and then hibernate ; but it has been noted that when reared in confinement, and supplied with privet, they nibble the stems during the winter. Occasionally, a caterpillar will feed up and assume the moth state in the autumn, but the usual

1. **Swallow-tailed Moth:** *caterpillar.*
2. **Orange Moth:** *caterpillar.*

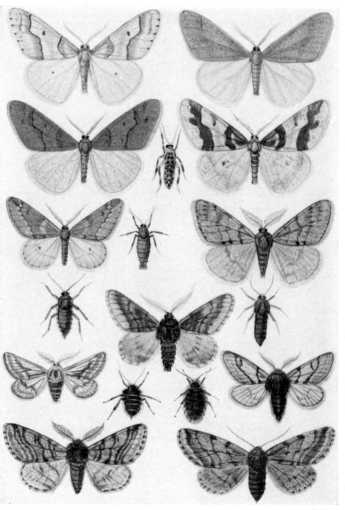

1. Mottled
Umber,
male.

2. Mottled
Umber,
male.

3. Mottled
Umber,
male.

4. Mottled
Umber,
female.

5. Mottled
Umber,
male.

6. March
Moth,
male.

7. March
Moth,
female.

8. Pale
Brindled
Beauty,
male.

9. Pale
Brindled
Beauty,
female.

10. Small
Brindled
Beauty,
male.

11. Small
Brindled
Beauty,
female.

12. Belted
Beauty,
male.

13. Belted
Beauty,
female.

14. Rannoch
Brindled
Beauty,
female.

15. Rannoch
Brindled
Beauty,
male.

16. Brindled
Beauty,
male.

17. Brindled
Beauty,
female.

habit is to complete growth in the spring, enter the chrysalis state in May, and appear as moths about the end of that month, if in captivity, or in June and July in the open. Various food plants have been given, among which are hawthorn, sloe, plum, birch, lilac, privet, and honeysuckle. The caterpillar is figured on Pl. **108,** 2.

The male flies in the early evening, but the female not until later. The species frequents woods, and may be disturbed by day from among the bracken and other undergrowth. It is more or less common in many woods throughout the southern half of England, and its range extends northwards to Yorkshire. In Ireland, it has occurred locally in counties Waterford, Cork, Kerry, Limerick, Clare, and Galway. It has been recorded from the Isle of Arran, but not from the main land of Scotland.

Abroad, the distribution spreads to Amurland, Korea, and Japan.

The Swallow-tailed Moth (*Ourapteryx sambucaria* Linn.)

This conspicuous-looking insect (Pl. **104,** 3) is frequently seen in gardens, lanes, and the outskirts of woods, pretty well all over England, Wales, and Ireland. In Scotland, it seems to be rare and confined to the south, but has been noted from Glasgow and Aviemore. Very rarely the cross lines of the fore wings are placed close together, but, except in the matter of size, there is, as a rule, little variation.

The caterpillar, of which a figure, from a coloured drawing by the late Mr. A. Sich, is given on Pl. **108,** 1, is brownish, variegated with reddish or purplish. It feeds, from August to June, on the foliage of hawthorn, sloe, elder, etc., but is especially partial to ivy.

The moth is out in July, and sometimes an odd specimen or two will appear in the autumn ; one was captured at Gravesend on October 22, 1904.

Abroad, it is found from central and southern Europe to Siberia.

The Scorched Wing (*Plagodis dolabraria* Linn.)

The crumpled or shrivelled appearance of the wings, coupled with the brown coloration of the streaks and other markings on the wings, no doubt suggested the English name of this species (Pl. **104,** 6).

The twig-like caterpillar is brownish, tinged with greenish or reddish, and variegated with darker, especially along the back of the first three rings, the hump on ring 8, and a cross stripe on the last ring. It feeds on oak, birch, and sallow, from July to September.

The moth, which inhabits woods, and is out in late May and in June, is sometimes attracted to sugar, but rather more frequently to light. It is, however, far more rarely seen than the caterpillar, which has been obtained in almost every English county up to Yorkshire. The moth has been recorded from Darlington, Durham, Northumberland, and Cumberland. It occurs in Wales and Ireland (Dublin, 1947), and several larvae were beaten from a beech hedge in Perthshire.

The range abroad extends to Amurland and Japan.

The Brimstone (*Opisthograptis luteolata* Linn.)

This generally distributed and often common yellow species (Pl. **104,** 7) has the front margin of the fore wings marked with reddish, and occasionally a stripe of this colour extends along the front margin from the base to the tip ; the discal mark is whitish outlined in reddish brown ; the wavy cross lines are often faint, and not infrequently quite absent. White specimens, ab. *albescens* Cockerell, have been recorded from Cheshire and Durham, and probably have occurred elsewhere, since South had a specimen said to have been taken in Staffordshire ; an orange yellow form has occurred in the last-named county.

The twig-like caterpillar is brownish tinged with greenish or purplish ; there is a double-pointed hump on the back of ring 6 and smaller projections on 8. It feeds on hawthorn

1, 2. **Oak Beauty**, *male and female*.
3. **Peppered Moth**, *female*.
4. **Peppered Moth (ab.** *carbonaria*)**.**   5. **Peppered Moth**, *male*.

1. **Dark Bordered Beauty:** *eggs, natural size and enlarged.*
2, 2a. **Bordered Beauty:** *eggs, natural size and enlarged, and caterpillar.*
3. **Little Thorn:** *caterpillar.*

chiefly, but sometimes on sloe, plum, etc. It may be found after hibernation in the spring, and a second generation occurs in the summer.

The moth seems to have been noted in each month from April to August and in October, but it is most frequent in May and June. The moths emerging in April from over-wintering pupae, produce a second brood in August, the larvae from which hibernate and pupate in the spring of the following year giving rise to a June emergence. These moths in turn produce the over-wintering pupae from which the April moths emerge. This " leap-frogging " sequence ensures an almost continuous emergence throughout the summer months.

The Bordered Beauty (*Epione repandaria* Hufn.)

The orange yellow moth whose portrait is shown on Pl. **104,** 10, has the outer margins, beyond the second blackish line, more or less shaded with purplish grey, inclining to purple near the line ; on the fore wings, the first cross line is angled at the middle, and the second line runs to the tips of the wings. Gynandrous specimens of this and also the following species have been noted.

The early stages are figured on Pl. **111,** 2, 2*a*. The eggs, which are laid in July and August on the food plant, are pale yellow at first, then reddish, with white dots and patches. The caterpillars generally emerge in the following spring, but sometimes, at least in captivity, they hatch in about a fortnight, feed up quickly, and attain the moth state in September or October.

Caterpillar, brown, with a greenish or ochreous tinge ; along the back of rings 3 to 6 is an ochreous patch, and within this a black mark, and on the rings following 6 there are more or less distinct ochreous diamonds ; a dull yellowish line low down along the sides ; head, dull reddish brown. It feeds, in May and June, on willow, sallow, alder, etc. The moth is out in July and August, and is not uncommon in many parts of Southern and Eastern England. Its range extends through England, Wales, and Scotland to Sutherland. In Ireland, it is widely distributed, and not at all scarce in some northern localities.

Abroad, it is found in central and southern Europe and in various localities between the Caucasus and Amurland.

The Dark Bordered Beauty (*Epione vespertaria* Fabr.)

As will be seen on referring to Pl. 104 the sexes of this species are strikingly different. The male (Fig. 9) is very similar to the last species, except that the first cross line is curved and reddish brown in colour ; the second line runs to the front margin before the tip, and the outer margin beyond is almost entirely purple. The female (Fig. 8) has the ground colour pale yellowish, and the outer borders narrowed, especially on the fore wings. Very occasionally, the ground colour in the male approaches that of the female. The eggs (Pl. 111, 1) are pale yellow when deposited, but afterwards become honey yellow, freckled with reddish, and later they are red all over. The caterpillar is dingy brown, inclining to greyish on the back of the first four rings, a dark mark about the middle of the back, and on each side of this two slender whitish lines are fairly distinct ; underside, whitish tinged with pale violet. It feeds, in May and June, sometimes later, on dwarf sallow and willow, birch, aspen, etc.

The moth is out in July and August, sometimes later. Although odd specimens have been recorded from Norfolk, St. Ives (Huntingdonshire) and Newbury (Berkshire), the species is a northern one, occurring chiefly near York (Sanburn Moss). Rare in Ireland.

In 1863, two specimens were secured at Learmouth Bog, near Cornhill-on-Tweed, and in 1890, Bolam found it at Newham Bog, on the Northumberland border. Renton states that it is fairly common in good seasons at Adderstone-lea

Moss, Roxburghshire; and Salvage found it widely distributed in Sutherlandshire.

Abroad, its range is similar to that of *repandaria* Hüfn., but rather more local.

The Little Thorn (*Cepphis advenaria* Hübn.)

This species (Pl. **107,** 1) is usually whitish, freckled and clouded with grey brown; cross lines rather darker. The markings may be tinged with ochreous, or with red.

A uniform brown-coloured specimen with white fringes (ab *fulva* Gillmer) has been taken in Surrey.

The caterpillar is greyish brown, minutely freckled with blackish; two white spots on front of ring 5, and two smaller ones on 11; the rings between 5 and 11 with pale diamonds on the back, and whitish marks on the sides; head, black, white dotted. It feeds, in July and August, or even later, on dogwood, bilberry, sallow, etc. The late Mr. A. J. Scollick, who kindly provided the caterpillar figured on Pl. **111,** 3, informed South that in rearing larvae from the egg he found that they preferred dogwood as a pabulum, and that in the locality where he took the moth in June there is no bilberry, but plenty of *Cornus sanguinea*. This local species, which is out from late May well into June, is generally associated with bilberry, but by no means confined to localities where this plant flourishes. In some of its haunts it affects bramble, and in others rose. It occurs, in woodlands, in Essex, Kent, Surrey (Leith Hill, Horsley, Chilworth, etc.), Berkshire and Oxfordshire (near Watlington), Sussex (Abbots Wood, St. Leonards Forest, etc.), Hampshire (New Forest), Devon (Haldon), in the west to Shropshire, and South Wales; Derbyshire and South Yorkshire. Rare in Ireland, being only found in Limerick and Waterford.

The range abroad extends to Amurland, Korea, and Japan, thus it has a more eastern distribution than either of the species of *Epione*, which only reach Amurland.

The Speckled Yellow (*Pseudopanthera macularia* Linn.)

This pretty blackish-spotted yellow species (Pl. **107**, 2) varies somewhat in the tint of ground colour, but more so in the number and size of the markings ; occasionally some of these are united, forming bands or blotches ; or they may be reduced in number and size, leading up to ab. *quadrimaculata* Hatchett (Pinion-spotted Yellow), a form that used to occur rarely in the Dartford district, Kent.

The caterpillar is green, with white lines and stripes ; head, shining green. It feeds, in July and August, on wood sage (*Teucrium*), woundwort (*Stachys*), and dead nettle (*Lamium*).

The moth is a lover of the woodlands, and as it flies in the daytime, especially when sunny, will be almost certainly noted on the wing by any one rambling through the woods in June, or even late May. It is generally plentiful in the south and west of England, but although its range extends through the northern parts of the country, and widely over Scotland to Sutherland, it is more or less local and often rare in the northern area indicated. In North Wales and South-west Ireland, it is local, but not uncommon.

Abroad, it extends to Asia Minor and central Asia.

The Peacock Moth (*Semiothisa notata* Linn.)

Whitish, with an ochreous tinge, and clouded with ochreous grey ; three indistinct cross lines on the fore wings, commencing as brownish spots on the front margin ; a larger brownish spot, inclining to reddish, on the front margin beyond the angle of outer line, and a large blackish or brownish divided spot below it ; a shallow notch under the tips of the wings, edged with dark brown, and fringed with smoky brown (Pl. **107**, 4).

The caterpillar is green, with brown markings on the sides, or brownish with green markings ; head, black as a rule, but occasionally green. It feeds, in late June and in July, on birch and sallow ; there is a second brood in August and Sep-

1. Waved Umber.   2. Waved Umber (ab. *fuscata*).
3, 4. Ringed Carpet.
5, 6. Willow Beauty.
7, 8. Satin Beauty.
9, 10. Mottled Beauty.

1, 1*a*. **Sharp-angled Peacock**: *eggs, natural size and enlarged, and caterpillar.*
2, 2*a*. **Tawny-barred Angle**: *caterpillar and chrysalis.*

tember. The moth may be beaten out from birch bushes in May and June, and again in July and August. Woods are its favourite haunts, especially those where heather and small birch abound, but it is very local in the south of England, although it occurs in most of the counties from Kent to Cornwall. Barrett states that it is rather common in heathy woods in Staffordshire and Cheshire, and Forsythe gives it as local and uncommon in the Lancaster district; also recorded from Cambridgeshire, Suffolk (Bentley Wood, 1901), Hertfordshire, and Gloucestershire; Glamorgan, South Wales; Inverness and Ross, in Scotland. Rare and restricted to Kerry in Ireland.

Abroad, it is distributed in central and northern Europe, Transcaucasia, Persia, and locally in Siberia.

The Sharp-angled Peacock (*Semiothisa alternata* Schiff.)

Whitish clouded and suffused with greyish; fore wings crossed by three dark lines, commencing in blackish spots on the front margin; a greyish band follows the outer line, a reddish brown spot at the costal end, and a blackish spot about the middle, the spot broken up by the veins, which are here ochreous; a rather deep notch below the tip is edged with black and fringed with blackish. Hind wings with a black central dot, and a greyish band beyond (Pl. **107**, 3).

The late Mr. A. J. Scollick has recorded that some caterpillars, presumably about a week old on June 24, 1905, went into chrysalis July 7 to 12. One moth emerged July 18, but no other appeared until December 20. A third came up on January 5, 1906, and a fourth on February 5.

The caterpillar is pale green, with reddish brown blotches on the sides, and sometimes the back is also reddish brown. It feeds on alder, sallow, and sloe, in June, and as a second generation in the autumn. (Eggs and a caterpillar, the latter after Hofmann, are figured on Pl. **113**, 1, 1a.) The moth flies in May and early June, and occasionally in July or August.

This species, which is always local, is perhaps most frequently met with in the New Forest, Hampshire, but it is not uncommon in some parts of the Isle of Wight, Dorset, Devon, and Kent. Also noted from a few other southern counties, and from Suffolk, Norfolk, Westmorland, and the Isle of Canna in Scotland. In Wales, it has occurred at Neath, Glamorgan. The range of this species abroad extends to Amurland.

The Tawny-barred Angle (*Semiothisa liturata* Clerck)

One of the more frequent forms of this species is shown on Pl. **107, 5**. In some examples the cross lines are almost absent, but in others they are very distinct and blackish in colour ; the orange yellow band in the outer marginal area varies in width and in strength, but it is usually present, even in the sooty brown form ab. *nigrofulvata* Collins described from Delamere, Cheshire, also found in Shropshire, Warwickshire, North Lancashire, Kendal, Surrey, and Buckinghamshire.

The caterpillar (Pl. **113, 2**) is green, with white or creamy transverse lines and stripes ; head, reddish. Another form is pale ochreous grey or brownish, with pale grey lines and stripes ; head, almost black, with purple tinge. It feeds on the needles of larch and Scots pine (*Pinus sylvestris*), in July and August, and occasionally in September and October. A photograph of the chrysalis by the late Mr. H. Main, enlarged to twice natural size, is shown on Pl. **113, 2a**.

The moth is to be found in fir woods, where it lurks among the branches or sits on the trunks, or on the fallen needles on the ground. The moths of the first generation appear in June and July and, where it occurs, the second flies in August and September. Widely distributed over the British Isles, but not noted north of Moray, in Scotland.

Abroad, it ranges from Europe to Transcaucasia and eastern Siberia. In north-eastern Siberia and north Amurland it is represented by a race, subsp. *pressaria* Chr.

The Early Moth (*Theria rupicapraria* Schiff.)

Although generally common, and often abundant, over England, Wales, the south of Scotland, and Ireland, this species (Pl. **107**, 8 ♂, 7 ♀) hardly ever comes under notice unless hedgerows and hawthorn bushes are examined in January and February, by the aid of a lantern, after darkness has set in. Then the males, and almost wingless females, will be found in numbers, sitting at the ends of the twigs.

The caterpillar is whitish green, clouded with darker green, striped with white along the back, and marked with white on the sides. The general colour is sometimes very dark green, approaching black, and in this form the white markings are more striking. It feeds, in April and May, on hawthorn, sloe, plum, and bilberry.

Abroad, it is found in central Europe, where it is later in appearance, and also in Transcaucasia.

The Spring Usher (*Erannis leucophaearia* Schiff.)

On Pl. **107** are shown the typical and more usual forms of this variable species. Fig. 6 represents the male, and Fig. 10 the female. The form with blackish base and outer margin is ab. *marmorinaria* Esp. (Pl. **107**, 9). Ab. *merularia* Weymer, is entirely black, and a modification of this form is shown in Fig. 11. Between each of these extremes and the type there are various gradations.

The caterpillar is usually some shade of green, with yellowish lines on the back, and some have brownish marks on the sides ; in others there are dark brown marks on the back of each ring. It feeds on the leaves of oak, in April and May.

The moth rests on tree trunks, fences, etc., and the males may be thus found during the day in February, earlier or later in some seasons ; the female is less often obtained on trees and fences, but may be beaten, together with the male, from the dead leaves which remain upon oak and other bushes.

The species appears to occur, more or less locally, in most of

the English counties ; it has also been recorded from Cardiganshire, Pembrokeshire and Flintshire, in Wales. In Scotland,
it is obtained in the south, and northwards to Aberdeenshire
and Inverness-shire. Rare and local in Ireland, having been
reported only from Wicklow.

Abroad, the range extends to Amurland and Japan.

The Scarce Umber (*Erannis aurantiaria* Hübn.)

One specimen of each sex of this orange yellow species will
be found on Pl. **107,** where Fig. 12 represents the male, and
Fig. 13 the female ; the cross lines, in the male, are usually
distinct on all the wings, but those on the hind pair are sometimes very faint, and occasionally absent. The ground colour
is paler in some specimens than in others, and there is variation in the amount of purplish speckling, in the purplish clouding following the second line, and in the submarginal series
of purplish marks of the fore wings. The marginal dots are
sometimes absent from the hind wings, most frequently in
specimens with faint cross lines on these wings. The melanic
ab. *fumipennaria* Hellweger, is firmly established in south-
west Yorkshire.

The eggs (Pl. **114,** 2), when South received them in
February, were purplish, or violet brown.

The caterpillar is yellowish, inclining to ochreous, lined with
brown on the back, and striped with purplish on the sides ;
underside, dark purplish brown, inclining to blackish, and
striped with yellowish. It feeds in the spring, sometimes to
June, on oak, birch, blackthorn, etc., and may be found on the
leaves during the day. The moth is out in the latter part of
the year, from October, and is best obtained at night, when
sitting on the twigs of trees and bushes, but a specimen or two
may be found on tree-trunks, palings, etc., in the daytime.

The species is widely distributed over England, and in some
parts it is common in woods ; also occurs in Wales and the Isle
of Man. In Scotland it is very rare and local in Roxburgh-

shire ; local and uncommon in the Clyde area, and has been recorded from other parts of the country up to Aberdeen and Inverness-shire. Rare in Ireland, but noted from Tyrone (local among birches at Cookstown), Monaghan, Fermanagh (Enniskillen), Donegal, Down, and Galway.

The moth is common in central Europe and is also found in the Taurus.

The Dotted Border (*Erannis marginaria* Fabr.)

On Pl. **107** four specimens of this rather variable species are depicted. Figs. 14♂ and 16 ♀ show the more usual form ; Fig. 17 represents the blackish ab. *fuscata* Mosley, which was confined to northern England but now occurs in Surrey and Essex, and Fig. 15 an intermediate form resulting from a cross-pairing of *fuscata* ♀ with a southern ♂. Somewhat

FIG. 11.—DOTTED BORDER, MALE, AT REST.

similar forms to the last have been captured in Weardale, Durham.

The caterpillar is figured on Pl. **114**, 3, from a coloured drawing by the late Mr. A. Sich. It is described by Fenn as dull yellow, olive green, or greenish brown ; a series of dark grey X-like marks on the back, most distinct on rings 5–11 ; the spiracles are white, each placed in a black cloud, and the spaces between them paler, sometimes yellowish; the last ring is often brown without marking, and the front rings have a purplish stripe above; under surface, paler throughout. It feeds, in April and May, as a rule, but has been found later, on hawthorn, sloe, oak, birch, alder, sallow, etc., and may be obtained in the daytime.

The moth is out in March and April; and after their short evening flight the males may be seen in numbers on hedgerows and the twigs of trees. It is not infrequent at sallow catkins, and sometimes is not scarce on palings and tree-trunks. The female may occasionally be detected in the crevices of bark on tree-trunks, but is more easily obtained on the twigs at night.

The species is common over the whole of England and Wales, also in Ireland. As regards Scotland, it is abundant in the south, but its range does not seem to extend beyond Inverness-shire and the Outer Hebrides; the ab. *fuscata* occurs in Renfrewshire.

Abroad, it is widely distributed in Europe, the Urals, Caucasus, etc.

The Mottled Umber (*Erannis defoliaria* Clerck)

A female (Fig. 4) and four examples of the male of this variable species are shown on Pl. **109**, 1, 2, 3, 5. The ground colour of the fore wings in the male varies from whitish, through ochreous brown to dull russet brown; the cross bands (when present) range in colour from reddish brown to dark purplish, almost blackish, brown; in all the paler specimens the ground colour is more or less sprinkled or suffused with brownish; the darker specimens are sprinkled with dark purplish or blackish. Ab. *obscurata* Staud., is almost uniformly dull brownish, and an example approaching this form is represented by Fig. 3. This form is becoming common in Epping Forest.

When deposited the eggs (Pl. **114**, 1b) were deep straw yellow.

The caterpillar (figured on Pl. **114, 1**, from a coloured drawing by the late Mr. A. Sich) has various shades of reddish brown on the back, and yellowish on the sides and beneath ; the line above the red-marked white spiracles is black, and this has an interrupted edging of white.   Fig. 1*a* shows a pale form. It feeds on the foliage of birch, oak, and other forest trees, also on fruit trees, rose, honeysuckle, etc.   It often occurs in great abundance, and is largely responsible for the leafless condition of the trees, sometimes noticed in May.

The moth appears from October to December, and occasionally in January, February, or March.

Generally abundant throughout England and Wales ; widely distributed, and often common in Ireland ; not uncommon in the south of Scotland, but becoming less frequent northwards to Perthshire and Aberdeen.   Heslop Harrison reports it from the Western Isles.

Abroad, it is distributed throughout Europe and Armenia.

The Pale Brindled Beauty (*Phigalia pilosaria* Schiff.)

The fore wings of this species (Pl. **109,** 8 ♂, 9 ♀) are greyish, tinged with greenish or brown, and sprinkled with darker grey or brownish ;   the irregular cross lines are blackish. Occasional specimens in the north of England are more or less sprinkled with yellow buff or orange buff, and in these the cross-markings may be present or absent.   A more frequent form of aberration in the north is a general darkening of the colour in the direction of ab. *monacharia* Staud., which is smoky black with the veins black, and occurs chiefly in South Yorkshire, but is also found around London.

The caterpillar, figured on Pl. **116, 1**, from a coloured drawing by the late Mr. A. Sich, is dull reddish brown, relieved with rust red mottling ;   the notched head is greyish brown.   It feeds, in the spring, on birch, oak, elm, lime, poplar, sallow, hawthorn, sloe, plum and other fruit trees, rose, etc.

The moth is out as a rule during the first two or three months of the year, but it has been noted in November and December, and also in mid-June. It may be seen in the daytime on tree-trunks, palings, etc., but the female secretes herself in any convenient cranny, and is not easily detected. The male flies at night, and comes freely to light.

The species is pretty generally distributed throughout England and Wales, and Scotland up to Aberdeen. It has been recorded from the Isle of Man. Heslop Harrison reports it from the Inner Hebrides. In Ireland, it has a wide distribution, but Kane states that, except in the Belfast district, it is decidedly scarce in the country.

Abroad, it is common from central Europe to the Urals.

The Small Brindled Beauty (*Apocheima hispidaria* Schiff.)

In the male (Pl. **109,** 10) the fore wings are ochreous grey inclining to brownish, usually much paler on the outer margin ; cross lines black. Hind wings, greyish white, with a blackish central band. Fringes of all the wings chequered with blackish. Often the central area of the fore wings, between the first and second lines, is more or less blackish ; less frequently the whole of these wings, up to or just beyond the submarginal line, is blackish (ab. *obscura* Kühne) ; and sometimes the pale outer marginal area is broken up by the blackish nervules. Very rarely, the ground colour is almost white, and the cross-markings on the fore wings dusky grey. The female (Pl. **109,** 11) varies from brown to blackish.

The caterpillar is brown, inclining to blackish or purplish, the raised spots are black, and occasionally the sides are freckled with orange (Pl. **116,** 2, from a coloured drawing by the late Mr. A. Sich). It feeds in May and early June on oak, and will also eat hawthorn, birch, and elm.

The moth, which is out in February and March, appears to be local, but has a wide distribution through England from Durham to Hampshire, and even Devon. It has also been

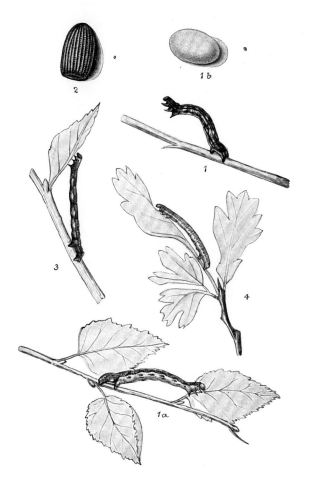

1, 1*a*, 1*b*. **Mottled Umber:** *egg, natural size and enlarged, and caterpillars.*
2. **Scarce Umber:** *egg, natural size and enlarged.*
3. **Dotted Border:** *caterpillar.*
4. **March Moth:** *caterpillar.*

1, 2. Brussels Lace.
3. Great Oak Beauty.
4, 5. Dotted Carpet.
6. Speckled Beauty.
7, 8. Pale Oak Beauty.

recorded from Cardiganshire and Denbighshire in Wales. A well-known locality is Richmond Park, in Surrey, and here it is found resting on oak trunks or on the grass stems, etc., under or around the trees. The male is attracted by light.

Abroad, it is rather local in central and south-eastern Europe.

The Rannoch Brindled Beauty (*Poecilopsis lapponaria* Boisd.)

The sexes of this species are shown on Pl. **109,** where Fig. 15 represents the male, and Fig. 14 the female. It was not known to occur in the British Isles until 1871, when a male specimen was captured in Perthshire, on April 20 of that year. The late Mr. W. M. Christy, in 1895, bred some moths from larvae obtained in the Highlands of Scotland, and he sent eggs to the late Mr. F. W. Frohawk, who worked out the life history, and described and figured all the stages from egg (Pl. **116,** 3*b*) to perfect insect (*Entom.*, xxviii. 237). In July, 1900 and 1901, Dr. E. A. Cockayne found caterpillars, in Perthshire (Rannoch district), on ling, heath, and bog-myrtle ; and in June, 1904, he published (*Entom.*, xxxvii. 149) some interesting observations on the habits of the species in its native haunts. The greenish yellow eggs are laid in batches of 10 to 150 in the dry corollas of the cross-leaved heath, and less frequently between the stem and sheath of reeds, or in cracks in dead bracken stems, etc. The caterpillar (Pl. **116,** 3) is pale drab, inclining to a yellowish tint ; irregular yellow stripes along the back and sides, and lines of blackish streaks between the stripes. It will eat birch, sallow, and hawthorn, in captivity ; but in the open it feeds on heather and bog-myrtle : May-July. The chrysalis is reddish brown, rather paler on the wing covers (figured on Pl. **116,** 3*a* from a photo, twice natural size, by the late Mr. H. Main). The moth is out in April and May, and sits on the twigs of heather and the stems of bog-myrtle. It has been recorded from Perthshire, Ross-shire, and

Inverness-shire, and is very local, frequenting damp places near streams.

Abroad, it is found in northern Europe, Siberia, and the Alps.

The late Mr. A. W. Mera obtained hybrids from crossing the female of this species with *N. zonaria* (hybr. *merana* Burrows)—(Tutt, " Brit. Lep.," vol. v., p. 542) ; the reciprocal hybrid has been named *smallmani* by Harrison.

The Belted Beauty (*Nyssia zonaria* Schiff.)

Two males and a female of this species are depicted on Pl. **109,** 12 ♂, 13 ♀). There is variation in the ground colour of the male, from white to greyish, and the markings are sometimes greyish brown and sometimes blackish. Kane states that, in Ireland, a large number of Connemara specimens have the fore wings entirely white, broken by dark veins, front margin, and three streaks parallel to the outer margin. The caterpillar is greenish, with dusky grey lines and freckles on the back, and a yellow stripe low down along the sides ; the latter is edged below with blackish ; the underside is black and striped with grey ; head, greyish, freckled with darker. It feeds on sallow, dandelion, dock, plantain, clover, yarrow, grass, etc. : May to August (Pl. **116,** 4 ; chrysalis 4*a* ; eggs, Pl. **122,** 4). The moth is out in March and April, and rests by day on or among herbage. The male has been known to fly in the sunshine, but its more usual time of flight is the early evening.

The species is locally common on sand hills, on the coast of Cheshire, Flintshire, and Carnarvon ; Wallasey is a noted locality, and the earliest British specimens were taken in that district about 1832 ; it also occurs on the Lancashire coast, in the Liverpool and Blackpool districts. In Ireland, it was first noted in Co. Antrim, where caterpillars were found at Ballycastle, and about 1885 moths were captured at the same place. Other Irish localities are Achill Island, off the coast of Mayo ;

Slyne Head and Roundstone, Connemara coast. There are records of its occurrence in the Isles of Skye, Canna, Tiree, an Harris ; the small race subsp. *atlantica* Harrison, was reported by Heslop Harrison as being abundant from Barvas (Lewis) to the Isle of Pabbay (Barra Isles).

Abroad, it is found in central Europe and the Caucasus.

The Brindled Beauty (*Lycia hirtaria* Clerck)

A male and a female are shown on Pl. **109**, 16 ♂, 17 ♀), and these represent the more usual form of the sexes in the London district. Some specimens are paler, others are darker ; and not infrequently the wings are sprinkled with yellowish.

Examples of a large race were taken by the late Mr. H. McArthur in 1908 at Aviemore, in Scotland. One of these males

FIG. 12.—CATERPILLAR OF BRINDLED BEAUTY.

is of a remarkable ochreous coloration, whilst in the other the contrast of grey ground and black marking is equally striking. The female is blackish sprinkled with ochreous. A melanic form has been taken in London but is considered very rare.

The caterpillar is purplish grey or reddish brown clouded and freckled with darker, and spotted with yellow on rings 5–8 ; the first ring is also marked with yellow in front, the head is freckled with black, and about the jaws with yellow. It feeds on lime, elm, willow, and fruit trees, especially plum and pear, in May, June, and July. For the example figured on Pl. **119**, 1, South was indebted to Mr. Norman Riley. The chrysalis (Pl. **119**, 1a) is dark reddish brown inclining to blackish. The moth comes out in March and April and is a common object on tree-trunks, etc., in the London parks, squares, and gardens. Its range extends over the south of England, and northwards to Yorkshire and Cumberland, but it is nowhere so plentiful in England as throughout the Metropolitan area. It occurs in Wales, in Ireland, and in Scotland up to Inverness.

Abroad, its range extends to Asia Minor.

Hybrids have been reared from this species crossed with several others. That from a male *hirtaria* × female *zonaria* is said only to produce males (*denhami* Harr.).

The Oak Beauty (*Biston strataria* Hufn.)

The fore wings of this species (Pl. **110**, 1 ♂, 2 ♀) are white, sprinkled and cross lined with black ; the first line is bordered inwardly, and the second line outwardly with brownish ; frequently these two lines fall closely together on the inner margin, and sometimes they are united by a blackish blotch at this point ; the brownish borders of the lines vary in width, and in some specimens the outer area beyond the second black line is almost entirely brownish ; in other specimens the central and outer areas are almost free of black speckling, and in such examples the brownish borders of the lines stand out conspicuously. The caterpillar (Pl. **119**, 2) is usually some shade of brown—greyish, violet, or purplish—mottled and freckled with a darker hue. It feeds on oak, birch, and elm,

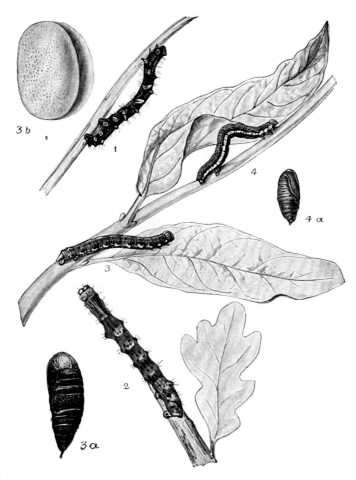

S 288

1. **Pale Brindled Beauty**: *caterpillar.*
2. **Small Brindled Beauty**: *caterpillar.*
3, 3*a*, 3*b*. **Rannoch Brindled Beauty**: *egg, natural size and enlarged, caterpillar and chrysalis.*
4, 4*a*. **Belted Beauty**: *caterpillar and chrysalis.*

1, 2. **Small Engrailed.**

3. **The Engrailed.** 4. **Small Engrailed** (ab. *delamerensis*).

5, 6. **Square Spot.**

7, 8. **Brindled White-spot.**

9, 10. **Grey Birch.**

11. **Grey Birch.** 12. **Dusky Carpet.**

will also eat sloe, plum, rose, etc., and is found from May to July. In confinement, larvae hatched in early May have gone down to pupate during the second week in June.

The moth is out in March and April as a rule, but has been noted in late February, and also in early May. It may be seen resting during the day on trunks of trees, palings, etc., generally near the ground; when on the wing at night the male will come to light. Although not generally common it is widely distributed over England and Wales. It has been recorded from Argyllshire in Scotland. In Ireland it is scarce but locally spread throughout the country.

Abroad, it is local in central and southern Europe, Asia Minor, and Transcaucasia.

Hybrids resulting from a cross between *strataria* ♂ and *betularia* ♀ have been named *herefordi* Tutt (Tutt, " Brit. Lep.," vol. v., p. 30).

The Peppered Moth (*Biston betularia* Linn.)

Typically (Pl. **110**, 5 ♂, 3 ♀) the wings are white, " peppered " with black, and with more or less distinct cross lines, also black. The black speckling varies in amount, in some examples it is almost absent, whilst in others it is so dense that the wings appear to be black sprinkled with white. Specimens of the last form are intermediate between the type and the melanic ab. *carbonaria* Jordan (Fig. 4). This black form, which seems to have been unknown about 1847, is now much commoner than the type in the South-west Riding of Yorkshire, and has spread into Lancashire, Cheshire, and southwards to Lincolnshire. On the wolds of the latter county, and on Cannock Chase, Staffordshire, it is said to be the dominant form of the species. The aberration also occurs in the eastern and the southern counties of England to Hampshire. Northwards, the form has extended to Clydesdale in Scotland, where one was reared from a caterpillar obtained near Paisley. In Wales *carbonaria* is in the ascendant at Newport,

Monmouth, and in Ireland one example of this variety together with some intermediate and typical specimens were reared from caterpillars collected at Castle Bellingham, Co. Louth (*vide Entom.*, lxxviii. 174).

FIG. 13.—THE TYPICAL AND MELANIC FORMS OF THE PEPPERED MOTH.

What is known as the buff aberration of this species dates back to the year 1874, when a buff female, paired with a black male, was captured at Heaton Park. From the eggs she deposited caterpillars hatched, and in due course pupated, but the moths reared from them were all either typical, or black. Some of the female moths were, however, given to other collectors to pair with black males with the result that buff specimens appeared among the moths reared by seven collectors. Subsequently, by breeding only from buff males and females 80 per cent. of this form were said to be obtained. By the year 1880, however, the form was extinct. In all the examples of the buff aberration that South had seen, including a pair in his own collection, the ground colour is normal, but the usual black markings of the wings are brownish buff; he understood, however, that there are specimens in which the ground colour is ochreous. The vapour of chlorine will change an ordinary specimen to a buff form; and it is said that caterpillars reared in an apartment where this vapour is present will produce these buff forms. Mr. Mansbridge has described ab. *ochrearia*, and in this form the typical black markings are present on an ochreous ground. The specimen, a female, was captured at St. Annes, Lancashire, June, 1891.

Gynandrous examples have been obtained, and seven of these abnormal forms occurred in a single brood reared from eggs by the late Mr. A. Harrison.

The caterpillar (Pl. **119**, 3, from a photo by Mr. H. Main) is green, brownish green, or purplish brown; in the green form, which is minutely dotted with white, there is generally a faint purplish line along the back, two purplish knobs on ring 8, and a purplish patch enclosing two ochreous spots on ring 11; the deeply notched head is ochreous, shaded with purplish; the last ring of the body is tinged with purplish, as also are the two small points thereon. It feeds, from July to September, on oak, birch, elm, beech, sallow, plum and other fruit trees; also on rose, bramble, etc. The moth is out in May and June, sometimes in July. The species is generally distributed, and sometimes common in the caterpillar state, but seems to be absent from the Scottish Isles.

Abroad, it ranges from Europe to Japan.

The Waved Umber (*Menophra abruptaria* Thunb.)

A male specimen is figured on Pl. **112**, 1. The males are usually darker than the females, but they vary in the amount of darker clouding and suffusion. Three forms of the species have been named as follows—ab. *brunneata* Tutt, a modification of the female rather more strongly coloured than the darkest typical male. Ab. *fuscata* Tutt, sooty brown, tending to blackish ; both sexes somewhat paler in central area of fore wings.   Ab. *unicolor* Tutt, similar to ab. *fuscata*, but without pale marking ; the thorax is also darker (Pl. **112**, 2, ab. *fuscata*).   The eggs, furnished by Mr. Norman Riley, were verdigris green when laid, but on the third day changed to greyish.

In general colour the caterpillar is greyish brown some- times tinged with green ; pinkish brown blotches along the back, often united on the front and hind rings.   In some cases the caterpillar is almost black, with a lighter mark on front of the first ring.   It feeds on privet and lilac, and is said to eat currant, broom, and jasmine :   May to August (Pl. **122**, 3).

The moth is out in April and May, and is fond of resting on palings, trees, and even walls.   It appears to be most plentiful in the London district, in the north and east of which the dark forms occur ;   but it is found more or less frequently over the greater part of England, and in South Wales ;   single speci- mens were taken at Hartlepool, Durham, in 1874 and 1875. One example has been recorded from Kincardineshire, Scot- land ;   and there are only two records from Ireland.

Abroad, it is found in central and southern Europe as well as North Africa.

The Ringed Carpet   (*Cleora cinctaria* Schiff.)

Two specimeus are showu on Pl. **112**.   Fig. 3 represents the more or less typical form, and Fig. 4 depicts an example in which the central orea is almost free of dark speckling, so that the whitish ground colour comes out distinctly.   There is a good range of variation)n the direction of both darker and paler forms than thore figured.   In some specimens with a cleor white central area, the basal and outer marginal areas of the fora win/s, and the outer area of the hind wings, are black or blackish; similar aberration ir sometimes found in the more speckled specimens also.   Occasionally, there is a

3. The Annulet.

1, 2. The Annulet.

4. The Horse Chestnut.

5, 6. Scotch Annulet.

7. Netted Mountain Moth.   8. Black Mountain Moth.   9. Rannoch Looper.

10. Netted Mountain Moth.   11. Black Mountain Moth.   12. Rannoch Looper.

13. Frosted Yellow   14. V-Moth.

15, 16, 17. Common Heath.

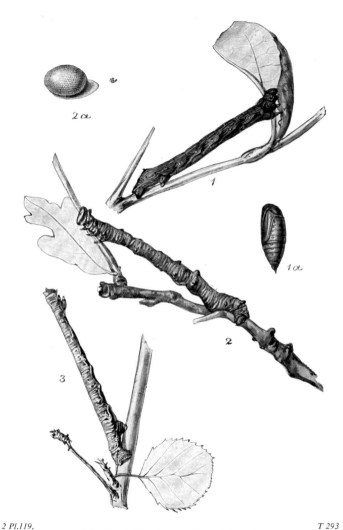

1, 1*a*. **Brindled Beauty**: *caterpillar and chrysalis.*
2, 2*a*. **Oak Beauty**: *eggs, natural size and enlarged, and caterpillar.*
3. **Peppered Moth**: *caterpillar.*

projection from below the middle of the second black line to the basal band.

The caterpillar is green, with darker green and whitish lines along the back and sides. It feeds on birch, sallow, and heath (*Erica cinerea*), and may be reared on knotgrass. In Scotland its food is chiefly bog myrtle. The moth is out in May, sometimes late April or early June. The New Forest in Hampshire is the district *par excellence* for this species, the most favoured locality being the heathy tract near Lyndhurst, where the moths are very common, in some years, on tree-trunks, especially birch, and on heather. Other localities in England are Poole Heath, Parley Heath, and Bloxworth in Dorset ; Tilgate Forest, etc., in Sussex ; Rempstone, Nottinghamshire ; Chiddingfold, Surrey ; Reading district in Berkshire, first noted in 1891. It has been recorded from N. Wales. In Ireland, it is widely distributed, and is abundant at Killarney and some other parts of Kerry. It is sometimes locally abundant in Argyllshire and Perthshire. The Scottish race differs in the almost complete absence of brown in the ground colour and markings and has been named subsp. *bowesi* Richardson.

The range abroad extends to Amurland and Japan.

The Willow Beauty (*Cleora rhomboidaria* Schiff.)

The two portraits on Pl. **112**, 5, 6 represent the best known forms of this species. Stephens in 1831 referred the smoky or dark slaty grey form which is the ordinary one in the London district, now as then, to *rhomboidaria*. Newman subsequently named this form *perfumaria*, and he, and other entomologists of the time, considered that it was a species distinct from *rhomboidaria*. We now know that the smoky grey specimens are not peculiar to the metropolitan area, but occur in other parts of England (Warwickshire, Yorkshire, Lancashire, etc.), and are found, with the type, at Howth and other localities in Ireland. The more general forms throughout

England, Wales, Ireland and Scotland up to Perthshire, are pale brown, or greyish brown (typical), sometimes—chiefly in Devon and Cornwall—it is more ochreous ; the latter is referable to ab. *australaria* Curtis. Black forms (ab. *rebeli* Aign.) have been recorded from Kent and Norfolk, and blackish specimens have been noted from Ashdown Forest, Sussex ; from Cannock Chase, Staffordshire ; and from the south of Scotland.

The eggs (Pl. **120,** 1*a*) are green at first, changing to pink mottled with green, and finally to dark grey ; the latter change indicates early hatching of the caterpillar, which usually occurs about a fortnight after the eggs are deposited.

The caterpillar (Pl. **120,** 1, after a coloured drawing by the late Mr. A. Sich) is dull reddish brown, mottled more or less with ochreous ; traces of diamond-shaped marks on the back, the latter sometimes well defined. It feeds on ivy (in London gardens especially), hawthorn, birch, privet, lilac, rose, clematis, broom, and many other shrubs, and also on yew and fir, in August, and after hibernation in the spring. The moth is out in July and August ; sometimes a second brood occurs in September.

Abroad, it is fairly common in Europe, Syria to Persia, Altai.

This species is the *gemmaria* of Brahm (1791), but *rhomboidaria* Schiff. (1775), although little more than a catalogue name until figured by Hübner, about 1797, is here adopted.

The Brussels Lace (*Cleorodes lichenaria* Hufn.)

The greenish grey species shown on Pl. **115,** 1 ♂, 2 ♀, varies in tint ; the fore wings are often clouded with olive, and occasionally with blackish ; there is frequently a tinge of ochreous between the black cross lines, but sometimes this area is flushed with orange.

Two figures of the caterpillar will be found on Pl. **122,** 2. In colour and marking it so closely resembles the greenish grey lichen upon which it feeds, that its detection thereon is not always easy. May and June are the best months in which to collect the caterpillars (although they may be found during the autumn and early spring), and they may then be jarred from the lichen, etc., growing on branches of trees and bushes, or searched for among the lichen on the tree tru ks, or on wooden pales and fences.

The species is widely spread over the southern half of England, but is more or less rare from the Midlands northwards. It has occurred in South Wales and the Isle of Anglesey ; and Kane states that it is widely distributed and locally common in Ireland. It has been recorded from the Isle of Man. In some parts of South Scotland it is not uncommon, and its range extends to Aberdeen and Ross.

Abroad, it is local in parts of central and southern Europe, Taurus, and Transcaucasia.

The Satin Beauty (*Deileptenia ribeata* Clerck)

As an inhabitant of Britain this species was first noted from Hampshire, and in 1825 was figured and described by Curtis as *Alcis sericearia*, but this name is now restricted to the dark form. Two specimens, from the New Forest, are depicted on Pl. **112**, 7, 8 ; but paler, and also darker, examples are found in this locality, and, occasionally, melanic specimens occur as well. The latter form, some examples of which might be described as sooty black with black veins, is more prevalent among the yews and firs of Surrey.

The caterpillar, for the example of which (and also the egg), figured on Pl. **125**, 1, 1*a*, South was obliged to the late Mr. A. J. Scollick, is, in one form, ochreous brown with paler cream-coloured patches on the back ; and in another dark grey brown with paler patches, sometimes of a light cinnamon brown ; a pale, thin line along the middle of the back runs through a series of brownish diamonds ; there are other pale lines on the back and sides, and these are edged with brownish, and partly with blackish ; spiracles outlined in black.

(Adapted from Buckler.) It feeds on spruce, pine, yew, oak, birch, sallow, etc., from August to June. A larva has been found on bilberry in Devon.

The moth is out from late June to early August, but captured specimens are not often suitable for the cabinet, they are generally more or less frayed or scarred.

Beside Surrey and Hampshire, previously mentioned, the species occurs in Sussex (Tilgate Forest), Buckinghamshire (Halton), and has been recorded from Berkshire; Egg Buckland, Oxton, Bickleigh Vale, and other Devon localities; also from Cornwall, Somerset, Gloucestershire (the Cotswolds), Cheshire, Monmouthshire, and Cardiganshire. It has also been reported from Ireland.

Abroad, it is found in central Europe, Russia, and Japan.

The Mottled Beauty (*Alcis repandata* Linn.)

Two examples of the more ordinary mottled form of this species are shown on Pl. **112**, 9 ♂, 10 ♀. Dark brown forms, inclining to blackish, are not uncommon in the London district, but in South Yorkshire coal-black specimens with whitish submarginal lines occur; these melanic forms are referable to ab. *nigricata* Fuchs. Broad dark banded specimens are recorded from Arran and Argyll, and a melanic form occurs at Rannoch.

The caterpillar (figured on Pl. **120**, 2, after Sich) is brownish inclining to ochreous; a dark brownish line along the middle of the back, and a series of brownish diamond-shaped marks most distinct on the back of the middle rings; a line of blackish marks along the sides shows up in the paler examples. Sometimes the general colour is dark reddish brown, freckled with dark brown; but in all cases the underside is paler than the upper, and is striped and lined with dark and pale brown. It feeds on hawthorn, birch, elm, hazel, bilberry, heather, etc., from July to May.

The moth is out in June and July, and specimens of a second

generation have been reared in September. Generally common throughout the British Isles.

Abroad, it ranges eastward to Transcaucasia.

The Speckled Beauty (*Alcis arenaria* Hufn.)

Stephens, who in 1831 figured this insect as *Cleora viduata* Schiff., remarks, " All the examples I have seen of this beautiful species, were captured in the New Forest : the first about June, 1822, the remainder in 1825 and 1826 : I believe in the vicinity of Lyndhurst." Barrett states that the late Mr. Samuel Stevens obtained a number of specimens " by sweeping the upper branches of oak trees in the New Forest with a long pole." This was in 1849 ; and between that year and 1872, about which time it seems to have disappeared, the moth was found, by those who knew where to look for it, in the Forest between Brockenhurst and Lyndhurst. Specimens have also been taken, in the past, in Tilgate Forest, Sussex, by the late William Tester, and by Mr. Merrifield, at Holm Bank, near Henfield, in the same county. There had been some rumours of its reappearance in the New Forest, but South was unable to verify this (Pl. **115,** 6).

The caterpillar, stated by Hofmann to feed on lichen growing upon oak and birch, is brownish variegated with paler shades.

Abroad, it is local in central Europe.

The Dotted Carpet (*Alcis jubata* Thunb.)

This species (Pl. **115,** 4, 5) has long been known as *glabraria* Hübn., but as authorities are agreed that *jubata* Thunb., is an earlier name, it must be adopted. The general colour is whitish, powdered with dark grey and black ; there are four black spots on the front margin and from these blackish markings cross the wings, but only the first line is generally distinct, although a second line, beyond the large black discal spot, is sometimes clearly defined and entire ; occasionally a central shade and a submarginal line are both in evidence. The hind wings have a black central spot and a blackish line beyond, but the latter is often absent. Exceptional aberration takes the form of leaden black blotches, clouds, and streaks on the fore wings, and dusky clouding on the hind wings, chiefly on the basal area.

The caterpillar is of a faint bluish green, inclining to greenish white on the back ; a row of black spots along the back, and a broken black narrow stripe along each side. It feeds on tree lichens (*Usnea barbata*), etc., from September to June or July. Three figures of this caterpillar are given on Pl. **122,** 1.

The moth is out in July and August, and may be found at rest on tree trunks now and then, but is more frequently obtained by jarring the lichen-clad branches of oak. Although it is known to occur very locally and somewhat rarely in the counties of Somerset, Wiltshire, Dorset, and Devon, the New Forest in Hampshire is the English district where one is most likely to meet with this species. It has been recorded from Cornwall (Falmouth district, 1904), Herefordshire, Pembrokeshire, Carnarvonshire (Beddgelert), and Cumberland. Charlton Forest, Sussex, has also been mentioned. In Scotland, Renton states that it is generally common in Roxburghshire ; it occurs in several of the woods in Clydesdale, and has been noted from Argyllshire.

Abroad, it is found in central Europe, eastern Siberia, and Japan.

The Great Oak Beauty (*Boarmia roboraria* Schiff.)

The fine Boarmid moth shown on Pl. **115,** 3, has all the typical markings well defined. Occasionally the black cross lines are more distinct, but sometimes they are more or less absent, or obscured. An almost black specimen is mentioned by Barrett as taken in the Reading district, Berkshire ; and the same author states that a black example was captured in the Midlands about the year 1887, but no other specimen was observed until 1893, when a female was obtained, and from eggs deposited smoky black moths were reared.

The caterpillar is very like an oak twig in shape, especially when in repose. In colour it is reddish brown, inclining to ochreous brown ; brownish grey on the humps on rings 5 and 11, and on the skin folds. It feeds on oak during the autumn, and, after hibernation, in the spring. The moth is out in June and July, and may be found on oak trees rather high up the trunks. When on the wing at night it will visit the sugar patch and also light.

The species occurs most frequently in the New Forest, Hampshire, where, in some years, it is very common. Other English counties in which it has been found, or still exists, are—Devon (Cann Woods), Dorset (Cranborne and Bloxworth), Wiltshire (Savernake Forest), Sussex (Abbots Wood, Charlton Forest, Holme Bank, etc.), Surrey (Addington, June, 1902), Kent, Essex (Epping Forest), Middlesex, Berkshire, Buckingham, Warwick (Princethorpe Wood), Worcester (Wyre Forest), Stafford (Cannock Chase), Cheshire (Dunham Park), Yorkshire (wood near Selby), Lancashire (Corporation and Quernmore Woods), Hertfordshire.

Abroad, it ranges from Europe to Japan where it is represented by the race *arguta* Btlr.

The Pale Oak Beauty (*Pseudoboarmia punctinalis* Scop.)

Some specimens are rather greyer. and the cross markings are occasionally less distinct than in Figs, 7 ♂ and 8 ♀ on Pl. 115, which represent the typical forms of this species in England. Examples of a blackish form, ab. *humperti* Humpert, have been noted from Sutton Coldfield, but the Kentish specimens South had seen had the second line of the fore wings edged with white, and a white submarginal line (*consobrinaria* Borkh.)

The caterpillar, which in shape is somewhat like that of the last species, varies in colour. One form is greenish grey, with three lines, the central one darker than those on each side. In another the colour is pale brown mottled with reddish and a darker brown. It feeds on oak, birch, and sometimes sallow, in July and August.

The moth is out in June and July, and specimens have been recorded as captured in September. It may be found on the trunks of oak and fir trees, and will come to sugar and light at night. Although local it is not uncommon in the New Forest and other woods in Hampshire ; also in Sussex, Surrey, Kent, and Berkshire. It has been recorded from Buckingham-shire, Wiltshire and Dorset ; and as local and scarce in the Lancaster district. Ireland, Glengariff, Co. Cork.

The range abroad extends to Amurland and Japan, and in both countries it is represented by subsp. *conferenda* Btlr., which may, however, be a distinct species.

The Engrailed (*Ectropis biundulata* de Vill.)

Like its close relative, some confusion has existed over the name of this species, which has hitherto been known as *bistortata* Goeze. It is far more variable than *crepuscularia* Schiff. On the average it is browner and the lighter forms develop brown or ochreous lines across the wings. Several forms have received names ; the first brood is usually large, has a brighter ochreous appearance and was named *laricaria* by Haworth. The second brood of this race, *baeticaria* Scharf., is smaller and more weakly marked (Pl. **117**, 3).

The eggs and larvae, like the imagines, are confusingly similar to those of *crepuscularia* Hb. A photograph of the caterpillar, by the late Mr. H. Main, is reproduced on Pl. **125**, 3, 3*a*. The general colour is grey, inclining to yellowish or brownish, sometimes it is reddish brown ; two broken dark grey lines on the back and some pale blotches on the sides. It feeds on a wide range of trees, being found sometimes on yew. There are two broods, May and June and again at the end of July and August.

1, 1a. **Willow Beauty**: *eggs, natural size and enlarged, and caterpillar.*
2. **Mottled Beauty**: *caterpillar.*

1. Bordered White.
3. Bordered White.
5. Bordered White.

2. Brown Silver-line.
4. Bordered Grey.
6. Bordered Grey.

7. Latticed Heath.
8, 9. Grass Wave.

10. Grey Scalloped Bar, *male*.
11. Latticed Heath.

12. Grey Scalloped Bar, *female*.

13. Yellow Belle.

14. Straw Belle.

15. Black-veined Moth.

The moth appears in March and April, the second brood at the end of June and July. Occasionally specimens of

FIG. 14.—THE ENGRAILED AT REST.

a third brood are met with in September, October, and November.

It is found throughout England and most of Scotland and has been recorded from Co. Cork in Ireland. Abroad, it has a much wider range than its relative, extending to Siberia and Japan.

Cross pairings between *biundulata* ♂ and *crepuscularia* ♀ resulted in the hybrid *ridingi* Tutt, *biundulata* ♂ and *delameren-sis* ♀ gave *ridingi-suffusa* Tutt. Many other combinations are mentioned by Tutt ("Brit. Lep.," vol. v., pp. 31–5)

The Small Engrailed (*Ectropis crepuscularia* Schiff.)

A great deal of confusion has arisen over this and the previous species, a confusion which originated in the days of the "old masters" and has not been completely cleared today.

In comparison with *biundulata* de Vill. the outer margin is less oblique, whilst the ground colour is whitish tinged with yellow. Prout says " never ochreous, ferruginous or umber brown." The postmedian is distinct. The moth is figured on Pl. **117,** 1, 2, whilst the form *delamerensis* B. White is shown by Fig. 4.

The eggs are smaller than those of *biundulata* but no other differences appear to be reliable.

The larva is very variable and usually darker with the markings less clearly developed. It feeds on the foliage of various deciduous trees during July and August.

The moth flies during May and June, very rarely during ate April.

It is generally common in England as far north as Sutherlandshire, and also in Ireland. Abroad, it is found in central Europe.

Cross pairings between *crepuscularia* ♂ and *biundulata* ♀ have been named *bacoti* Tutt, those of *delamerensis* ♂ and *biundulata* ♀ = *bacoti-suffusa* Tutt (" Brit. Lep.," vol. v., pp. 31–5).

The Square Spot (*Ectropis consonaria* Hübn.)

Two examples of this species will be found on Pl. **117** 5 ♂, 6 ♀. There is variation in the greyish or brownish speckling of the wings, and this in some typical examples is so sparse that the wings appear to be almost white with brownish basal band and brownish markings on the outer area ; the most conspicuous of the latter being the middle square spot between the second and submarginal lines, more or less distinct in all forms, to which the English name refers. In other specimens the wings are, especially the front pair, densely covered with the dark speckling. Some Surrey specimens, chiefly from the Leith Hill district, have an ochreous tinge ; and a black form of the species (ab. *nigra* Bankes) has occurred in a wood near Maidstone, in West Kent. In the Cotswolds the ab. *waiensis* Richardson occurs.

The egg (Pl. **125**, 2) is yellowish green when laid ; later it becomes yellow, and orange red markings appear, chiefly at one end.

The somewhat wrinkled caterpillar is ochreous brown above, inclining to greyish between the rings ; an ochreous line along the middle of the back is only clearly defined on the front rings ; the underside is greenish ochreous, and sometimes this colour extends to the upper side also ; the head, which is notched on the crown, is pale ochreous, more or less marked with brown. It feeds at night, in June and July, on birch, beech, oak, pine, etc.

The moth is out in May and June, earlier in some districts. In the daytime it may be seen on the trunks or boughs of trees, most frequently at too great a height to be easily secured ; but still a few sit low enough for capture, especially on the trunks of fir trees. The species is a decidedly local one, and seems to be largely confined, in Britain, to the southern parts of England, Wales, and Ireland. It occurs in some of the woods of Kent, Surrey, Sussex, Hampshire, Dorset, Devon, Cornwall, Gloucestershire, Oxfordshire, Buckinghamshire, Bedfordshire, Essex, and Suffolk. Edwards notes the species as rare at Malvern, Worcestershire. Forsythe, in " A List of the Macro-Lepidoptera of Lancaster and District " (*Entom.*, 1905, p. 182), states that the moth may be found sitting on the fir-tree trunks at the end of May, at Witherslack and Quernmore ; and a single specimen has been recorded from Upton, near Birkenhead, Cheshire. The occurrence of *E. consonaria* in the north of England seems open to question. The only county in Wales appears to be Glamorgan, as mentioned by Barrett. Kane (*Catalogue of the Lepidoptera of Ireland*) noted the species from Derrycunihy, and Mucross, Killarney, where he has taken it in moderate abundance ; he also gives Clonbullogue, in King's County. Cork (Donovan).

The range abroad extends to Amurland and Japan.

The Brindled White-spot (*Ectropis extersaria* Hübn.)

Two examples of this species (also known as *luridata*, Bork.) are depicted on Pl. **117**, 7♂, 8♀. There is variation in the amount of black speckling and in the strength of the cross lines.

The caterpillar is dull hazel or chocolate brown, often tinged with green ; a row of whitish dots on each side of a series of pale spots along the middle of the back ; rings 4 and 8 barred with black-brown or dusky rust colour. Sometimes the general colour is green. (Adapted from Fenn.) It feeds in July and August, or even later, on oak and birch, sometimes on alder and sallow. The moth is out in May and June, earlier or later in some seasons. In Britain apparently confined to England, where it occurs locally, in woods, from Worcestershire southwards to Kent and Cornwall, and eastward to Norfolk and Suffolk. In the New Forest, Hampshire, where it is often plentiful, it may be seen on the boles of trees, but is more easily obtained after dark when it comes to the sugar patch, or light.

Abroad, it is found in central Europe. A smaller, darker race (*obscurior* Staud.) represents it in south-eastern Siberia and Japan.

The Dusky Carpet (*Tephronia cremiaria* Freyer)

Newman (" British Moths," p. 69) figured this insect under the name of *Mniophila cineraria* Guenée. It was catalogued by Doubleday as British and stated by Stainton (*Man.* ii. 31) to have once occurred at Tenby, South Wales. It can only be regarded as an accidental visitor. The specimen is in the British Museum (Natural History) (Pl. **117**, 12).

The caterpillar is said to feed on lichens on walls.

The Grey Birch (*Aethalura punctulata* Schiff.)

An example of this greyish species is shown on Pl. **117**, 9–11. The wings are usually whitish grey in the ground colour, and sprinkled or dusted with darker grey ; there are three blackish, or black-dotted, cross-lines on the fore wings, often indistinct,

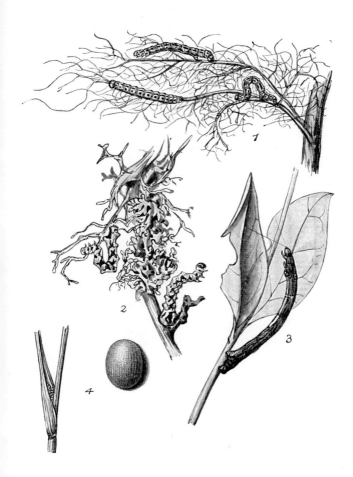

1. **Dotted Carpet:** *caterpillars.*
2. **Brussels Lace:** *caterpillars.*
3. **Waved Umber:** *caterpillar.*
4. **Belted Beauty:** *eggs, natural size and enlarged.*

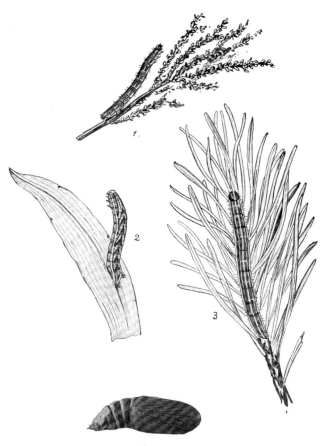

1. **Horse Chestnut**: *caterpillar.*
2. **The Annulet**: *caterpillar.*
3, 3*a*. **Bordered White**: *caterpillar and chrysalis, enlarged.*

but rarely entirely absent, and even then represented by black marks on the front margin. Sometimes the first and third lines may be well in evidence and the central one absent ; occasionally the second line is placed quite close to the first ; the sub-marginal line is whitish, inwardly shaded with dark greyish, especially at the middle and towards the front margin. The hind wings have two cross lines corresponding with the first and third on the fore wings. There is a good deal of variation in the amount of dark speckling, and this is occasionally so heavy that the insect becomes dark grey in colour ; South took such specimens at Oxshott in Surrey. Dark aberrations are perhaps more frequent in the north of England, but the species is more local and less plentiful in that part of the country.

The caterpillar, which may be beaten from birch, and sometimes alder, in July, is bright apple green with yellowish lines on the sides and back ; the ring divisions are yellow, and the head is tinged with that colour. (Adapted from Porritt.) Sometimes the caterpillars are brownish, or greenish grey in general colour. The moth, which is out in May and June, will be found in woods, or on heaths, where birches grow. It rests on the trunks of the trees and may be boxed, as a rule, with ease. On some occasions, however, it is very lively, and the net will have to be brought into action for its capture.

The distribution of this species extends through England, but it is far more plentiful in the south than in the north, although it has been recorded from several places in Yorkshire, and from Coal Law Wood in Northumberland. It is found also in Wales, and in Scotland up to Moray. In Ireland it is not frequent, but has been noted from Mucross, and the Upper Lake of Killarney, in Kerry, and from Tinahely in Wicklow ; Kane also gives Clonbrock in Galway, and adds that " some specimens from this locality have the spots very large on a clear whitish ground, so that they have a superficial resemblance to *Alcis jubata*."

The range abroad spreads to eastern Siberia, Amurland, and Japan.

The Horse Chestnut (*Pachycnemia hippocastanaria* Hübn.)

The rather long and somewhat oval fore wings of this species (Pl. **118,** 4) are brownish grey, inclining to purplish grey ; the two cross lines are blackish, edged with whitish, but generally indistinct ; when the lines are well defined, the enclosed central area is sometimes darker than the other parts of the wings ; there is a black central dot, and occasionally there is a well-marked dusky central shade. Hind wings, whitish, more or less tinged with smoky grey ; frequently there is a dusky, curved line beyond the middle, and this is sometimes outwardly edged with whitish.

The caterpillar is greyish brown, dotted with black, and marked on the back and sides with reddish brown. When at rest on the twigs of its food plant, heather or ling (*Calluna vulgaris*), this caterpillar agrees so well with its surroundings that it is not at all easy to see ; at least, we may see it, but fail to distinguish it from the twigs of the plant. It may be obtained in June and July, and again in the autumn. (Figured on Pl. **123,** 1 after Hofmann).

The first flight of the moth occurs in April and May ; the second in August, but specimens of the later generation are usually small in size and in number, as compared with those of the early brood.

In Britain, this species has so far only been found on the heaths of Kent, Surrey, Sussex, Hampshire, Dorset, Somerset, Berkshire, and Suffolk ; in all these counties it is more or less local, but it abounds in some of its haunts. It has been recorded from Hereford, and Edwards states that it occurs rarely in the Malvern district of Worcestershire.

Abroad, it is rather local in central and southern Europe and North Africa.

The Annulet (*Gnophos obscurata* Schiff.)

In a general way, all the grey specimens of this species are referable to the type form *obscurata* Schiff. ; the type form, however, appears to be rare in Britain, even if it occurs at all. It is, perhaps, best represented by well-marked dark specimens from peaty ground, or the lighter ones from limestone districts. At Folkestone and in other chalky localities on the Kentish coast, the bulk of the specimens are pale grey inclining to whitish, usually with the black cross lines showing more or less clearly. Sometimes the lines are obscured by heavy freckling (ab. *woodiata* Prout) ; not infrequently, at Folkestone chiefly, the inner and outer areas are pale, more or less free of freckling, but the central area, defined by black lines, is densely freckled ; this is the banded form (ab. *fasciata* Prout). A form occurs on the chalk hills at Lewes in Sussex, in which the wings are almost white, without freckling, but with distinct black lines and rings (ab. *calceata* Staud.) ; a modification of this whitish form from Lewes has been described by Prout as ab. *mundata*, " Amost pure whitish, with virtually no markings, excepting the annulets." On heaths in Surrey and Hampshire, and on the mountains of Aberdeen and Perthshire, a blackish form occurs (ab. *obscuriorata* Prout, *obscuraria* Hübn. 146=) ; and sometimes specimens are found in which the wings are of an intense and almost uniform black. In Devonshire and Cornwall, the species is darkish grey inclining to brownish (ab. *anthracinaria* Esp.) ; whilst on the coasts of North Devon and Wales it is of a slaty grey, more or less tinged with brown, and almost without markings ; the Welsh specimens are large, and the wings are rather shining (ab. *uniformata* Prout). A form, which South had not seen, of " a sandy or reddish colour " is referred by Prout (*Trans. City of Lond. Ent. Soc.*, 1903, p. 39) to ab. *argillacearia* Staud. ; it occurs in sandstone localities (Pl. **118**, 1–3.

The rather rough and dumpy caterpillar is dark greyish

brown above, inclining to purplish brown beneath ; the raised dots are capped with white, and there is a pair of white-capped warts on the last ring (adapted from Barrett). It feeds on rock rose (*Helianthemum*), cinquefoil (*Potentilla*), salad burnet (*Poterium*), etc. ; in moorland areas heather is the usual food ; or the larvae may be reared on groundsel, chickweed, and strawberry, both wild and cultivated : September to May (Pl. **123,** 2).

The late Mr. A. J. Scollick gave South some eggs, laid by a female taken in Surrey ; they were yellowish green at first, but changed to pale brownish. The caterpillars hatched and seemed to thrive on groundsel, but they died during the winter.

The moth is out in July and August, and is widely distributed in England, but except that it occurs in Surrey, Berkshire, Herefordshire, and Worcestershire, it seems to prefer the seaboard counties, and in them chiefly affects localities near the sea. It is found in Wales, and in Scotland up to Moray ; but in both these countries and also in Ireland it is most frequent on the coast.

Abroad, it ranges through Europe and Asia Minor.

The Scotch Annulet (*Gnophos obfuscata* Schiff.)

This species (Pl. **118,** 5 ♂, 6 ♀) was recorded, as a species new to Britain, by Curtis, who described and figured it as *Charissa operaria* in 1826, from specimens captured in Scotland. Subsequently, it was found to be the *obfuscaria* of Hübner, and also the *obfuscata* of the Vienna Catalogue (1775). Our ashy grey form of the species is referable to *obfuscata* and the fuscous grey form to *myrtillata* Thunberg.

The rather stout caterpillar is grey with darker lines and V-shaped marks along the middle of the back, and dark-edged pale lines on the sides ; two erect whitish points on ring 12. It feeds on heather (*Calluna*), and needle furze or petty-whin (*Genista anglica*), but it may be reared on knotgrass. September to June, sometimes later.

1, 2, Goat Moth.

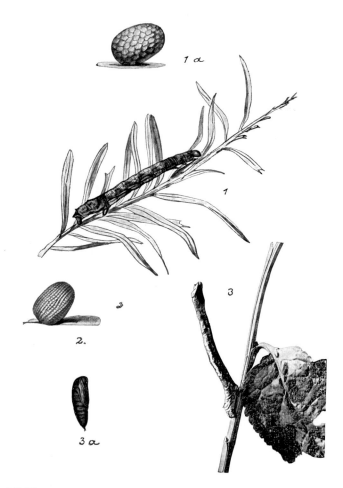

1, 1*a*. **Satin Beauty:** *egg, enlarged, and caterpillar.*
2. **Square Spot:** *eggs, natural size and enlarged.*
3, 3*a*. **The Engrailed:** *caterpillar and chrysalis.*

The moth is out in July and August, and frequents heaths, moor, and mountain, in Scotland from Clydesdale (including Bute and Arran) to Aberdeen and Ross, and the Isle of Lewis. Donovan reports it as being rare and very local in Ireland. It may be found resting upon rocks, stone walls, etc. ; where these have suitable holes, crannies, or projections they are selected as hiding places. Sometimes the moth has been noted on the wing during the day, but at night it flies freely, and will then visit light.

Abroad, it is locally common throughout Europe and the Caucasus.

The Black Mountain Moth (*Psodos coracina* Esp.)

The smoky-grey species represented on Pl. **118**, 8 ♂, 11 ♀ has two black lines on the fore wings ; these are often edged with whitish, and the space between them blackish ; the sub-marginal line is whitish, and the discal spot is black ; the hind wings have a black central spot and two pale lines or bands. The female is rather smaller and much paler. In both sexes the central band of the fore wings is generally narrowed below the middle, and sometimes it is completely divided at this point. It flies during July.

According to Gardner (1950, *Ent. Gazette*, 1, 47) eggs were deposited on July 8 and hatched on the 25th and 26th. Pale yellow at first they became gradually darker until almost black.

The larvae fed on *Calluna vulgaris* preferring the flowers but would eat the leaves. They hibernated through the winter and started to feed again in February. The general colour of the full-grown larva is light brown or greyish brown, becoming a glossy white on the middle segments. On the back of each of the first five abdominal segments are two oblique dark marks forming a sort of fishtail. On the hind segments these marks are replaced by a more or less continuous brown patch. Along the spiracles is a black line formed by a series of slightly arched streaks. There is a fine brown dorsal line and a broad brown line on the sides. The spiracles are black. The larva is stumpy and broadest in the middle, tapering towards head and tail. Length when full fed ⅜ inch.

More details of its life history are published by Richardson (1952, *Ent. Rec.*, lvi. 114) ; and by Cockayne, in the same volume.

As regards the British Isles, this species is known only to occur in the Highlands of Scotland. It is a day flyer, and very fond of sunshine, but its favourite haunts are situated at elevations of from 2000 to 4000 feet.

Abroad, it frequents the mountains of Scandinavia, Pyrenees, Alps, Carpathians, etc.

In *Jahresbericht des Wien, Ent.*, 1898, v., p. 85, a comparison is made between the larvae and pupae of *P. coracina* and *P. noricana* Wagner, and the larvae are figured on Taf. I. The larvae of *noricana* were fed in confinement on dandelion and *coracina* on knotgrass. A moth, supposed to be *Orphne tenebraria* Esp. = *torvaria* Hübn. was reported as taken in Ireland " many years " before 1843, but at the present time that specimen, apparently, does not exist and there is no exact description of it extant.

The Netted Mountain Moth (*Epelis carbonaria* Clerck)

The white wings of this species (Pl. **118**, 7, 10) are freckled with blackish and crossed by black stripes ; sometimes the freckling is so heavy that the white ground colour is much obscured and only distinctly seen as edging to the cross stripes.

The caterpillar is dingy ochreous or whity brown marked with wavy darker stripes. It feeds at night on birch and sallow ; *Vaccinium*, *Erica*, bearberry (*Arctostaphylos uva-ursi*) have also been mentioned as food plants.

In April and May, the moth, which is to be found locally, high up on the mountains of Scotland from Perthshire to Ross, is on the wing, and flies in the sunshine. Writing of this species at Rannoch in May (about 17th), 1905, Dr. E. A. Cockayne remarks that the moths began to fly about noon, when they appeared on all sides and were fairly active on the wing.

The distribution abroad is northern and Alpine, and the range extends to north-eastern Siberia.

The Frosted Yellow (*Isturgia limbaria* Fabr.)

This black-bordered orange-yellow species (Pl. **118,** 13) is not likely to be confused with any other occurring in Britain. The wings are more or less sprinkled with black, but this is usually most noticeable on the hind wings which are some-times thickly sprinkled, or, more rarely, the yellow ground colour is entirely obscured. The form with a black discal spot on all the wings has been named ab. *quadripunctaria* Fuchs. In ab. *fumata* Mathew, the orange yellow is replaced by smoky umber brown, tinged with orange, and dusted with black atoms (bred July, 1899).

The caterpillar is greenish with grey-edged yellowish lines along the back, and a black-edged yellow one along the sides. The ground colour is sometimes purplish brown. It feeds on broom chiefly, but will eat other Genisteae. There appear to be two broods, one in June, and the other in September, or earlier sometimes. The moth is out in May and early June, and again in July and August, but it has been known to remain in the chrysalis for four years. It flies in the sunshine, and when resting, it sits like a butterfly, with its wings brought together over its back.

Stephens (1831) states that the species was " not uncommon among high broom in the vicinity of Birch-wood in Kent." Later authors give Stowmarket (common), Needham, Barham, and Ipswich, in Suffolk. There are no recent records from the county of Kent ; and not much has been heard of the species from Suffolk, although it may still exist, in greatly reduced numbers, in some of its old haunts therein. A specimen was reported from Ross-shire (*Entom.*, lxxvii. 12).

Abroad, it is found locally in central Europe.

The Common Heath (*Ematurga atomaria* Linn.)

Three specimens of this variable species are shown on Pl. **118**, 15 ♂, 17 ♀). The general colour of all the wings in the male is ochreous, inclining to whitish or to brownish. Usually the wings are speckled with brown, and the cross lines, or bands, are dark brown. Occasionally the cross markings are absent; but more frequently the three lines on the fore wings are much broadened and more or less united, sometimes forming a central band in which are a few ochreous scales towards the front margin : ab. *obsoletaria* Zett. Dark brown or blackish specimens (ab. *unicolorata* Staud.) are captured now and then in the southern counties of England, but such uniform dark varieties are more frequent in the north (Staffordshire and Yorkshire). The female is white in colour, and usually only lightly speckled with blackish ; the cross lines are more conspicuous, as a rule, than in the male, but they are subject to pretty much the same kind of aberration. Sometimes examples of this sex greatly resemble *Isturgia carbonaria*, and have been confused with that species by Haworth and other entomologists in the past. An abnormal specimen with six wings has been recorded, and Barrett mentions a gynandrous example—the right side like a small dark female, and the left an ordinary male ; both antennae shortly pectinated.

The caterpillar, according to Fenn, is variable in colour and markings, all shades of brown, greenish brown, ochreous, purple, and grey ; in some examples there are pale diamonds, and in others whitish spots, along the back. It feeds on ling and heath, and will eat clover, trefoils, broom, etc. : July and August, and occasionally September. The moth is out in May and June, and sometimes there are specimens on the wing in

August. Abundant on almost every heath throughout the British Isles, except in the Shetlands.

Common over most of Europe to Siberia.

The Bordered White (*Bupalus piniaria* Linn.)

Two forms of the male of this species are represented on Pl. **121**. Fig. 3 shows the yellow English form (ab. *flavescens* White), and Fig. 5 the white North English and Scottish forms. In southern localities, however, specimens occur which are almost as white as the northern or even Scottish examples ; South had two such specimens from Surrey. There is considerable variation in the size of area occupied by the pale colour, both in white and yellow forms. In one of the former, from Forres, in Scotland, the white is represented by a small oval spot and dappled streak on the fore wings ; an entirely black specimen (ab. *nigricarius* Backhaus) has been noted from Berkshire. In other specimens there is an unusually large proportion of pale colour. The females are usually orange, or orange yellow, in the south (Pl. **121**, 1) ; and yellowish brown, or dingy orange brown, in the north. The brownish-coloured females occasionally occur in the south, and the brighter form of this sex is sometimes taken in the Midlands, where the two forms of the species seem to overlap.

The long, greenish caterpillar is marked with whitish or yellow lines ; those along the back are edged with black, and along the sides with dark green. It feeds from August to October on the needles of the pine, and also on other firs. (Pl. **123**, 3 ; Fig. 3*a* shows a photo of the chrysalis, twice natural size, by the late Mr. H. Main.) The moth is out in May and June, later in the north ; it is generally common in pine woods throughout England, Wales, and Scotland, sometimes occurring in such numbers as to cause damage to pine plantations. Local in Ireland.

Abroad, it is found in suitable localities in Castile, central and northern Europe, Transcaucasia, Altai, and eastern Siberia.

The Bordered Grey (*Selidosema brunnearia*
subsp. *scandinaviaria* Staud.)

D. S. Fletcher (*Entom.*, lxxxii. 217) has shown that the
British race is comparable with that from north-western
Europe, ssp. *scandinaviaria* Staud.

Portraits of the male and female of this species (known also
as *ericetaria* de Vill. will be found on Pl. **121,** 4 ♂, 6 ♀. The
cross markings are more distinct in some specimens than in
others, and the central one of the fore wings varies in width.

The caterpillar (Pl. **126,** 3, from a photograph by the late
Mr. H. Main) is grey, with a dark brown or blackish irregular
double line along the back, and pale lines along the sides, the
lower one edged above with reddish brown ; spiracles, black,
as also are the dots on the back ; the last ring ends in a point.
(Adapted from Porritt.) It feeds on broom, restharrow,
trefoils, and ling (*Calluna*), from September well on into the
following spring.

The moth occurs on heaths and mosses in July and August,
but it is local. On warm days the males are very active, but
about dusk they are not difficult to capture. In southern
England, the New Forest, Hampshire, appears to be its special
home, but it is also found in other parts of that county, including the Isle of Wight, in Dorset, and in Surrey ; also noted
from Berkshire. It is scarce in Cheshire, fairly common on the
Witherslack mosses in North Lancashire, and at Ullswater in
Cumberland. It has been recorded from the Isle of Arran
1882), Mallaig, Inverness-shire (1909), Isle of Canna (1954)
and Loch Shiel, Argyllshire (1913). It has also been recorded
from the Isle of Man. In Ireland it is widely distributed, and
is abundant at Kinsale, Co. Cork. Cockayne (*Ent. Rec.*, lx. 79
described a subspecies from Tyrone under the name *tyronensis*.

Abroad, it occurs in Scandinavia, western Europe, North
Africa, and Asia Minor.

The V-moth (*Itame wauaria* Linn.)

The popular name of this species (Pl. **118,** 14) refers to the black discal mark on the more or less violet-tinged, pale greyish fore wings ; but there is a good deal of variation in this character. Occasionally the wings are suffused with smoky (ab. *vau-nigraria* Hatchett), or more rarely with blackish brown (ab. *fuscaria* Thunb.).

On Pl. **126,** 1, is a figure of the caterpillar, from a coloured drawing by the late Mr. A. Sich. The general colour is greenish, or some shade of brown ; the lines on the back are white, and that low down along the sides is broad, and yellow ; the raised dots are black with short bristles. It feeds in April, May, and June on the foliage of gooseberry and currant, and is especially fond of the tender shoots.

The moth, which is out in July and August, is often common in gardens and orchards where bush fruit is grown, pretty well throughout the United Kingdom. It appears to occur only rarely in Ireland, but has recently been taken abundantly near Dublin.

Abroad, the range extends to Amurland.

The Rannoch Looper (*Itame brunneata* Thunb.)

All the wings are of a rusty ochreous colour, sometimes, chiefly in the male, inclining to a purplish tint on the fore wings ; the brownish cross lines are usually most distinct in the female, which sex Hübner figured as *pinetaria* (Pl. **118,** 9 ♂, 12 ♀).

The caterpillar is reddish brown, with a black-edged dark green irregular line along the middle of the back ; a white line on each side of the central one, and following this are a dark brown shade-like stripe and some brownish green lines ; the line along the spiracles is whitish, inclining to yellow. In general appearance it closely resembles a twig of bilberry (*Vaccinium*), upon the foliage of which plant the caterpillar feeds in the spring.

The moth is out in June and July, but in the British Isles it is only to be obtained in Perthshire and northwards in Scotland. Black-wood, Loch Rannoch, is the original, and a now well-known, locality for this species, which Curtis in 1828 figured as *Speranza sylvaria*. Odd specimens have been taken in Cambridgeshire, Norfolk, Staffordshire, Essex, Surrey, and Kent.

The range abroad extends to Amurland and Japan, and to North America.

The Brown Silver-line (*Lithina chlorosata* Scop.)

The two cross lines on the pale brown, sometimes pinkish, fore wings, are edged with whitish, but this is most distinct on the outer one. In some specimens there is a distinct submarginal line, but this character is only faintly in evidence as a rule, and occasionally it is entirely absent (Pl. **121**, 2).

The caterpillar feeds in June, sometimes earlier, on bracken or brake-fern (*Pteris aquilina*). It is olive green marked with reddish brown lines, and there is a whitish line under the black spiracles.

In most English and Welsh localities where bracken is plentiful, this moth should be found in May and June ; also in the south of Scotland, but its occurrence in that country north of Clydesdale appears to be only casual. J. L. Campbell reports it from the Isle of Canna in the Hebrides. It is common in several parts of Ireland.

The distribution abroad includes Amurland and Japan.

The Latticed Heath (*Chiasmia clathrata* Linn.)

In its ground colour this species (Pl. **121**, 7 ♂, 11 ♀) varies from ochreous of some shade to white. The dark-brown or blackish cross lines and veins give a latticed appearance to the wings, hence both the Latin and popular names for this insect. There is much variation in the width of the cross markings ; sometimes two or more unite and so form bands;

1. **V-moth**: *caterpillar*.
2. **Yellow Belle**, *caterpillar*.
3. **Bordered Grey**: *caterpillar*.
4. **Grey Scalloped Bar**: *caterpillar*.

1, 2. The Festoon.
3. Reed Leopard.
4, 5. The Triangle.
6, 7. Leopard Moth.
8. *Syntomis phegea.*   9. *Dysauxes ancilla.*

more rarely, perhaps, the outer lines are absent, and the others broken up into dashes ; or the blackish cross lines may be slender and the veins remain of the ochreous ground colour (ab. *cancellaria* Hb.). A less frequent aberration has the wings dark brown or blackish all over, except a row of whitish or ochreous spots on the outer margins (ab. *nocturnata* Fuchs).

The caterpillar, which feeds on clovers and trefoils, is green, with white lines along the back and sides ; the slightly notched head is rather glossy, and the mouth is brownish : June to September, in two broods.

The first generation of the moth is out in April and May, and the second in July and August. It may be found in clover fields and on chalk slopes, etc., where the food plants flourish ; although it is an active day flyer, it is not difficult to capture with the net. It is most plentiful in southern and eastern England, but its range extends throughout the United Kingdom to Clydesdale. The Irish subspecies, *hugginsi* Baynes, is single brooded and has the ground colour of the wings white. It occurs in the northern half of Ireland, extending southwards to Co. Clare in the west and to Cos. Dublin and Kildare in the east. There is a single record from Tipperary.

The distribution abroad extends to eastern Siberia, Amurland, and Japan.

The Grey Scalloped Bar (*Dyscia fagaria* Thunb.)

In its typical form this species (synonym *belgiaria* Hübn.) is grey, more or less tinged with ochreous, speckled with brownish grey, and crossed by black-marked brownish grey lines. The bulk of British specimens, especially those from southern localities, are whitish grey, thinly sprinkled with darker grey scales in the male, and sometimes heavily powdered in the female ; a pair are figured on Pl. **121**, 10 ♂, 12 ♀. The whiter form of the male, occurring in Britain chiefly in the New Forest, Hampshire, has been named *albidaria* Staud.

The roughened caterpillar is figured on Pl. **126**, 4 (photo by

the late H. Main).   In general colour it is dingy brown, with a
whitish stripe along the back and some greyish marking on the
sides.   It feeds on ling and heath ; growing slowly in the late
summer, but more quickly in the spring, after hibernation,
when it may be obtained at night from the tips of the heather
twigs, either by searching or by means of the sweeping net.
The moth is out in June and July in the south, and later in
the north.   It is found on moist heaths, moors, and mosses ;
when resting on the dark-coloured earth it so closely resembles
a stone that it is probably frequently passed unnoticed.

The species is apparently more plentiful in the New Forest
than in its other known southern localities (Kent, Surrey,
Berkshire, Sussex, and Dorset).   Its range northwards in
England extends from Worcestershire (Malvern, rare) to Cumberland and Northumberland.   It seems to be distributed
over the greater part of Scotland, including the Hebrides and
the Orkneys.   In Wales it has been recorded from Flint,
Denbigh, and Carnarvon ; and it is widely spread over Ireland, occurring chiefly on the bogs.

Abroad, it is found in northern central Europe, Russia, and
the Caucasus.

The Black-veined Moth (*Idaea lineata* Scop.)

This slightly ochreous-tinged silky white moth has the veins
of the wings blackish, and this is especially noticeable on the
underside of the fore wings.   A male specimen is shown on
Pl. **121,** 15; the wings of the female are slightly smaller, and
the body is stouter and shorter.   This species is the *dealbata*
of Linnaeus, but *lineata* Scop. is older by four years.   The
long caterpillar is greyish inclining to ochreous or brownish ;
several irregular darker lines on the back and sides.   It feeds,
in confinement, on knotgrass, docks, bird's-foot trefoil, etc.,
but in the open is said to eat wood grasses, such as *Brachy-
podium*, upon the blades of which the female moth has been
seen to deposit eggs : July to May.   The moth is out from

late May through June ; it flies in the sunshine, or rests among long grass, etc., from which it is readily disturbed. Its chief British haunts are in Kent (Higham, Wye, etc.) ; but it has been recorded from Sussex, Dorset, Somerset, Gloucestershire, and Herefordshire, chiefly in single specimens.

Abroad, the range extends to Amurland.

The Straw Belle (*Aspitates gilvaria* Schiff.)

This straw-coloured species (Pl. **121,** 14 ♂) will be easily recognised by the brownish stripe on the fore wings, which extends from the front margin, near the tip, almost to the inner margin ; this is sometimes faint, but rarely quite absent. The hind wings are paler and have a dusky central dot and incomplete band. The caterpillar, which in shape is somewhat similar to that of the next species, is ochreous grey inclining to pinkish on the sides ; a dark almost blackish line along the middle of the back is edged on each side with pale ochreous, and there are other pale and dark lines along the sides. It feeds on thyme, cinquefoil, yarrow, and other low-growing plants ; it may be reared on knotgrass : September to June. The moth is out in July and August, and, although very local, is not uncommon on downs and hilly fields on the chalk in Kent and Surrey—Dover, Folkestone, and Rochester in the former county, and Leatherhead, Box Hill, and Reigate in the latter, are the best-known localities. It has also been reported from Sussex (Brighton, Horsham, near Polegate, Shoreham). In Devonshire it is said to occur at Braunton and Ilfracombe, but is scarce. In his catalogue of the Lepidoptera of Suffolk (1890) the Rev. E. N. Bloomfield noted the species as very plentiful in clover fields about Tuddenham. Also recorded from Somerset, Gloucestershire, Cheshire (West Kirby and Hale), and from near Harrow in Middlesex.

Very local in Ireland (Kane). During a visit to the Burren, Co. Clare, in 1950, Messrs. Classey and Robinson took a short series of a form which differed so much from the typical form that Dr. Cockayne has described it as a subspecies and named it *burrenensis* (*Ent. Gaz.*, 1951, ii. 100).

The range abroad extends to East Siberia and Amurland.

The Yellow Belle (*Aspitates ochrearia* Rossi)

As will be seen from Fig. 13 ♂ on Pl. **121**, this species differs from the last in its yellower colour and rather smaller size ; the fore wings have two cross bands, generally well defined, but in the male they are sometimes very faint and slender, and specimens have been recorded in which the bands were missing.

The roughened caterpillar, figured on Pl. **126**, 2, from a coloured drawing by the late Mr. A. Sich, is pale ochreous brown, lined and striped with darker brown. It feeds on wild carrot, plantain, hawks'-beard, etc., and will thrive on knotgrass. There are two broods, one feeding in the spring, after hibernation ; and the other in June and July, sometimes later. The first generation of moths flies in May and June, and the second in August and early September. The species occurs in all the southern sea-board counties of England from Kent to Cornwall, frequenting the downs and rough fields near the coast ; also in the Breck district of the eastern counties. It occurs in South Wales ; and odd specimens have been reported from Cheshire (Delamere), and from Cumberland.

The range abroad extends to North-west Africa and Asia Minor.

The Grass Wave (*Perconia strigillaria* Hübn.)

A male and a female of this species are depicted on Pl. **121**, 8 ♂ and 9 ♀. There is variation in the amount of dark speckling on the wings, and in the number and width of the cross markings ; sometimes the first and second on the fore wings are united throughout their length, or towards the inner margin ; coupled with this there is sometimes considerable increase in the width of the first cross marking of the hind wings. A rare variety in Britain is ab. *grisearia* Staud.,

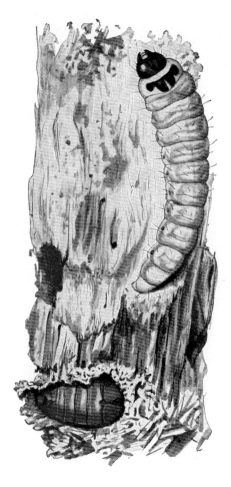

Goat Moth: *caterpillar, chrysalis and cocoon.*

1, 2. **Transparent Burnet.**
3. **Scotch Burnet.**   4. **Slender Scotch Burnet.**
5, 6. **New Forest Burnet.**
7, 8, 9, 10. **Five-spot Burnet.**

which is of an almost uniform greyish or greyish brown colour, with the markings obscured.

The caterpillar is purplish grey, marked with paler and darker ; two warts on the back of rings 7-10, the middle pair the largest and most prominent. It feeds on ling, heath, broom, and the flowers of gorse or furze, and is best obtained in the spring after hibernation.

The moth, which is out in June and July, occurs on most of the heaths and moors throughout England ; apparently commoner and more generally distributed in the south than in the north ; but it seems to be rare on the eastern side of the country altogether. From Cheshire it spreads into Flint and Denbigh, North Wales. In Scotland, it is found in Roxburgh (Bellion Moor), Clydesdale (local, but common), and north-wards to Ross. It is found on the boggy heaths of Ireland, and Kane states that it is abundant where it occurs.

The range abroad extends to Scandinavia and eastward to Asia Minor.

COSSIDAE

Of the eighty-six Palaearctic species referred to this family, by far the larger number are eastern, only about eight appear to be found in Europe, and but three of these occur in Britain.

Meyrick separated *Cossus cossus* from our other two species, adopted *Trypanus* Rambur, as the generic name, and removed it to the Tortricina as a family of that group under the name Trypanidae.

The Goat Moth (*Cossus cossus* Linn.)

The English name of this species (Pl. **124,** 1 ♂, 2 ♀) applies more especially to the caterpillar, as this creature gives off an odour which has been compared with that of the he-goat. In general colour the caterpillar is pinkish ochreous, inclining to dark reddish on the back; the small head is black and glossy, and the mark on the first ring of the body is black. It feeds in the solid wood of various trees, especially elm, ash, birch, and willow, but is three or four years in completing

FIG. 15.—GOAT MOTH AT REST.

growth. When mature, it often leaves its burrow and wanders in search of a suitable place for pupation. When met with at such times it should, if taken, be placed in a roomy tin box with a good supply of sawdust or decayed wood, when it will make its cocoon, and appear as a moth in due course. The early stages are shown on Pl. **128.**

Caterpillars are more likely to come under the notice of the country rambler than are the moths; examples of the latter, however, may be seen occasionally, in June or July, resting on a tree-trunk, a fence, or a gate post; sometimes, although practically tongueless, the female moth visits the sugar patch and either settles on the tree or flutters around, presumably attracted as to a tree exuding sap and therefore suitable for egg-laying.

The species seems to occur in all parts of the British Isles, except perhaps the extreme north of Scotland and the Hebrides.

Abroad, the range extends to Amurland and to North-west Africa.

The Leopard Moth (*Zeuzera pyrina* Linn.)

As will be seen from the portraits of this blue-black spotted white species on Pl. **127,** the male (Fig. 6) is smaller than the female (Fig. 7) ; it will be further noted that the antennae of the male are bi-pectinate on the basal half, and thread-like on the outer half ; the antennae of the female are thread-like throughout.

The caterpillar (Pl. **135,** 1, from a coloured drawing by the late Mr. A. Sich) is dull whitish, more or less tinged with yellow ; the spots are black, and the head and plates on the first and last rings of the body are blackish brown. It feeds in branches and stems of trees and shrubs, and is often a pest of fruit trees. The food plants of the larva are maple, sycamore, ash, elm, oak, horse-chestnut, hawthorn, sallow, lilac, pear, apple, cherry, and laurel. Hatching from the egg, say in the late summer of 1960, the caterpillar will not be full grown until May or June of 1962, or possibly 1963 ; forming a cocoon of silk and wood particles, it turns to a reddish brown chrysalis in the burrow, and near the bark of the stem or branch. The moth comes out in the summer, and is most often seen in the London district, where the female especially is not infrequently found on tree-trunks or on grass, etc., under trees. It visits light, and the electric arc lamps are very attractive to it.

The species occurs in the south and east of England, and through the north-west counties to Cheshire. It has been recorded from Cardiff, South Wales, and doubtfully from Ireland. Recently recorded from Uppingham.

Abroad, the range extends to Korea and Japan. In America it seems to be established in parts of the State of New York.

The Reed Leopard (*Phragmataecia castaneae* Hübn.)

A male of this species (*Macrogaster arundinis* Hübn. of some authors) is shown on Pl. **127**, 3. The female is rather larger, with longer body, and the antennae are without pectinations.

The wrinkled and rather shining caterpillar is ochreous white with reddish brown stripes along the back. It feeds at the base of the stems of reed (*Phragmites communis*) and is full grown in the spring of the second year following that in which it left the egg in late summer. Thus, a caterpillar hatching in August, 1960, would be mature about May, 1962, pupate in that month, or the next, and the perfect insect would appear in June or July.

The moth flies at night, and may be attracted by a brilliant light. The earliest known British locality for the species was Holme Fen in Huntingdonshire (1841–8). In 1850 it was found abundantly at Whittlesea Mere. Its haunts in the present day are Wicken and Chippenham fens in Cambridge-shire, but specimens from these localities are somewhat smaller than the old Huntingdonshire examples; also in Dorset. Barrett states that he put down some eggs of the species in Ranworth Fen, Norfolk, and that five years later two males were captured within a short distance of the spot where the eggs had been placed. In 1901 Edelsten took two males at light close to Ranworth and in 1904 one at Horning.

The range abroad extends to China and Japan.

LIMACODIDAE

This family of moths mainly comprises tropical species, and is but poorly represented in the Palaearctic Region. Only two species are European, and both occur in Britain.

1. New Forest (ab. *confusa*).
2, 3, 4, 5. Five-spot Burnet, *varieties*.
6, 7. Six-spot Burnet, *varieties*.

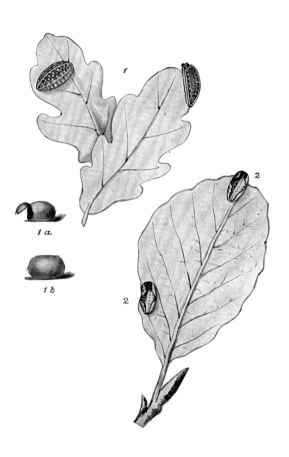

1, 1*a*, 1*b*. **The Festoon:** *caterpillars and cocoons.*
2. **The Triangle:** *caterpillars.*

Apoda Haw., supersedes *Limacodes* Latrielle, but the name of the family so long known as Limacodidae, will not have to be changed as *Limacodes* still remains in the synonymy. Meyrick, who had rightly sunk *Limacodes* in favour of *Apoda* Haw. uses Heterogeneidae as the family name.

The Festoon (*Apoda avellana* Linn.)

The fore wings of the male are orange brown, more or less smudged or clouded with blackish ; two oblique black lines, the first inclined inwards, and the second outwards and apparently terminating on the outer margin just above the inner angle, but there is a slender dusky curve from this point enclosing a clear, orange-brown spot. Hind wings blackish, except on the inner margin, which is broadly orange brown. Female, ochreous brown, with lines on the fore wings as in the male ; hind wings suffused with dark grey or blackish, except on the inner area ; generally rather larger than the male (Pl. **127**, 1 ♂, 2 ♀). Not infrequently, the fore wings of the male are so much clouded with blackish that the cross lines are obscured, and the spot on the inner margin alone remains clear.

The caterpillar (Pl. **131**, 1, from a coloured drawing by the late Mr. A. Sich) is green, with two reddish-edged yellow lines on the back ; between these lines are yellowish spots ; a yellow line along the sides extends along the front edge of the second ring, where it is marked with red. It feeds on oak, and may be beaten from the boughs in the autumn. The brownish cocoon is depicted on Pl. **131** ; Fig. 1*a* shows the hinged lid which covered the opening through which the chrysalis protruded previous to the moth's escape ; Fig. 1*b* represents one from which the moth has not emerged, and in nature this would be attached to a leaf and covered with a delicate film of silk. The moth is out in June and July, and both sexes may be beaten from the branches of trees, or seen flying around their tops in the sunshine.

This species, though often referred to as *Limacodes testudo* Shciff. is the *avellana* of Linnaeus, and is an inhabitant of oak woods, and occurs in Hampshire, Sussex, Kent, Surrey, Essex, Suffolk, Oxfordshire, Buckinghamshire, Gloucester-shire, and Worcestershire. A male and two females have been reported from Clonbrock, Co. Galway, Ireland.

The Triangle (*Heterogenea asella* Schiff.)

The fore wings of this little species (Pl. **127**, 4 ♂ and 5 ♀) are of triangular shape ; in the male, which sex is smaller than the female, they are dark brown, sometimes almost blackish (ab. *nigra* Tutt), and those of the female yellowish brown varying to ochreous yellow (ab. *flavescens* Tutt). The hind wings of the male are blackish, and of the female clouded with blackish.

The curious woodlouse-shaped caterpillar is green, sometimes inclining to yellowish ; the broad reddish band on the back broadens out before the middle, thus giving the idea of a rough cross, or, as sometimes described, a blunt spear head. It is found, by searching, in August and until October, on the foliage of beech and oak. Birch has also been mentioned as a food plant, and on the Continent it is said to feed on poplar, lime, hazel, and hornbeam. Fig. 2 on Pl. **131** is from a photo by the late Mr. H. Main.

Although the caterpillar constructs its gall-like cocoon on a leaf or in the fork of a twig in the autumn, it does not change to a chrysalis until late in spring, sometimes not until June. The moth is out in June and July and flies in the sunshine, chiefly in the afternoon, and might easily be confused with the Lechean Tortrix (*Ptycholoma lecheana* Linn.).

The species appears to be very local in England and confined to the south. Its chief haunts seem to be in Buckinghamshire, where it is not uncommon in beech woods at Marlow, and in Hampshire, especially parts of the New Forest. It has been found in Epping Forest, Essex ; rarely in Abbot's Wood and

Rewell Wood, Sussex; also recorded from Bickleigh Vale and the Plym Valley, Devon.

The range abroad extends to Amurland.

ZYGAENIDAE

The moths belonging to this family are popularly known in Britain as Burnets and Foresters. Of the former seven kinds occur in the British Isles, and of the latter there are only three species.

All the species live in colonies, so that when a specimen is seen or captured others may be expected to occur on, or somewhere around, the same spot. The caterpillars bear a close resemblance to each other, and are not always easily distinguished.

Over thirty species of *Zygaena* are found in Europe, and about sixty more have been described from other parts of the Palaearctic Region. There are at least twenty-five Palaearctic species referred to the genus *Ino*, and about ten of these are European.

By most authors *filipendulae* is regarded as the type of the genus *Zygaena* Fabr.; but others refer this species, and its allies, to the genus *Anthrocera* Scop., using the Fabrician genus for *phegea* Linn. The latter species and its allies are perhaps more frequently referred to *Syntomis* Ochsenheimer, the typical genus of the family Syntomidae, the systematic position of which is near the Arctiidae.

For a discussion of the British subspecies, some of the aberrations and the synonymy of the British representatives of the genus *Zygaena*, see W. G. Tremewan, 1960, *Ent. Gazette*, 11 : 185–194. In revising the text of the *Zygaena* species in the following pages, the information contained in Mr. Tremewan's paper has been freely drawn upon.

The Transparent Burnet (*Zygaena purpuralis* Brünn.)

Three subspecies of *Zygaena purpuralis* have so far been recognised in the British Isles. Compared with other races, subsp. *segontii* Tremewan from Wales has the first basal streak on the fore wing shorter ; the other streaks are narrower and widely separated and are, together with the hind wing, scarlet, not crimson. The ground colour of the fore wing is mixed with green. Head, thorox and abdomen slightly hairy. The antennae end abruptly, with blunt tips. Abersoch, Carnarvonshire, and Cardiganshire.

Subspecies *hibernica* Reiss (Pl. **129**, 1, 2) is thickly scaled, with the hind wing and the streaks on the fore wing scarlet, not crimson ; the ground colour of the fore wing is blue-black. The type series is from Ardrahan, Galway. Not all Irish specimens, however, appear to be identical to *hibernica*. Specimens from Ballyvaughan, Co. Clare, are much closer in appearance to the race from western Scotland, subsp. *caledonensis* Reiss and are named f. loc. *sabulosa* Tremewan.

Subspecies *caledonensis* is rather smaller than *hibernica* ; the head, thorax and abdomen are densely covered with black hairs. The wings are thinly scaled ; the hind wing and the streaks on the fore wing are crimson, not scarlet. The antennae end with short, thick clubs.

A rare aberration from Wales has the spots and the hind wings more or less suffused with blackish (ab. *obscura* Tutt), but a still rarer variety from Ireland has the crimson of spots and hind wings replaced by yellow (ab. *lutescens* Tutt).

The caterpillar (Pl. **132**, 1) is dark green inclining to olive above and paler below ; the spots are black (outer row) and yellow (inner row) ; the line along the back is obscure whitish ; hairs, whitish. It feeds on thyme : in late summer, and after hibernation, in the spring. The moth flies in June, and is locally common in Ireland (Clare and Galway), Wales (Abersoch), and Scotland (Oban, Loch Etive). It has been reported from Tintagel, Cornwall, but there is some doubt about the identification of these specimens. It has now been recorded from the Inner Hebrides (Harrison).

This species was figured by Brünnich, in 1763, as *purpuralis*, and authorities are now agreed that this name must be adopted in place of *pilosellae*, Esper (1781), or *minos*, Fuessly (1782).

The Scotch or Mountain Burnet (*Zygaena exulans* subsp. *subochracea* White)

This semi-transparent and rather greyish moth has five reddish spots on the fore wings (Pl. **129,** 3). So far as concerns the British Isles it is only known to occur in Aberdeenshire, where it was discovered on the mountains at Braemar in July, 1871, and where it forms colonies here and there on the mountain top. The late Dr. Buchanan White named the Scottish form *subochracea*, but others consider that it is not readily separable from *vanadis* Dalman, which in turn is said by Tutt to be pretty much the same form of the species as that described as the type *exulans* Hohenwarth. Cockayne considered these colour forms are due to fading in the sun as bred specimens are always red. However, the marginal border of the hind wing is usually wider and more distinct in the Scottish race.

The caterpillar is dark green above, and paler below ; two velvety black stripes on the back, each stripe interrupted by yellow spots ; warts with black hairs ; head, black. It feeds on crowberry (*Empetrum nigrum*) but on the Continent is said to eat various alpine plants. In confinement it has been known to eat dock and knotgrass : August to June. Cockayne said that judging from the different sizes of the larvae he found it possibly hibernates four times. The larvae all disappear before the moth is out and perhaps aestivate. The life history requires more investigation. The cocoon is usually hidden on the underside of crowberry stems, very few on heather, grass, or rocks. The moth is out in July, and, like the rest of its kindred, delights in the sunshine

The Slender Scotch Burnet (*Zygaena loti*
subsp. *scotica* Rowland-Brown)

Cockayne (*Ent. Rec.* xx. 73) was the first to introduce this species as British, from specimens sent him as *purpuralis* by Renton in October, 1907, who had taken them near Oban earlier in that year. Rowland-Brown (*Entom.*, lii. 217–25) in an article on the distribution and variation of this species, named the Scottish race subsp. *scotica* (Pl. **129,** 4). Sheldon (*Ent. Rec.*, xiii. 136–7) had already recorded a very worn *Zygaena*, taken by him near Glencoe on July 8, 1898, which if not *exulans* with which species Tutt (" Brit. Lep.," vol. i., p. 453) included it, was a species not hitherto recorded as British. He afterwards thought it might have been *achilleae*.

In some respects *loti* is not unlike some of the forms of *filipendulae* with confluent spots, but it is a more slender-looking insect, the body is more hairy and the legs are yellower beneath. Further the upper basal spot of the fore wing is lengthened almost to the upper spot of the middle pair, and the fifth and sixth spots together form an almost oval mark. A yellow form ab. *flava* Oberthür is known on the Continent. In the *Entomologist* for 1919, p. 188, Mr. P. C. Reid describes a hunt for this species. The caterpillar in Scotland feeds on *Lotus corniculatus* and the oval cocoon is spun on the ground. The moth is on the wing from the middle of June and in early July. It is distributed in Argyllshire, Mull, Raasay, and probably elsewhere.

The New Forest Burnet (*Zygaena viciae* subsp. *anglica* Reiss)

Two examples of this, normally, five-spotted little species are shown on Pl. **129,** 5 ♂, 6 ♀ ; a variety, referable to ab. *confluens* Tutt (spots run together forming streaks somewhat as in *purpuralis*), is depicted in Pl. **130,** 1. Occasionally a sixth spot is in evidence (ab. *sexpunctata* Tutt). A form in which the body has a red belt is known abroad as subspecies *stentzii* Freyer, and examples having traces of this belt have been recorded from the New Forest, which, it may be added, was the only locality in Britain producing this species.

The caterpillar is of a dull pale greenish colour, with numerous black speckles ; three whitish lines on the back, the central one greenish tinged and broader than the others, which are interrupted on each ring by a yellow spot ; between the lines is a series of black dots, one on the outer edge of each ring ; hairs, from greenish warts, white and short ; head, black, dotted with white. It feeds on bird's-foot trefoil (*Lotus corniculatus*), and other trefoils and clovers ; August to May. Sometimes the caterpillars do not complete growth until they have passed two winters in hibernation. The cocoon, which is yellow or yellowish white, has been found on a grass stem, but it is generally placed so low down among herbage that it seems to be rarely detected.

The moth is out in June and early July.

As previously stated the only part of Britain that the species inhabited was the New Forest, Hampshire. Here it was first met with in Stubby Copse, about 1869, but was apparently not distinguished from *Z. trifolii* until 1872. It has now disappeared from its old haunts.

The Five-spot Burnet (*Zygaena trifolii* Esp.)

Four specimens of this species are portrayed on Pl. **129**. In the typical form (Figs. 7 ♂, 8 ♀) the central pair of crimson spots are united and often form a large blotch ; ab. *orobi* Hübn. (Figs. 9 ♂, 10 ♀), has the spots placed well apart. Other more or less frequent aberrations are depicted on Pl. **130** where Fig. 2 represents ab. *glycirrhizae* Hübn. (spots 3, 4 and 5 united) ; Fig. 3, ab. *basalis* Selys (spots 3 and 4 united with the basal pair) ; and Fig. 4, ab. *minoides* Selys (all the spots united, forming an irregular patch). An extreme development of the last-mentioned form has been named ab. *extrema* Tutt (see *Entom.*, xxix. p. 341, Fig. 2). Specimens with a sixth spot as in *Z. filipendulae* have been occasionally recorded, and an example with the lower spot of the central pair absent was taken in West Sussex by the late W. M. Christy, who also obtained a number of specimens of a yellow form (ab. *lutescens* Cockerell) in the same locality. The yellow form is shown on Pl. **130**, 5. Some of the yellow aberrations also exhibit variation in the spots pretty much as in the ordinary form. In some localities, especially marshy ones, the spots on the fore wings and the hind wings are occasionally dull orange ; and South noted specimens in the Weybridge district, Surrey, with the spots on the fore wings of a pinky ochreous colour, whilst the hind wings were of the usual crimson. Such " aberrations " as the last-mentioned probably result from weather exposure. In 1899, Mr. G. B. Corbin recorded the capture, near Ringwood, Hants, of a specimen which had the spots on the fore wings and the red of the hind wings darkened over with dull smoky black, so that the insect when seen at a distance seemed to be wholly black. The late Dr. Hodgson obtained several of these melanic specimens in Sussex. A form with the spots and hind wings suffused with blackish has been named ab. *obscura* Tutt.

The caterpillar (Pl. **132**, 3, 3*a*) is green inclining to yellowish and to bluish, with black marks on the back ; a series of black streaks low down along the sides. It feeds on *Lotus corniculatus*, and on other trefoils and clover ; July to May. Sometimes takes two years to complete its changes.

There are two subspecies occurring in England. (1) A smaller insect appearing in May–June on downland (subsp. *palustrella* Verity), the caterpillar of which feeds chiefly on *Lotus corniculatus*, and whose cocoon is hidden below the herbage, and (2) a larger insect (subsp. *decreta* Verity (*palustris* auctt. =)) inhabiting marshes, which emerges in late July–early August. Its caterpillar feeds on *Lotus uliginosus* and its cocoon is spun well up on grass stems.

In 1891 and 1892 Fletcher succeeded in rearing hybrids of both the crosses obtainable between *trifolii* and *lonicerae*.

1. **Transparent Burnet:** *caterpillar.*
2, 2*a* **Narrow-bordered Five-spot Burnet:** *caterpillar, chrysalis and cocoon.*
3, 3*a.* **Five-spot Burnet:** *caterpillar and cocoon.*
4. **Six-spot Burnet:** *caterpillar.*
5. **Forester:** *caterpillar.*

1, 2. Narrow-bordered Five-spot Burnet.
3, 4, 5. Six-spot Burnet.
6, 7. Scarce Forester.
8, 9. The Forester.
10, 11. Cistus Forester.

In the British Isles, the species is apparently confined to England, North Wales, and Isle of Man. In the former country it is locally common in most of the southern counties, but more local in the eastern counties. There are records from Armagh and Fermanagh, but Kane appears to doubt the occurrence of the species in Ireland. There is no doubt that the next species has frequently been mistaken for the present one, therefore the actual range of *trifolii* in the British Isles has probably not been fully ascertained.

The Narrow-bordered Five-spot Burnet
(*Zygaena lonicerae* subsp. *transferens* Verity)

As will be seen from the two specimens represented by Figs. 1 ♂ and 2 ♀ on Pl. **133**, this species bears considerable resemblance to ab. *orobi* of *Z. trifolii*. The chief differences are in the rather longer fore wings and the more pointed tips of the hind pair ; the borders of the hind wings are often narrower. In a broad way, it may be stated that the general tone of colour in the male of *lonicerae* is bluer than that of *trifolii* and the antennae are longer. The union of any two or more spots is rarely seen in this species in Britain, but specimens with all the spots joined together have certainly been noted. A yellow form, ab. *citrina* Speyer (*flava* Oberthür =), occurs regularly in Gloucestershire. In ab. *lutescens* Hewett, the hind wings are orange. Ab. *eboracae* Prest, is semitransparent, steel blue ; the spots and the hind wings are pink. the border of the hind wings brown, and the fringes of all the wings are whitish. Specimens with the fore wings nearly all red (ab. *incendium* Oberth.) occur in Northamptonshire. Form loc. *latomarginata* Tutt from the coast of Yorkshire is larger, with broader fore wings ; the hind wings have a wide blue-black border extending along the costa.

The caterpillar (Pl. **132**, 2, 2*a*) is very similar to that of the last species, but the black marks on the sides are heavier, and the hairs of the body are longer ; the ground colour, however, is whiter than in *trifolii* and *filipendulae*. It feeds on trefoils and clover, and sometimes passes two winters before becoming full grown. The cocoon, which is attached to stems of grass, etc., is generally placed well up above the ground, so that it is readily seen.

The moth, which is out in late June and in July, occurs in woods and plantations ; also said to be found in meadows, and on rough waste ground, as well as in marshes and salterns. The distribution extends from Cumberland, Northumberland and Durham southwards as far as Kent and Surrey in the east and to Gloucestershire in the west ; it is plentiful in East Yorkshire. Local in the northern half of Ireland (subsp. *insularis* Tremewan).

The Six-spot Burnet (*Zygaena filipendulae* subsp. *anglicola* Tremewan)

This species (Pl. **133**, 3–5) is the most generally common of our Burnets. Perhaps the most frequent form of variation in the spots of the fore wings is that in which the outer pair run together, and so form a blotch ; but union of the middle pair is not an uncommon occurrence. In ab. *cytisi* Hübn., the three pairs of spots are each united, so that the fore wings have three separate blotches. Occasionally, the spots are united, as in ab. *cytisi*, and the blotches thus formed are connected by reddish streaks in various modifications leading up to ab. *conjuncta* Tutt, which has all the spots merged into a large blotch, extending over the disc of the fore wings. From the normal crimson, the spots and the hind wings vary now and then to orange, ab. *aurantia* Tutt, or to yellow, ab. *flava* Robson (*cerinus* Robson and Gardner =) ; intermediate shades between these two extremes, and the typical coloration, are rather more frequent. The late Mr. R. Adkin kindly loaned the example of the yellow form shown on Pl. **130**, 6. Pink, and orange, forms have been noted from various parts of

England, but they seem to occur more especially in Cambridge and the north-east corner of Essex. Pl. **130**, 7, represents an example of ab. *chrysanthemi* Hübn., and is copied from Oberthür's *Etudes d'Entom.*, xx., Pl. 8, Fig. 134. Many *chrysanthemi* have been taken at Fleetwood and Birmingham, odd ones in the New Forest and Epping Forest, and specimens with pale brown spots and hind wings at Orpington, Kent.

In typical *filipendulae* the dark blue border of the hind wings is narrow, but in the seasonal form *stephensi* Dupont, the borders are rather broader. Another character of this form, though not constant, is that the nervule upon which the sixth spot is placed is here of the ground colour, and therefore divides the spot (Pl. **123**, 5). At Northwood, Middlesex, South found this form in May and June. Although it has been suggested that *stephensi* is a hybrid, Cockayne states that he examined the genitalia of a number of Tutt's own specimens and they proved to be quite typical *filipendulae*. During 1889 and 1890 Fletcher succeeded in breeding hybrids between *lonicerae* and *filipendulae*. Cockayne (*Ent. Rec.*, liii. 113) mentions wild hybrids between *lonicerae* and *filipendulae* taken near Bedford, the genitalia of which were intermediate. Hybrids between *filipendulae* and *trifolii* are difficult to rear in captivity and wild ones must be very rare indeed.

Subspecies (? ab.) *lismorica* Reiss, from the Isle of Lismore, Scotland, has the spots and hind wings dull red, not the usual scarlet and crimson.

From a number of cocoons collected in a Yorkshire locality for *lonicerae*, South reared, in 1907, a good many examples of that species, and also about a dozen six-spot specimens, which agree in colour with *filipendulae*, but they have the vein-interrupted sixth spot and broader border to hind wings, as in *stephensi*.

The caterpillar (Pl. **132**, 4) is greenish, with black markings and some yellow spots, the latter chiefly on the hind edges of the rings. It feeds in the autumn and after hibernation, on trefoils, clover, bird's-foot (*Ornithopus*), and kidney-vetch (*Anthyllis*), completing growth in the spring.

The moth flies on sunny days in July and August, on chalk downs, etc., inland, and on cliffs, and sand hills on the coast. Common throughout Ireland.

The Scarce Forester (*Procris globulariae* Hübner)

Of the three species occurring in Britain this is slightly the largest, at least in the male. The fore wings are green, some-times with a slightly golden sheen ; fringes, greyish. The male is best distinguished from *statices* by its more slender body, and by the pectinated and rather pointed antennae. The female is a good deal smaller than the male ; the antennae are simple, and somewhat thread-like, compared with those of the females of *statices* and *geryon* (Pl. **133**, 6 ♂, 7 ♀).

The description of the caterpillar given in previous editions is incorrect. It had probably been taken from Buckler who had received ova and larvae of supposed *P. globulariae* from the Continent. Sheldon (*Entom.*, liv. 240) pointed out that the caterpillar of the British species was brownish and Cockayne who gave a detailed description (*Ent. Rec.*, xliv. 17) also described it as pale greyish brown (greyish olive, Ridgway) with the large tubercles pink or avellaneous (Ridgway). Just external to the dorsal tubercles is a fairly broad stripe, whitish, cream coloured, or clear pale yellow, jutting inwards towards the middle line in the intervals between the tubercles and some-times running up the sides of each tubercle. Occasionally this stripe is bordered externally at a point opposite each tubercle by a narrow bright red line. Head small, blackish ; anal plate small, dark brown ; spiracles small, oval and black. It feeds in knapweed (*Centaurea nigra*).

The moth is out in June and July ; it is partial to blossoms of salad burnet (*Poterium sanguisorba*), and only flies in the sunshine. The late Mr. J. Jenner Weir, who found the species commonly on the downs near Lewes, Sussex, was the first

Intomologist to record it as British. The best known localities in Sussex are Hollingbury Vale and Cliffe Hill, but it also occurs at the Devil's Dyke near Brighton. In Kent it is found on the downs behind Folkestone and Shorncliffe Camp; it also occurs in the Cotswolds and in 1952 was found at Devizes in Wiltshire.

The Forester (*Procris statices* Linn.)

In its most frequent form in Britain, this species is bronzy green (ab. *viridis* Tutt) ; the typical bluish green type is much less frequent. The female is smaller than the male, but the difference in size is hardly ever so marked as in the sexes of *globulariae*. The antennae of the male are pectinate, but the tips are thickened (Pl. **133,** 8 ♂, 9 ♀).

The caterpillar (Pl. **132,** 5) is whitish, inclining to green, yellow, or pinkish, on the back, and the sides are pinkish brown ; the hairy warts are brown or pinkish brown, and the small head is glossy black. It feeds on sorrel (*Rumex acetosa*), and it attains full growth, after hibernation, about the end of April. On leaving the egg-shell in the summer, the young caterpillar bores into a leaf, and eats the tissue between the upper and lower skins ; later on it attacks the foliage from the underside, but leaves the upper skin intact ; or the process may be reversed, and the under skin left.

The moth is on the wing in June, sometimes late May. It occurs, locally, in meadows, frequently damp ones, where there is plenty of ragged-robin (*Lychnis flos-cuculi*), the blossoms of which plant it seems to prefer to all others.

Widely distributed over England, but in Wales only recorded from Capel Curig and Barmouth, in the north of that country (1900). In Scotland its range extends to Moray ; and in Ireland it is found in counties Wicklow, Cork, Clare, Westmeath, Monaghan, Sligo, Galway and Tyrone.

The Cistus Forester (*Procris geryon* Hübn.)

This species is much smaller than the last ; the fore wings, the outer margins of which are somewhat rounded, **are** bronze green, but, in the male, rather dull in tint, sometimes tinged with golden towards the base.   The antennae are more stumpy than those of *statices*, but in other respects they are similar in appearance.   The female is not much smaller than the male (Pl. **133**, 10 ♂, 11 ♀).

The caterpillar is yellowish white, with bristle-bearing warts of pretty much the same colour ; three lines on the back, the central one whitish, edged on each side with purplish, the others waved and of a claret colour ; a reddish brown stripe low down along the sides ; head and plate on first ring of the body black, the latter edged in front with yellowish.   It feeds on rock rose (*Helianthemum vulgare*).   At first it attacks the leaf from the upper side, and partly burrows therein ; when older it clears away patches from the under surface, leaving the upper skin of the leaf more or less transparent ; as it approaches full growth it likes to take its meals in the sunshine, and then eats the top skin as well as other parts of the leaf, and also tender shoots : July to May.   The moth is out in June and July, as a rule, but is sometimes observed in May.   Its haunts are on warm slopes of chalk downs and limestone hills, where it flies in the sunshine.

This species was first noted as British in March, 1860, when specimens from Worcestershire were recorded as *Procris tenui-cornis* Zell.   It seems, however, to have been considered doubtfully distinct from *statices* until 1863, when the caterpillar was found, and the occurrence of the species in several other English counties recorded.   At the present time *P. geryon* is known to inhabit Sussex (Brighton and Lewes districts), Kent (Canterbury and Shorncliffe), Buckinghamshire (Ayles-bury and Tring), Oxfordshire (Chinor), Gloucestershire (Cots-wolds), Worcestershire (Malvern Hills), Derbyshire and North Staffordshire (Bakewell and Dovedale), Yorkshire (Richmond, Barnsley, Sheffield, etc.), and Durham (banks on the coast). In Wales, it is sometimes common on Great Orme's Head, Carnarvonshire.

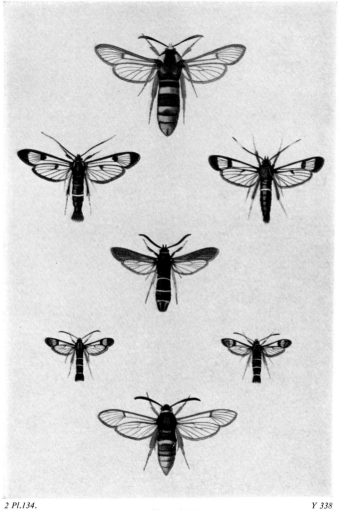

1. Hornet Moth.
2. Welsh Clearwing.   3. White-barred Clearwing.
4. Dusky Clearwing.
5, 6. Currant Clearwing.
7. Lunar Hornet Moth.

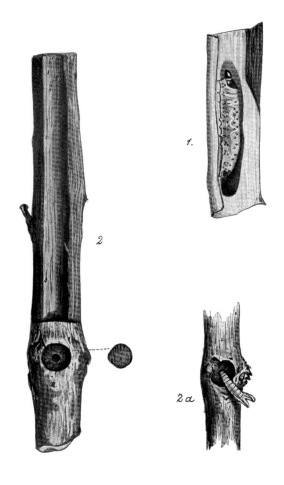

1. **Leopard Moth**: *caterpillar.*
2, 2a. **Orange-tailed Clearwing**: *caterpillar's burrow and exit hole, chrysalis skin.*

SESIIDAE

This family—the Aegeriidae of some authors—has over one hundred Palaearctic species assigned to it ; these are represented in Britain by five genera. Fourteen species are found in the British Isles, but to obtain fine specimens of most of them the mature caterpillars or the chrysalids will have to be collected and the moths reared. All species emerge from the chrysalis early in the forenoon, and then only under the influence of sunshine.

The caterpillars are somewhat maggot-like, and live in stems, branches, and roots of trees and shrubs ; or in the crowns and roots of low-growing plants. The majority, possibly all, are nearly two years in arriving at full growth.

The Hornet Moth (*Sesia apiformis* Clerck)

As indicated by the English name this moth, and also that next to be mentioned, are very like the hornet (*Vespa crabro*). On turning to Pl. **134,** 1, it will be seen that this species has a yellow head and patches of yellow on the shoulders ; these characters at once separate it from *Sphecia bembeciformis* Hübn.

The caterpillar is yellowish white, with a red brown head, and a yellow plate on the first ring of the body. It feeds on the roots and lower portion of the trunks of poplar, probably living three years. In its last year it changes skin once and grows very little more. The brown shining chrysalis is enclosed in a cocoon of wood scrapings woven together with silk, made in late summer, in the bark or in the earth. The larva does not change to a chrysalis until the spring. The moth is out in May and June ; and has been found, newly emerged, sitting on stems of poplar in the morning.

The eastern counties of England appear to be most favoured by this species, but it also occurs northwards to Yorkshire, southwards to Devon, and a specimen has been recorded from Rhyl, North Wales. In Scotland, it has been reported from some localities in the south ; Kane states that he has reason to believe that the species occurs in the northern half of Ireland, and that he found caterpillars plentiful in young poplars growing in a marsh near the city of Waterford.

Donovan records it from Cork.

The Lunar Hornet Moth (*Sphecia bembeciformis* Hübn.)

Another hornet-like moth, best distinguished from that just mentioned by the yellow collar behind the black head (Pl. **134**, 7). The male is rather smaller, but otherwise similar.

The caterpillar is yellowish white, with dark brownish head, and a blackish-edged yellow plate on the first ring of the body. It feeds in stems of sallow, willow, and poplar, probably living two years. In late June and through July the moth is on the wing, and may occasionally be seen at rest on leaves or stems of sallow, etc.

The species, known also as *crabroniformis* Lewin, is generally distributed throughout England, Wales, and Ireland ; in Scotland its range extends into Perthshire.

Abroad it seems pretty much confined to Holland, northern and central Germany, Austria, and Bohemia.

The Dusky Clearwing (*Sciapteron tabaniformis* Rott.)

This species is the *Trochilium vespiforme* of some British authors, and the *Aegeria asiliformis* of Stephens and others.

Stephens, writing of it in 1828, remarks : " Occasionally taken on poplars, near London, in June. I have obtained it from the neighbourhood of Bexley, and from Birchwood ; but it is doubtless a rare species, and exists in few collections : of the male, I have hitherto seen but two specimens, one of which I possess." Both places mentioned by Stephens are in Kent, and one or two specimens of the species have since been reported from Ashford in the same county. The late Henry Doubleday took specimens at Epping, Essex. Colney Hatch Wood in Middlesex has also been given as a locality in the past ; two specimens have been recorded from Chiswick, and

1. Orange-tailed Clearwing.   2. Sallow Clearwing.
3. Yellow-legged Clearwing.
4, 5. Red-belted Clearwing.
6. Large Red-belted Clearwing.
7. Red-tipped Clearwing.   8. Thrift Clearwing.
9, 10. Fiery Clearwing.
11. Six-belted Clearwing.

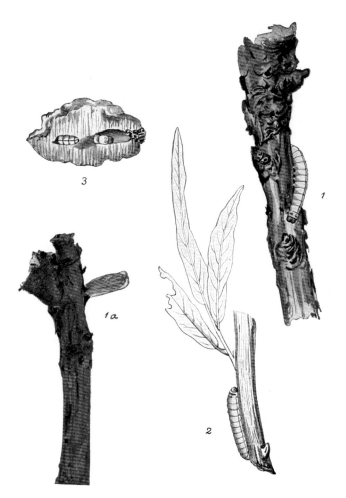

1, 1*a*. **Currant Clearwing,** *caterpillar and chrysalis skin.*
2. **Red-tipped Clearwing** : *caterpillar.*
3. **Welsh Clearwing** : *caterpillar.*

one was captured on a poplar trunk close to Portsmouth in
July, 1909, also recorded from Durham. The occurrence of
this species in Britain is probably due to the larva being
brought in with imported Lombardy poplars. (Pl. **134,** 4).

The caterpillar lives in the side shoots of Lombardy poplars
in which it causes a swelling. It pupates within the shoot,
and the moth flies in June and July.

The Welsh Clearwing (*Aegeria scoliaeformis* Borkh.)

As a British species this insect was first noted from Llangollen, in North Wales, somewhere about 1854. In 1867
it was found to inhabit birch woods in the Rannoch district
of Scotland, and later on its presence was detected in Sutherlandshire. It has been recorded from Hereford ; one example
was reported from Wiltshire in 1857 ; and two from Delamere
Forest, Cheshire (1901 and 1905). A pupa obtained June,
and a moth captured in July, 1913, Cannock Chase, Staffordshire. Kane states that moths have been taken at Killarney, and
caterpillars obtained in the same district, and also at Kenmare.

The caterpillar (Pl. **137,** 3 ; after Hofmann) feeds on the
inner layer of bark of large birch trees, living three years, the
last year changing skin once, and growing very little more.
It makes its cocoon in July–August but does not pupate until
the spring. It turns to a dark brownish chrysalis, in a cocoon
formed close up to the bark, which thinly covers the outer end
of the burrow. The moth flies in June or sometimes July,
and assembles freely. It is of comparatively large size, and
may be distinguished from the next species by the yellow belts
on its body, and the chestnut coloured tuft at the tail
(Pl. **134,** 2).

The White-barred Clearwing (*Aegeria spheciformis* Schiff.)

Although generally smaller, some specimens run very close
to the last species in size. It may be distinguished by the
single pale yellow belt on the body and the black tail (Pl. **134,**
3). One of the best known localities for the species in England

is Tilgate Forest, in Sussex ; but it also occurs in Surrey, Berkshire, Hampshire (Basingstoke), Herefordshire (Tarrington), Worcestershire (Wyre Forest), Staffordshire (Burnt Wood), Warwickshire, Cheshire (one, Delamere Forest, 1901), Denbighshire (Llangollen), Lancashire (Chat Moss), and Yorkshire (Bishop's Wood, 1894).

The caterpillar feeds in stems of alder, and sometimes birch, and is full grown in May of the third year after hatching from the egg. It is said that the chrysalis may sometimes be found by bending and twisting the stems of alder, so as to cause the thin skin of bark over the exit hole of the burrow to crack, and so disclose its whereabouts. The burrow is generally low down the stem. The moth is out in June and early July, and is sometimes to be seen on sunny mornings at rest on alder leaves, or flying over and around the bushes. It assembles freely.

The Orange-tailed Clearwing (*Aegeria andrenaeformis* Lasp.)

Although known to be a British species since 1829, when a specimen was taken in a wood near Greenhithe, Kent, this insect continued to be very rare until 1905–6 (Pl. **136**, 1). For a long time the caterpillar was supposed to feed in the stems of dogwood, but it is now known to live in the stems of the wayfaring tree (*Viburnum lantana*), and the guelder rose (*V. opulus*). Unfortunately the caterpillar is much infested by parasites, and comparatively few escape attack. It lives for at least two years. Notes on the life history of this moth, by the Hon. N. Charles Rothschild, Mr. Eustace Bankes, and Dr. Chapman, were published in the *Transaction of the Entomological Society of London* for 1906 (Part IV, pp. 471–82).

Most of the known localities for the species are in Kent, but it has also been found in Surrey, Dorset, Somerset, Gloucestershire, Hertfordshire (Tring district), Buckinghamshire, N. Essex, Huntingdonshire, Cambridgeshire, and Northamptonshire (Oundle). For the caterpillar mine in stem of *Viburnum*

(Pl. **135**, 2, 2a) thanks are due to Mr. Rayward, who kindly sent a living pupa, from which the moth duly emerged, but unfortunately escaped from the box in which the stick containing the chrysalis was kept.

Newman, in 1833, described this species as *Trochilium allantiformis* Wood, and in 1842 it was figured by Westwood and Humphreys as *T. andreniforme*. It is distinguished from *Aegeria tipuliformis* by the two yellow belts of the body (the first sometimes indistinct) and the orange-yellow tuft in the blue-black tail ; on the underside of the body there is a broad yellow band on the fourth ring, sometimes extending to the fifth and sixth.

The Currant Clearwing (*Aegeria tipuliformis* Clerck)

In this species the body is narrowly belted with yellow, usually four belts in the male and three in the female ; the tail tuft is black in both sexes. The outer marginal border of the fore wings has a bronzy tinge, due to orange patches between the veins (Pl. **134**, 5 ♂, 6 ♀).

The caterpillar lives in the stems and shoots of black and red currant bushes and gooseberry ; it feeds on the pith, and works its way downwards. When full grown about May, it gnaws an outlet to the side of the stem, but does not penetrate the outer skin, although it reduces this to a very thin layer, through which the reddish brown chrysalis is able to force itself when the moth is ready to emerge. A figure of the caterpillar will be found on Pl. **137**, 1 ; the chrysalis protruding from currant stem (Fig. 1a) is from a photo by the late Mr. H. Main. In June or July, the moths are not infrequently seen on leaves of shrubs in gardens where there are currant bushes in or around such gardens, but the foliage of the food plant is a favourite resting place.

Generally distributed throughout England, the range extending into Wales, and South Scotland, but is apparently rare in these countries and also in some of the northern counties of

England. Kane states that the species is common near Dublin, and is probably widely distributed in Ireland.

This species seems to have been introduced into North America, where its caterpillar is known as the " currant borer," and, as in England, is regarded with little favour by bush-fruit growers.

The Sallow Clearwing (*Aegeria flaviventris* Staud.)

This clearwing was first recorded as occurring in Britain by W. Fassnidge (*Ent. Rec.*, 1926, xxxviii. pp. 113–15, Pl. III). It may be distinguished from *tipuliformis* as follows : no yellow ring at back of head, tegulae black, segments four to six, all yellow on underside of abdomen, anal tuft of female yellow on sides (Pl. **136,** 2). The larva, which lives for two years, feeds in sallow branches, causing a swelling somewhat similar to that made by the beetle *Saperda populnea*. It has been reported from Hampshire, Dorset, Devon, Wiltshire, Sussex Kent, Surrey, Berkshire, Buckinghamshire, Oxfordshire, and Durham (*Entom.*, lxi. 282).

The Yellow-legged Clearwing (*Aegeria vespiformis* Linn.)

This species (Pl. **136,** 3), known also as *asiliformis* Rottemburg (1775), and *cynipiformis* Esper (1782), is now held to be correctly referred to *vespiformis* Linn. (1761). The crossbar of the fore wings is orange red in both sexes ; the body of the male has two more or less united yellow spots at the junction with the thorax, four yellow belts, and the tail tuft is black above, mixed with yellow below ; in the female the body belts are usually one less than in the male, the yellow spots at the junction are generally run together, and the tail tuft is almost wholly yellow. As indicated by the English name, the legs are largely yellow in both sexes.

The caterpillar feeds under the bark of oak, sweet chestnut, and elm, is full grown in May or June, and turns to a brownish chrysalis in a cell formed in the bark. The stumps of felled

trees about two years after felling are a favourite habitat
for larvae and pupae. A well-known locality for this moth,
which is out in July and early August, is Hyde Park, London.
It is also found in woods or oak-timbered parks in Kent (Tun-
bridge Wells), Surrey, Sussex (Abbot's Wood, Tilgate, etc.),
Dorset (Glanvilles Wootton, etc.), Devon (Devonport, Plymouth, Topsham, etc.), Essex (Epping), Cambridgeshire,
Suffolk, Oxfordshire, Gloucestershire, Leicestershire, Staffordshire, and Yorkshire (Doncaster).

The Red-belted Clearwing (*Aegeria myopaeformis* Borkh.)

One example of each sex is shown on Pl. **136,** where Fig. 4
represents the male and Fig. 5 the female ; both have a single
belt on the body ; as a rule, the belt is red, but occasionally it
inclines to orange or yellow.

The caterpillar feeds on the inner bark of the trunks or
boughs of apple, and sometimes pear trees, also hawthorn.
It is nearly two years in maturing, but is full grown about
June. The moth is out during the summer months, and is to
be seen early on sunny mornings, newly emerged from the
chrysalis on the trunks of the trees in which the caterpillar
lives ; the chrysalis skins will also be noted at the same time,
sticking out from holes in the bark. Later in the day it sits
on leaves, etc., after its flights, and South had even found
it occasionally on a gravel path, and once on the pavement
of a road in North-west London.

The species seems to be most frequent in gardens and
orchards around London, but it has been recorded from as far
north as Lancashire and Yorkshire ; it is probably widely
distributed over England. The Irish localities, mentioned by
Kane, are Dublin, Cork, Killarney, and Clonbrock.

The Large Red-belted Clearwing (*Aegeria culiciformis*
Linn.)

This species (Pl. **136,** 6) is very similar to the last, but
it is larger, and the fore wings are dusted with reddish scales

towards the base, sometimes also along the inner margin. The belt on the body is generally red, not infrequently with an orange tinge, but it is sometimes yellow or far more rarely white.

The caterpillar, which is full grown in May, feeds on the inner bark of birch trees and bushes, apparently preferring the stumps left in the ground where stems have been cut down. It is not difficult to find, but as it is about two years in this stage it should not be taken until nearly or quite full grown, and it is safer to leave it until it has entered the chrysalis state. The moth is out in June, or sometimes at the end of May ; it flies over birch and rests on leaves, and has been known to visit flowers of the wood spurge and the rhododendron.

Kent and Sussex appear to be the counties most favoured by this species, but it occurs in most of the other English counties in which there are birch woods, certainly up to Yorkshire, and probably further north, as it is found in Scotland (Clydesdale, Perthshire, and Aberdeen). The Irish localities are Killarney, Ballinasloe, and Derry.

The Red-tipped Clearwing (*Aegeria formicaeformis* Esp.)

This is another red-belted species, but it differs from either of the two immediately preceding in having the fore wings tipped with red (Pl. **136,** 7).

The caterpillar feeds in the twigs and stumps of osier (*Salix viminalis*), sometimes called " withe " ; it is full grown about June ; also in other species of sallow, often several larvae close together. It likes bushes injured by *Cossus* and beetles (Pl. **137,** 2 ; after Hofmann). The moth is out in July and August ; it is partial to marshes and other wet spots, and is fond of a leaf as a resting place. Like the rest of its kind, it is very alert, and skips off quickly on one's approach. Probably the species is more widely distributed in England, but from the records, it only appears to have been noted from

Surrey, Kent, Hampshire, Somerset, Devon, Gloucestershire, Herefordshire, Derbyshire, Yorkshire, Norfolk, Suffolk, Cambridgeshire, Huntingdonshire, Hertfordshire, and Essex. Ireland scarce, Kerry and Cork.

The Thrift Clearwing (*Aegeria muscaeformis* Esp.)

This is our smallest species of the genus, and it is further distinguished by narrow clear spaces on the blackish, or bronzy, fore wings, three whitish bands on the body, and traces of a whitish line along the middle of the back (Pl. **136,** 8).

The caterpillar feeds on the roots of thrift or sea-pink (*Armeria vulgaris*), and is full grown about June. The moth is out in June and July, and seems to have a liking for the flowers of thyme.

This species (also known as *philanthiformis* Laspeyres) frequents rocky places on the coasts of Devon (Torquay, Lynmouth, etc.); Cornwall; Wales ; Isle of Man; Scotland (Aberdeenshire) ; and Ireland (Saltee Islands, Wexford, and Seven Heads, Cork. Gregson recorded it from Howth).

The Fiery Clearwing (*Aegeria chrysidiformis* Esp.)

The orange red colour on the fore wings, and of the tail tuft, at once distinguish this species (Pl. **136,** 9 ♂, 10 ♀) from either of its British allies. The blackish body has two pale-yellow belts, but in the male the lower one is often double. As a rule, the body of the female is stouter than that of the male, but the bodies of some males appear quite as thick as those of the females, and the true sex is only disclosed by the ciliated antennae, which is a character of the male alone.

The caterpillar feeds on the roots of dock and sorrel, and it is full grown about May. In June and July the moth is on the wing and flies in the sunshine, about noon, over the food plants.

The species occurs not uncommonly in the Warren at Folkestone, Kent. This locality, well known to entomologists, is a long stretch of rough broken ground lying between the railway and the sea ; and is probably the only spot in the British Isles where the Fiery Clearwing is almost certain to be found, either in its early or its perfect stage, at the proper season. The moth has been recorded from Eastbourne, Sussex (1874), and from the Forest of Dean, Gloucestershire (1902).

The Six-belted Clearwing (*Dipsosphecia scopigera* Scop.)

The inner and outer margins of the fore wings are tinged with orange, and there is an orange mark on the outer edge of the cross bar ; the body of the male has seven yellow belts, and that of the female one less (Pl. **136, 11**).

The caterpillar feeds in the roots of bird's-foot trefoil (*Lotus corniculatus*), and kidney vetch (*Anthyllis vulneraria*) ; it is full grown about June. July and August are the months for the moth, and its haunts are on chalk downs, and on banks by the sea ; it seems partial to the edges of chalk pits, sloping banks, and broken ground of undercliffs, etc. In such places it is to be seen on the wing in the early evening, and South thought in the early morning also. It has frequently been obtained by sweeping the net over herbage in the vicinity of the food plants.

Mr. W. H. Flint records (1902) the species from the Forest of Dean district, where, he states, he could easily have captured two dozen a day, as they flew over trefoils, etc.

The species occurs in most of the southern seaboard counties of England, from Kent to Cornwall and including the Isle of Wight ; Surrey, Buckinghamshire, Essex, and other eastern counties, including Cambridge ; and it has been recorded from Yorkshire. On the western side of the country it is found in Somerset, Gloucestershire, Herefordshire, Worcestershire, Staffordshire, and in South Wales. (Also known as *ichneumoniformis* Schiff.)

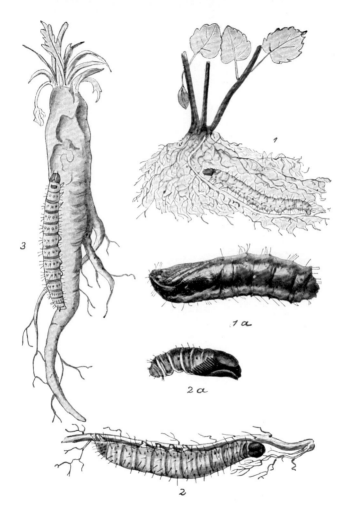

1, 1*a*. **Common Swift**: *caterpillar and chrysalis, enlarged.*
2, 2*a*. **Ghost Moth**: *caterpillar and chrysalis.*
3. **Orange Swift**: *caterpillar.*

1, 3. Ghost Moth, *male and female.*
2, 4. Ghost Moth (ssp. *thulensis*), *male and female.*

HEPIALIDAE

Of the twenty-eight Palaearctic species belonging to this family, eleven appear to occur in Europe, and the range of five of these extends to the British Isles.

In some of the more recent systems of classification, this family is relegated to almost the bottom of the scheme, and therefore occupies a much lower place than do the bulk of the families comprised in the old style " Micro-Lepidoptera." As, however, these insects, commonly called " Swifts," have long received the attention of collectors, and in collections usually occupy a position among the so-called " Bombyces," they have been included in the present volume.

The Ghost Moth (*Hepialus humuli* Linn.)

On Pl. **139** are portraits of a male and a female of the typical form of this species (Figs. 1 ♂ and 3 ♀) ; and two male examples (Figs. 2 and 4) of the Shetland race subsp. *thulensis* Newman, better known perhaps as *hethlandica* Staud., but the former is the older name. It will be noted that in the ordinary form the male has white wings, and that the female has yellowish fore wings marked with orange, and smoky hind wings. The Shetland male, represented by Fig. 2, has the fore wings whitish buff in colour with brownish markings similar in pattern to those of an ordinary female ; the hind wings are blackish. The second example of *thulensis* (Fig. 4) approaches in appearance a typical female. In other male specimens of this insular race the wings are pretty much of the typical colour, but the markings on the front pair are reduced both in number and size. Mr. H. McArthur, who collected a good deal in the Shetland Isles, stated that in Unst, the most northern island of the group, more or less typical *humuli* were found on the cliffs facing south-east, whilst the majority of the specimens obtained in boggy meadows, etc., were of the *thulensis* form.

The caterpillar feeds on the roots of plants, such as burdock, dandelion, dead-nettle, etc. It often causes damage to agricultural and horticultural crops. It is full grown in May, and the moth is out in June and July (Pl. **138**, 2, 2*a* ; after Hofmann). The males may be seen in the evening, sometimes in numbers in grassy places, swaying themselves to and fro without making progress, and appearing as though they dangled from the end of an invisible thread ; the female flies straight, and, as a rule, in the direction of one or other of the pendulous males.

The species is generally distributed over the British Isles.

The Orange Swift (*Hepialus sylvina* Linn.)

The male of this species (Pl. **139**, 5 ♂, 6 ♀) is usually some shade of orange brown, with greyish-edged white markings on the fore wings. Sometimes the female is orange brown, but more often it is some shade of grey brown.

The caterpillar (Pl. **138**, 3 ; after Hofmann) feeds on the roots of dock, bracken, viper's bugloss, etc., and is full grown about July. In late July and in August the moth may be seen in the early evening flying among bracken, and not infrequently around trees fairly high up. Occasionally, specimens are seen in the daytime on tree-trunks, fences, etc. At one time this species was known in the vernacular as " The Tawny and Brown Swift " ; it is also " The Orange or Evening Swift " of Harris (1778) and the " Wood Swift " of Newman. It is common in many southern and eastern parts, but widely distributed over England, Wales, and Scotland to Moray. Only doubtfully recorded from Ireland.

The Map-winged Swift (*Hepialus fusconebulosa* de Geer)

At one time this species (the *velleda* of Hübner) was known as the " Northern Swift," but as it is plentiful in North Devon and Somerset, and occurs less commonly in other southern English counties, that name is hardly suitable. Haworth's English name for it—" The Beautiful Swift "—does not quite

Eupithecia phoeniceata **Rambur.**

1, 2, 3. **Map-winged Swift.**
4, 5. 6. **Common Swift.**
7, 8. **Gold Swift.**

meet the case, because, although the insect is prettily marked, it is scarcely beautiful.   We have then to fall back on Donovan's Map-winged Swift as a popular name, and this seems a fairly apt one, as the markings on the fore wings are somewhat map-like in pattern, especially in the more typical specimens.

There is much variation in colour and in marking ; some examples, chiefly those from Shetland, are prettily variegated. A uniform reddish brown variety, ab. *gallicus* Lederer, is depicted on Pl. **141**, 3 ; and a more or less typical specimen of each sex is shown on the same plate (Figs. 1 ♂, 2 ♀).

The caterpillar is ochreous white, with orange-brown plates, and rather paler raised dots ; head, reddish brown, and spiracles black.   It feeds on the roots of the bracken, and is full grown about May.   The moth is out in June and July, and flies, in the gloaming, on hill slopes, heaths, and the edges of mosses and woods ; it seems to be more active than either of the other British " Swifts " ; at all events, South always found it less easy to capture with the net.

The species is pretty generally distributed throughout the British Isles.

The Common Swift (*Hepialus lupulina* Linn.)

Three examples of this species are shown on Pl. **141**. Fig. 4 is a typical male, Fig. 5, a whitish suffused aberration, and Fig. 6 is a female.   The latter sex is generally devoid of marking, and in the male the stripes and dashes are far more conspicuous in some specimens than in others.

The glossy whitish caterpillar has a brown head ; the plate on the first ring of the body is brownish, and the raised dots are pretty much of the same colour.   It feeds on the roots of grass and other plants, and is full grown about April.   It is often a pest to both the horticulturist and agriculturist.   A figure of the caterpillar, from a drawing in colour by the late Mr. A. Sich, and a photo of the pupa by the late Mr. H. Main, are shown on Pl. **138**, 1 and 1*a* ; the latter is twice natural size.

The moth is out in June, or sometimes late May, and occasional specimens have been noted in September. It is more frequently seen at rest, on fences, etc., than either of the other species of the genus ; but towards dusk it is on the wing, and may then be observed in large numbers careering over grass meadows or along stretches of green turf by the wayside.

Generally distributed, and often abundant, throughout the United Kingdom ; and it occurs in Monaghan, Mayo, Galway, Tyrone, Kerry, and other counties in Ireland.

The Gold Swift (*Hepialus hecta* Linn.)

Both sexes of this species are shown on Pl. **141,** where Fig. 7 represents the golden-marked male, and Fig. 8 the more dingy, dull, purplish grey striped female. There is variation in number and in size of the markings on the fore wings of the male, and occasionally the hind wings in this sex are adorned with golden spangles on the outer area.

The pale greyish brown caterpillar has glossy darker brown plates on rings 1–3, and the raised dots and the spiracles are black. It feeds on the roots of bracken, and is full grown about May. Buckler states that at first it burrows in the root, hibernates when small, resumes feeding in April, attains full growth before winter, and hibernates in the earth for a second time ; in the spring of the second year it gnaws cavities in the young shoots of the bracken, and apparently drinks the flowing sap.

The moth is out in June. The males fly at dusk, something in the manner of *humuli*, over and among the bracken ; but the females fly in a more or less direct line. An odour given off by the males of this species has been likened to that of the pineapple ; whilst the " scent " of the Ghost Moth is said to be more of the billy-goat character.

In most woody localities, where the bracken flourishes, this species will be found throughout England, Wales, Scotland to Aberdeen and the Hebrides, and Ireland. It also occurs where there is no bracken so must have other food plants.

INDEX OF ENGLISH NAMES

INDEX OF SCIENTIFIC NAMES

359

Printed in Great Britain by Butler & Tanner Ltd., Frome and London
639.973